MEN OF SPACE

Volume 1

*Profiles of the Leaders in Space Research,
Development, and Exploration*

Advisory Committee

Chairman:

HOLGER N. TOFTOY
Major General, United States Army (Ret.)

Members:

THE HONORABLE STYLES BRIDGES
United States Senator from New Hampshire
Member, Senate Committee on
Aeronautical and Space Sciences

JAMES H. DOOLITTLE
Lieutenant General,
United States Air Force (Ret.)

GRAYSON MERRILL
Captain, United States Navy (Ret.)

DR. FRANK E. SORENSON
Chairman,
Department of Educational Services
University of Nebraska

THE HONORABLE STUART SYMINGTON
United States Senator from Missouri
Member, Senate Committee on
Aeronautical and Space Sciences

Volume 1

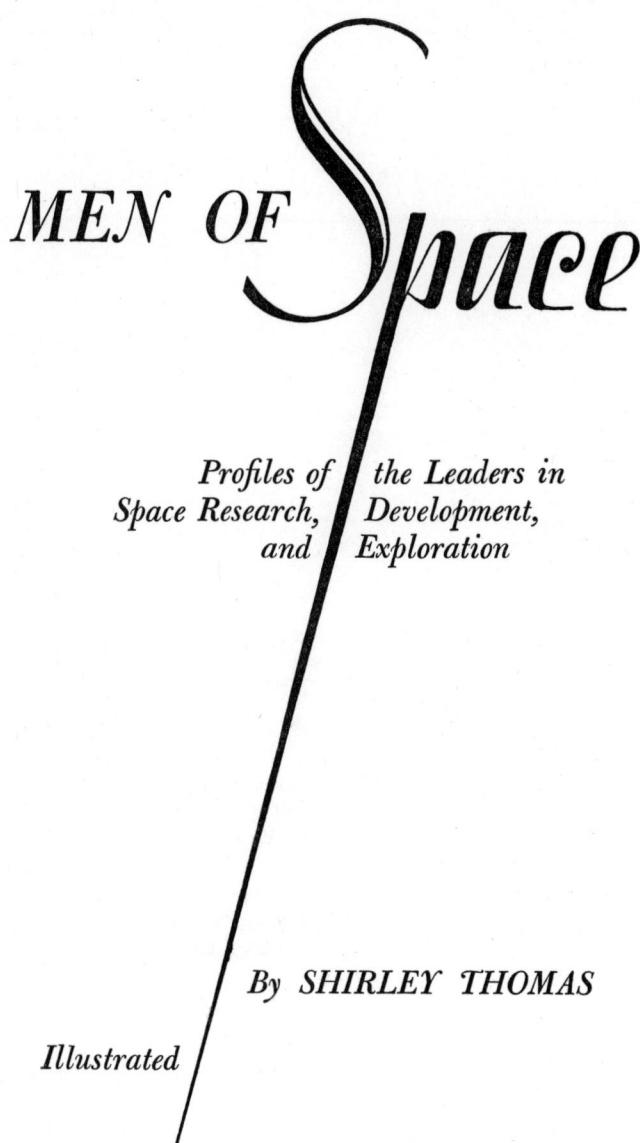

MEN OF Space

Profiles of the Leaders in
Space Research, Development,
and Exploration

By SHIRLEY THOMAS

Illustrated

CHILTON COMPANY · BOOK DIVISION
Publishers
PHILADELPHIA AND NEW YORK

Foreword

The development of human flight—beginning early in this century with the first crude attempts to fly in air and now culminating in projected journeys across airless space to the moon and the planets—is one of the boldest and most outstanding ventures ever undertaken by the mind and spirit of mankind. Man ceases to be an earth crawler and flies through the heavens.

Men who have made significant contributions to the development of rockets and astronautics are the subject of this book. They are currently changing the history of the human race. Some of these men about whom the author writes are already well-known names throughout the world; others are less familiar. In a time when we stand poised on the very threshold of manned space flight and extra-terrestrial exploration, it is both fitting and important that these men become well and even intimately known to their fellow-humans.

The Russians have a saying that the road to the stars runs through Kaluga, because in that city Konstantin Edouardovich Tsiolkovsky served as schoolmaster in the Czarist days of the late 1800's and wrote his pioneering ideas on aeronautics and astronautics.

It might also be said that the first passable road to space lies through Worcester, Massachusetts, for in that city Dr. Robert H. Goddard began his work in developing the mathematical theory of rockets, commenced the experiments that produced the world's first practical examples of this vehicle of the Space Age, and formulated his own arresting and original proposals for flight away from earth.

The path to space also lies through Kai-Feng, China, where the whole story began in A.D. 1232, with the battle between the Chinese and Tartar defenders of the city against the Mongol invaders under Ogdai Khan—a battle in which rockets were used for the first time, so far as history records. In the western world it also leads through Berlin, Peenemünde, White Sands, Cape Canaveral, Vandenberg Air Force Base, Pasadena, San Diego, Detroit, Azusa, California, and Denville, New Jersey. All of these places, and many others, have figured prominently in the story of man's progress from the mere idea of flight in space to actual accomplishments along the road to this bold venture.

In reality no one place has been the only source, and no one man the true and only progenitor of rocketry and the Space Age. The dream of astronautics has long been growing in many minds. It began perhaps as far back as the year A.D. 1500, when the legendary Wan-Hu supposedly took off on the first rocket-powered passenger flight. It developed thereafter through many generations, pushed and propelled along the way by pioneer thinkers and achievers like Sir Isaac Newton, Roger Bacon, Claude and Gaetano Ruggieri, Sir William Congreve, the American William Hale, and writers like Bishop John Wilkins, Daniel Defoe, Bishop Godwin, Cyrano de Bergerac and, of course, Jules Verne and H. G. Wells.

A movement of such sweep and momentum must necessarily be sustained and powered by the minds and energies of many men, and by the dreams of the whole human race. Nevertheless, it often finds supreme expression in the lives and works of a special few, who in some unusual way are caught up in the idea and become the key achievers of it. They are the men who, by virtue of personality, genius, inspiration or opportunity, become the selected instruments of history.

It has been my privilege to be associated with the lives and achievements of two of the men Miss Thomas has selected for her first volume of *Men of Space,* and to have known some of the others. The pioneering work of Dr. Robert H. Goddard was supported from 1929 until 1941 by grants provided by my father, Daniel Guggenheim, and The Daniel and Florence Guggenheim Foundation. During that period I knew Dr. Goddard well, and often discussed with him the plans and ideas that bore fruit in many of his experiments in New Mexico. On occasions I visited him at the site of his workshop and launching tower near Roswell, and witnessed exciting, though sometimes abortive, rocket shots. (The rockets in those days often failed at take-off, just as they sometimes do today.)

Goddard was a man of many and varied abilities. His life was one of self-less devotion to rocketry and astronautics. He never tried to dramatize either himself or his ideas. He believed firmly that the ideas would carry conviction on their own merit. I used to look forward with interest to an-other discussion with him of rockets and the particular development prob-lems of the moment. His presentations were always factual, to the point, exciting but unemotional. The solutions proposed were equally clear and imaginative. His place in history is assured. He is this country's "Father of the Space Age."

In a similar way, grants made by my father and The Daniel Guggenheim Fund for Aeronautics made it possible for the California Institute of Tech-nology to bring Dr. Theodore von Kármán to this country in 1928, and sus-tained much of his later work at the Guggenheim Aeronautical Laboratory at Caltech. Dr. von Kármán is a truly unusual man, from whose sharp and active mind ideas fly like sparks. He has a gift for selecting able young peo-ple of high promise, the ability to train and inspire them toward outstand-ing achievement, and a talent for winning affection without loss of his in-tellectual leadership. Over many years Dr. von Kármán and I have been close collaborators in devising ways to further the progress of the flight sciences. My association with him has always been a delight.

One thing the men whose biographies are contained in this book have in common, beside their contributions to rocketry and astronautics: they are all dedicated and uncommon people. I am delighted to see their lives and achievements so ably presented as they are here.

The conquest of space is one of the truly great human achievements of all times—comparable with the taming of fire, the invention of the wheel, the development of agriculture and the voyages of discovery.

In this great movement, the men whose lives are outlined in this book are epoch makers.

HARRY F. GUGGENHEIM
President,
The Daniel and Florence Guggenheim Foundation

Preface

I've been asked why I risked losing some of my old friends by serving as Chairman of the Advisory Committee to the author of the biographies *Men of Space,* when it is obviously impossible to include all of the important people in the many fields which comprise the science of astronautics—even in this plus successive volumes.

My answer is simply that I feel there is a need for these factual biographies on a representative number of persons whose colleagues agree they have really contributed to the state of the art.

There is, for example, no single industry which is self-sufficient in the area of rocketry. The development of a successful guided missile is far from being a one-man job. Nearly every field of science finds application in a major missile project. Our country's most successful missiles have been designed, developed, and produced by large teams of specialists drawn from widely separated industries, educational institutions, and government agencies. For this reason key people in a project may have little or no personal contact with one another, but being interested in their colleagues they can get to know each other better through *Men of Space.*

Then, too, technological progress in the past fifteen years has exceeded many-fold the technological advancements which had taken place in the preceding several centuries. There is no reason to believe this acceleration in advancing the frontiers of science will slow down now. So in order to maintain its leadership this nation must continue to provide increasing numbers of graduates in science and engineering. It is my hope that these real life stories of men in astronautics, and the challenges that lie ahead, will inspire more of our country's youth to choose careers in the technical fields.

But above all, the fascinating story of our missiles and space effort, and the men behind it, is one of interest to every American, and one which will help to better understand today's problems in this rapidly changing world.

I visualize, then, that the volumes *Men of Space* will be quite useful in ways other than serving as reference material for students, writers, and historians, even though, as in other human endeavors, such as football, there are always unsung heroes whose dedicated work have insured the success of their team.

H. N. TOFTOY

May 14, 1960

Author's Introduction to the
MEN OF SPACE Series

Volume 1 contains the biographical profiles of ten of the many outstanding men engaged in astronautical research, development, and exploration.

Successive volumes will be comprised of other leaders in this vast new field—men who stand shoulder to shoulder with those in this volume.

The *Men of Space* Advisory Committee has rendered invaluable aid in performing the difficult task of selecting the men for inclusion in the volumes. The responsibility for compiling the biographies has rested solely with the author, who has also included a brief biography of each of the members of the Advisory Committee, as well as of Harry F. Guggenheim, immediately following this Introduction.

The limitless support that was extended to the author from many sources since the outset made it apparent that the basis of this book was a sound one. Without this ready help, such extensive research could never have been accomplished.

The author's "unofficial technical staff" is comprised of some of the most distinguished men from each field, who generously obliged by scrutinizing each chapter. Friends of the biographees have helped in another way—by clothing the skeleton of dates and facts with the human qualities of motivation and aspiration.

To all of the above mentioned, lexicons provide no better words than "thank you" for this assistance.

SHIRLEY THOMAS

HARRY F. GUGGENHEIM

Harry F. Guggenheim is a noted authority on aviation and the flight sciences, and through his leadership in the promotion of new ideas, his encouragement of outstanding men, his interest in scientific education and his furtherance of research, has had a distinguished part in the development of rocketry and astronautics.

Son of a famous American family noted for its business leadership and philanthropy, former ambassador to Cuba, author, newspaper publisher, he is head of The Daniel and Florence Guggenheim Foundation and The Solomon R. Guggenheim Foundation, and senior partner of the firm of Guggenheim Brothers.

During World War I Mr. Guggenheim was among the first naval aviators sent to Europe. In World War II he was recalled to active duty to organize and operate Mercer Field at Trenton, New Jersey. Commander Guggenheim served on the aircraft carrier, *U.S.S. Nehenta Bay,* on combat duty in the Pacific in the spring of 1945, including the actions against Okinawa and Sakishima.

His experiences in the First World War convinced him that there was a great future in aviation—a rare opinion in those days. He was able to communicate this enthusiasm to his father, Daniel Guggenheim, then head of the firm of Guggenheim Brothers. As a result, Daniel Guggenheim, at first through personal grants and later through The Daniel Guggenheim Fund for Aeronautics, provided money to organize several outstanding schools for aeronautics at major universities.

In 1929—at a time when rocketry was still considered by most Americans too visionary for attention, and astronautics a fantasy that could never be achieved—Daniel Guggenheim, and later The Daniel and Florence Guggenheim Foundation under Harry Guggenheim's direction, sponsored and financed the experiments of Dr. Robert H. Goddard, subsequently several university laboratories.

Through such activities, and his lifelong interest and devotion to the development of the flight sciences, Harry Guggenheim occupies a unique position in this field today, and is particularly qualified to write the Foreword for this book.

MEN OF SPACE
Advisory Committee

Chairman

HOLGER N. TOFTOY
Major General, United States Army (Ret.)

"Had it not been for Toftoy's big heart and sense of duty, there would be no Redstone, no Jupiter, no Explorers." This statement from Dr. Wernher von Braun summarizes the vital contributions which the General has made to the United States' activities in space.

When the President awarded General Toftoy the Distinguished Service Medal, its accompanying citation stated in part:

"Major General Toftoy distinguished himself by exceptionally meritorious service to the government in positions of great responsibility from June 1945 to February 1958. As Chief of Technical Intelligence for Army Ordnance in Europe during the closing phases of World War II, General Toftoy (then Colonel) recognized the wealth of German scientific and engineering knowledge that had developed the V-2 rocket at Peenemünde and foresaw it as a foundation for the envisioned Guided Missile Program within the United States Army. In June 1945, General Toftoy was ordered to Washington to direct rocket and guided missile research and development for Army Ordnance. At this time, he personally implemented the selection of approximately 130 of the finest German rocket scientists to be brought to the United States and assigned them to the Research and Development Laboratories at Fort Bliss, Texas. This provided the United States Army with their unique contributions in the preliminary phases of research and development work in the missile program. In September 1954, General Toftoy assumed command of Redstone Arsenal, Huntsville, Alabama. He is credited with personally directing the program that has led to the acquirement of a complete guided missile team and a system of utilizing technical talent that has contributed immeasurably to guided missile technology in the United States. . . . He secured appropriate technical objectives and necessary resources for the early developmental stages of REDSTONE far ahead of present widespread recognition of the military value of powerful ballistic missiles. It was a modified version of the REDSTONE, the JUPITER C, that successfully launched the 'EXPLORER,' the free world's first earth satellite, on 31 January 1958. Through his continuous outstanding devotion to duty and his keen ability for making sound decisions, he has earned the highest respect of personnel in the scientific and engineering field, as well as that of his superior and subordinate military associates. General Toftoy's accomplishments reflect highest credit on himself and the military service."

THE HONORABLE STYLES BRIDGES
United States Senator from New Hampshire

Senator Bridges is a member of the vitally important new Aeronautical and Space Committee. He is ranking Republican Member of the Senate and is one of a select group of Congressional leaders who confer frequently with the President to help chart the course of the Administration's program.

He holds important positions of leadership in many functions of the Upper Chamber, being Chairman of the important Republican Policy Committee, senior Republican Member of the Appropriations Committee and ranking Minority Member of the important Armed Services Committee; he is also the GOP Member of the Senate Preparedness Investigating Subcommittee and the Republican Personnel Committee.

When Bridges was elected Governor of his home state in 1934, he was not only the youngest Governor in the country at the age of 36, but he was also the only Republican Governor elected that year. Bridges was elected to his first term in the Senate at the age of 38. He voted then to strengthen American naval and air power just as he continues to advocate a strong defense setup today.

In addition to his long service as Chairman and as ranking Republican on vital Senatorial committees during his 23 years in the Senate, Senator Bridges has also served as Minority Leader and as President Pro Tempore of the Senate.

One of three children, he was born and raised on a farm and worked his way through the University of Maine, from which he was graduated in 1918. His Alma Mater later honored him with an LL.D degree, and he holds other honorary degrees from a number of outstanding colleges and universities.

JAMES H. DOOLITTLE
Lieutenant General, United States Air Force (Ret.)

In 1922, "Jimmy" Doolittle made the first cross-country flight from Pablo Beach, Florida, to San Diego, California. The international fame which this accorded him has deepened in each of the succeeding years as his achievements and contributions mounted. The unique niche which he occupies today in the aero/space panorama was built upon a remarkable foundation.

His service career started with his enlistment as a Flying Cadet in 1917. Though his was the era of "seat of the pants flying," he acquired an outstanding technical background, earning a Doctor of Science degree from the Massachusetts Institute of Technology in 1925. He was granted a leave of absence from the service in 1926 to go to South America on airplane demonstration flights.

The year 1928 marks another outstanding event in aviation chronology —one in which General Doolittle participated. He assisted in the development of fog flying equipment; during the assignment, the now almost universally used artificial horizontal and directional gyroscopes were developed and he accomplished the first flight completely by instruments. After advising on the building of the Floyd Bennett Airport in New York City in 1930, he resigned his Regular Army commission and accepted one as Major in the Officers Reserve Corps. He was named manager of the Aviation Department of the Shell Oil Company and in that capacity conducted numerous aviation tests.

At various times, he resumed active duty with the Army to conduct experiments; in 1932, the Doolittle name was attached to one more achievement—he set the world's high speed record for land planes. But his skill in the cockpit did not overshadow his acumen behind a desk. The Army appointed him to the Board to study Air Corps organization.

The decade of the '40's began with his election as President of the Institute of the Aeronautical Sciences. Soon after, he was ordered to active duty with the Air Corps. On April 18, 1942, he led the daring first aerial raid on the Japanese mainland. Later wartime assignments were as Commander of the 15th Air Force and the 8th Air Force. In the spring of 1946, he reverted to inactive status.

General Doolittle returned to the Shell Oil Company, later to become Vice President. The numerous top decorations which he had received as an officer were matched in number by his activities as a civilian advisor. Among his distinguished appointments was that to membership of the President's Science Advisory Committee.

Space, the logical extension of the air, long occupied his thinking—dating back to such activities as his visit to New Mexico to confer with Dr. Robert H. Goddard. Astronautics became his principal endeavor in January, 1959, when he accepted the position as Chairman of the Board of Space Technology Laboratories, Inc.

GRAYSON MERRILL
Captain, United States Navy (Ret.)

Grayson Merrill is editor of a comprehensive, ten-volume work entitled *Principles of Guided Missile Design,* editor of the *Dictionary of Guided*

Missiles and Space Flight, and co-author of an undergraduate textbook, *Fundamentals of Guided Missiles.* He is general manager of Fairchild Astrionics Division, Fairchild Engine and Airplane Corporation, Wyandanch, Long Island, New York, having joined the division in 1957 as Director of Engineering, following a distinguished career as a Captain in the United States Navy.

His experience in guided missile research and development dates from the very first pilotless aircraft operated by the Navy, and he has been awarded two commendations from the Secretary of the Navy as well as the Legion of Merit for his work in the missile field.

Among his many accomplishments, Mr. Merrill conceived and managed the development of the rocket-powered Gorgon, formulated the Navy's first program for launching a guided missile, and was named first Technical Director of the Fleet Ballistic Missile (Polaris) program in 1956, the position he held prior to his retirement from the Navy.

He played a key role in the establishment of the Naval Air Missile Test Center at Point Mugu, and was its first Test Director. In other important posts, Mr. Merrill was Plans Officer of the Guided Missiles Division, Bureau of Aeronautics, and Director of the Naval Electronics and Electrical Laboratory, Johnsville, Pennsylvania.

A naval aviator with 21 years of active flying, Mr. Merrill was graduated from the U.S. Naval Academy in 1934, and returned there for postgraduate training in radio engineering. He has also studied at MIT, Harvard School of Business, and George Washington University.

Mr. Merrill is an Associate Fellow of the Institute of the Aeronautical Sciences, a member of the Education Committee, American Rocket Society, and served on the Advisory Board of the U.S. Pacific Missile Range and on the Industrial and Professional Advisory Council of the College of Engineering and Architecture at the University of Pennsylvania.

DR. FRANK E. SORENSON

Chairman, Department of Educational Services, University of Nebraska

As one of the nation's most outstanding leaders in astronautical education, Dr. Sorenson is deeply conscious of the responsibility that rests with today's young people—the responsibility of guiding their country in the new and challenging Space Age.

He serves as a vigorous Chairman of the Aerospace Education Council which has the following objective: "Formed to assume leadership within the framework of the Air Force Association in the encouragement and support of aerospace education throughout the nation and the world." Leading educators from twenty countries gathered at the International Conference on Space Age Education at the World Congress of Flight, April 12–19,

1959. The Space Education Foundation co-sponsored the event together with the Federation Aeronautique Internationale, U.S. Office of Education, University Aviation Association, and the Link Foundation.

Dr. Sorenson is Executive Secretary of the latter Foundation, assisting in its program of grants to universities, colleges, and institutions throughout the country. Created seven years ago by Edwin A. Link, of the family of Link aviation training aids, this organization strives to advance scientific, technological, and general educational projects.

A most forward-thinking educator, Dr. Sorenson travels widely from his post at the University of Nebraska, to stimulate greater interest and more active participation of students in this field of expanding technology. He is convinced of the service that can be rendered by good quality literature in the aerospace category.

An unusual combination of interests has led Dr. Sorenson into many noteworthy positions: Administrator of the Nebraska Air Age Education Division, membership on the USAF Air Training Command Advisory Board, educational advisor to the Executive Committee of the United States Air Force Association.

An important tribute came to him in 1946 when he was awarded the Frank G. Brewer Trophy, regarded as the nation's top honor in aviation education.

THE HONORABLE STUART SYMINGTON

United States Senator from Missouri

As the nation's first Secretary of the Air Force in 1947, Senator Symington has long been one of the nation's strongest influences for a positive air/space program. As a member of the Aeronautical and Space Sciences Committee, his interest and advocacy are supported by those who see in the expanding astronautics area a great, progressive step.

His responsibilities with Government date from 1941 when he went to England at the request of the War Department to study airplane armament. On July 16, 1945, he entered full-time Government service as Chairman of the Surplus Property Board; became Assistant Secretary of War for Air, 1946; Secretary of the Air Force, 1947; Chairman of National Security Resources Board, 1950; Administrator, Reconstruction Finance Corporation, 1951.

During his service in the Executive Branch, Senator Symington was approved by the Senate six times for high office without a single dissenting vote, Democratic or Republican. He was awarded the Medal for Merit in 1947, and the Distinguished Service Medal in January 1952.

On November 4, 1952, Stuart Symington was elected United States Senator for Missouri, and was re-elected November 4, 1958, by the highest percentage of votes cast in the history of Missouri, for a term ending January 3, 1965.

Senator Symington is a member of the Armed Services and the Agriculture and Forestry Committees; and is an ex-officio member of the Senate Appropriations Committee on defense matters.

As a member of the Senate, he introduced in 1955 an international plan for disarmament, by which the nations of the world would divert resources from armaments and devote them to raising living standards. This resolution was passed unanimously by the Senate.

Senator Symington is the son of the late Judge William Stuart Symington and the late Emily Harrison Symington, of Baltimore, Maryland; and the grandson of Major Stuart Symington, who served throughout the Civil War in the Army of Northern Virginia under Major General George Pickett.

On completion of high school, Symington enlisted as a private in the Army at the age of 17. Following his honorable discharge in 1919, he earned a B.A. degree at Yale.

Contents

*Brilliant advocate of space, whose
knowledge and keen imagination have
laid steppingstones toward the
exploration of the universe*

KRAFFT A. EHRICKE

"Knowledge is tomorrow's most important tool. In a world that is becoming so crowded—crowded with people of different types of living—we must acquire a feeling of pride in the kind of civilization we can produce by daring, by searching, by placing the greatest possible value on knowledge.

"Science is the most exciting life you can lead, because in performing research and making discoveries, there comes a realization that you have contributed to mankind—that you understand one more facet of the workings of nature which neither you nor anyone else ever understood before.

"A force of nature is now within our control, capable of destroying us. That force is without intelligence; whether it will obliterate us or whether it will cut across every national or sociological boundary and open the universe to us depends upon our intelligence."

With such intense concern does Krafft Ehricke speak of our newly attained capability of space exploration. Enthusiasm and drive exude from this scientist who is but in his early forties. He has a mind as visionary as it is intelligent—witness his forward-looking space concepts of the past twenty years. His interest does not end with the designing of spacecraft.

Underlying his scientific and technical prowess there exists the reflective-ness of deep thinking. To Ehricke, the vehicles provide the means; beyond that must come inquiry into the purposes and implication of this challenge before us.

James Dempsey, Manager of Convair Astronautics in San Diego, the man who employs Ehricke, recently said, "I became so exasperated with Krafft that I had the guards forcibly eject him from the plant." This was a startling statement, until he further explained, "I want that man to stay alive for a long while, but I just can't find any way to make him slow down. He'll work at his desk right through the night. Even on that evening I had him thrown out, do you know what happened? His wife said that when he arrived home he went into his den and worked the rest of the night. Krafft has a drive toward the realization of space flight that is not equaled by any-one I know anywhere in the world. It's almost a religion with him."

This "complaint" coming from Dempsey—a man who is known as a dynamo himself—is one that is not usually voiced by any executive about one of his staff. But it might be expected of Krafft Ehricke, for there is nothing usual about him or the events of his life.

Most people immigrate into the United States via ocean liner or airplane —Ehricke's papers show that he arrived by bus. The event came about when our State Department took steps to legalize the status of the scientists who were brought into the United States in Operation Paperclip at the end of World War II. Ehricke (and the other scientists) had been working for the Army at Fort Bliss in El Paso for quite some time, so when questioned how he arrived at the offices of the immigration and naturalization service his answer was, "Via an El Paso City Line bus."

Ehricke's perceptive nature feasted on the opportunity to adjust to his new life during long walks he took out into the El Paso sands. He recalls, "I thought about the future, and about America. In studying the Constitu-tion of the United States and early American history, the one thing that struck me very strongly was the high degree of rationalism that was evi-denced. In the Revolutionary period there would have been plenty of rea-son for the people who lived in Philadelphia and Boston to have expressed great emotionalism against the British. Those men who formulated the Constitution could have reflected inflamed emotions in the determination of foreign policy and other important elements of the document. I felt that part of America's wonderful heritage was due to this fact—people were constantly trying to be rational from the very beginning."

Applying it to the present, Ehricke continued, "How can man really ad-just from the way of life he has led over the last few thousand years—with its agriculture, wars, famine, plagues, through a thoroughly industrial and incomplete civilization racked by many social problems—without blowing up? The only thing that can save us today is a rational type of approach, such as that used by the men who framed the Constitution."

Krafft Ehricke went to see the motion picture "The Girl in the Moon" in Berlin in 1929, as did many another boy. But when he emerged from the theatre, he was no longer like the other twelve-year-olds—his was a soul dedicated to space flight! The science fiction film so fascinated him that he saw it a dozen times—his enthusiasm mounting with each viewing. It was a masterfully penned story by Thea von Harbou; her husband, Fritz Lang, directed the film, and Hermann Oberth was technical adviser. Oberth, the great rocket pioneer, was one of a mere handful of men who foresaw the magnitude of space exploration. Ehricke terms Oberth's contribution "technical clairvoyance."

As the boy Krafft watched the unfolding of the film, he was entranced by the sudden realization that man could leave the earth's atmosphere. His spirit traveled with the fictional occupants of the pay-load section as they hurtled toward the moon. As he thrilled to the adventure, he savored the promise that was being offered. But the words—velocity, thrust, trajectory, orbital paths! This strange vocabulary must be mastered.

Read. Study. Think. The path to the moon was not easy. His next years were devoted to the reading of material which must serve as prelude to the understanding of Hermann Oberth's book *The Rocket into Interplanetary Space*. In Krafft's life ordinary schooling was a necessity; the luxury that filled every available moment was the study of space.

Krafft had built a foundation upon which this activity might suitably rest. His reading favorites since childhood were historical biographies of such scientific leaders as Kepler and Copernicus; respect for scientific accomplishment was well ingrained. When Christmas of 1929 approached, Krafft presented his mother with a list—books on astronomy, flight mechanics, and propulsion.

Mother Ehricke offered encouragement and indulgence. The latter was called upon when Krafft decided to run an experiment inspired by reading the moon atlas she had bought him. As he studied the face of his faraway object of fascination, photographs called his attention to the lunar cracks and craters. He wanted to learn how these formed. Since both his parents were dentists, equipment was available with which to conduct interesting tests. In the Bunsen burner intended for dental work, Krafft placed small spheres of gypsum; with various methods of heating and cooling he created his own parched and crevassed moons.

Then from the writings of the Belgian professor of experimental physics, Joseph Antoine Plateau, he learned how to create a sphere in a fluid. By getting oil underneath the surface of the liquid, then using one of his mother's knitting needles, he was able to rotate the oil into a sphere. As it whirled, it split off moons, just as had our own earth-moon system in evolution.

Krafft was creating the universe—equipped only with a glass, water, oil, and a knitting needle! He began to understand in this experiment that the moon had to rotate about the earth and at the same time had to rotate about its own axis. Then he extended this formula into creating the solar system, with the sphere of oil representing the sun; he split off planets with dexterity —large ones, small ones, fast rotating ones with high oblateness like Jupiter. So vivid were those simple experiments that they are still bright in the memory of the scientist who is today responsible for one of our country's most ambitious space efforts—Project Centaur.

The next acquisition of the boy Krafft was a telescope—which he promptly perched on the balcony and, ignoring Berlin's winter temperatures, studied the constellations. His first lecture on astronomy was delivered to a spellbound audience gathered in the waiting room of his mother's dental office. None who paid ten cents to hear this youngster's remarks went away disappointed.

His remarkable mental capacity was responsible for his nonconformity at times and begot problems when it came to routine school work. In history, one of Krafft's favorite subjects, what absorbed him were the great trends affecting the rise and fall of civilizations. So, wanting to learn these things, he was understandably bored when the teacher directed attention to the memorizing of dates and places. He recalls, "He wanted to know when Ivan the Terrible or Oscar the Cross-Eyed were born, when they married and died, and how many children each had. I thought this was a statistical and unimportant thing and so actively disliked it that I often would not do my homework.

"The same was true in other subjects—like botany. I wanted to know how one flower related to a group and how that group fitted into the over-all system of plants. Without that general survey, I was not very prone to go into the details which they wanted me to learn about one single flower."

But the most distressing of all Krafft's school troubles centered about his study of mathematics—to his mother's dismay he brought home unsatisfactory grades. This subject would be the basis for his work in space— which he well knew—yet he rebelled at the dull rote of classroom math. A private instructor was assigned the task of bringing Krafft to the level of the class and was soon bewildered that there should have been any problem. He said, "This boy is doing most advanced things. When I invite him to approach a problem more elegantly, he responds with clarity. He is only fifteen, yet he is doing logarithms!"

Krafft was no "average" student. Yet, sadly, general education must be for the average—it must strive for a middle balance between the lag of the slow ones and the forward push of the exceptionally bright. Therefore neglect of those at each end results. What can be accomplished to solve the problem for students like Krafft who deserve the encouragement to develop to their full potential? The problem is formidable, but it must never be accepted as insolvable.

While his talk of stars and moon, his dreaming of advanced ideas were shrugged off by the boys on his street in Berlin, his devotion to ideals was certainly understood. At the risk of being outnumbered, or being labeled an aggressor, he would stand up to any situation in which he believed. But this young man was most particular about what he did believe.

In his words, "I always had the tendency to reserve ardent judgment on important things. I would go along only so far, then I just wouldn't be told. No matter what it was, what the field, I wanted to think it out for myself. This was instinctive at first; later I was consciously afraid to surrender my capability of judgment. With the change in government, the advent of Hitler in 1933, this trait protected me—though it also got me into great difficulty.

"Once in a youth group we were standing at attention endlessly. I said, 'I think this is nonsense,' and the leader was outraged. He then ordered me to stand separately, until I stepped out and slapped him, not caring what the consequences might be.

"When I feel I'm going to be suffocated in some way, I become stubborn as a mule. This trait, of course, was something that helped me very greatly in holding a line of thought in the Nazi era. I think propaganda is one of the worst offenses to the human mind. First of all, if someone wants to sell you propaganda, he must assume that you are fundamentally, tremendously stupid—that you will go along with extremes. Propaganda is normally extreme and does not want to allow you to think in terms of the middle ground.

"I like to paraphrase the saying 'My home is my castle.' To me, my mind is my castle. A part of it no one may enter—it is completely and absolutely taboo. I must have this ultimate, internal refuge, in which I am myself completely; only then am I really an individual."

Ultimate, internal refuge! Every man could gain rich reward from such a sanctuary.

Ehricke's hopes for active participation in rocketry were dispelled in 1933 when the VfR—the famed German Society for Space Travel—was taken over by the military. Too young before that time to enter into the activities, his dreams of applying his knowledge, gained from years of concerted study, had to be shelved. Other factors interrupted the plan for his life. He was drafted into doing manual labor for the Third Reich.

The glimmer of his dedication sparked again, briefly, when he joined with Hans K. Kaiser in organizing a new Society for Space Research in Germany. In the Journal of that Society Ehricke published many articles;

among them was one entitled *Will Man Be Cold in a Spacecraft?* This dealt with temperature and temperature control in spaceships of various shapes throughout the entire solar system; it summarized the results in a chart, which presented the equilibrium temperatures as function of solar distance for various emission and absorption ratios resulting from different materials and spaceship attitudes. Recently—twenty-one years after this publication—a chart with essentially corresponding data made its first appearance at a technical meeting in this country. This long-range thinking of Ehricke has characterized all of his space research.

His major at the Technical University of Berlin was aeronautical engineering, augmenting his space studies in helpful fashion. This brought his efforts to the merging frontiers of science and engineering, where inputs are received from each. Ehricke's view is that "science is something passive . . . we learn . . . nature teaches us. Scientific engineering is specific . . . active . . . it's a creative form. After I have absorbed the knowledge, I emit it as a human being, in a creative form."

Among his teachers at the Technical University of Berlin were the famous experimental physicist Hans Geiger, for whom the Geiger counter was named. At the University of Berlin, he heard the world-renowned nuclear physicist, Werner Karl Heisenberg. Ehricke's plan was to continue his studies until he received his doctorate in aeronautical engineering, then to enter into a second study of theoretical physics or theoretical astronomy. But his schooling was abruptly halted. War.

When the name of Krafft Ehricke appeared on the official government register, he was quickly classified as ablebodied, single, and identified as having previously been drafted into military service. Hitler needed his services immediately. His pleas brought enough extension of time to complete two more semesters of university work. In the spring of 1940 he was sent into the fury of the West front. Wounded, returned to Berlin to convalesce, Ehricke resumed his studies for a snatched period. Military orders next sent him into the heavy battle of Hitler's thrust to the East. After critical maneuvers east of Leningrad, there was instituted a top-level review of policy. The government decided that it had made an error in sending to the front men who had specialized in important technical fields.

So in the spring of 1942 Ehricke was recalled and assigned to Peenemünde, the military base which developed the V-2 rocket. Major General Walter Dornberger, the commanding officer, invited Ehricke to accompany him in his car to travel from Berlin to Peenemünde. Ehricke vividly remembers the day: "As a Lieutenant in armored divisions, I had known many tough generals. Dr. Dornberger impressed me from the beginning as being more of a scientist than a general. In spite of his resoluteness, I sensed that this man who directed Germany's long-range (at that time) missile effort offered me much more than I had a right to expect—namely, guidance and tutorship in the face of the then greatest rocket challenge.

"In spite of many overwhelming problems which he had to face practically alone to keep our work out of the hands of political opportunists, I had his benevolent attention during the subsequent years and owe to him many challenging opportunities. His technical knowledge of rockets and his enthusiasm and realistic appraisal of space development impressed me deeply. As we drove to Peenemünde that day, Dr. Dornberger made some brief and to-the-point remarks: 'Dr. von Braun and Dr. Thiel are among the very few who really understand the technology and the future of rockets as the instrument of a new age.' In the years to come I had many opportunities to recognize the truth of his analysis."

Further describing his work, Ehricke says, "Although I was assigned as assistant to Dr. Walter Thiel, Director of Propulsion Development, I was not too eager to settle down in a plush office job. I am forever grateful to Dr. von Braun and Dr. Thiel that I did not have to. They gave me first the opportunity to work on the test stand with a monkey wrench, and in this manner I was able to acquaint myself thoroughly with the hardware on hand before theorizing on how to improve it. After all, that is the way they both started, so the benefits of such work were well illustrated. In the last years I have observed young engineers starting right off as experts without having done honest design work on one single component or having once gotten their hands dirty on lowly hardware. I feel regrets for them, because they are deprived of a wonderful opportunity which will never return after they have grown in status and responsibility.

"Eventually at Peenemünde more planning and theoretical work took over. In Dr. Thiel's office we were concerned with test planning, test evaluation, and liaison work to outlying research laboratories. I was later assigned to do an evaluation of the German nuclear development work, with respect to possible application to rocket propulsion." Ehricke adds, "I didn't get very far with it, for the work in Germany was much less developed in the nuclear field than it was in the United States. Following the big attack on Peenemünde in 1943, in which Dr. Thiel and his family died, we did other advanced studies; but they gradually diminished because it became apparent that none of them would be realized." As Germany's downfall came, Dornberger, von Braun, and many others, exerted great effort to get to where they might surrender to American officers. Ehricke was among them. "I once escaped through a rear door while Russian soldiers were storming through the front door," he vividly recalls in an interview which appeared in the *San Diego Evening Tribune* on March 24, 1958.[1]

When the Allied occupation began, following V-E Day, many of the German scientists were invited to go to America in Operation Paperclip—the remarkable project headed by the then Colonel H. N. Toftoy (now Major General U.S.A. Ret.), which brought to our shores 127 of the scientists who had furthered the art of rocketry in Germany. But Ehricke was not in this initial group.

His wife, Ingeborg, was in Berlin. There was no transportation to get there—absolutely none. So he walked for thirty days to get from Bavaria to the capital. Traveling with him were two ladies from the staff at Peenemünde who soon became too footsore to walk. He found a wagon used for carrying hay and used it to convey them, pulling the load for the many long miles to the area of their homes in the Harz Mountains. Then he turned east and continued his trudge to Berlin. Relief welled within him when he found Inge was all right—though, of course, living under most difficult conditions.

For Krafft and Inge only the first week of their meeting had been free from the pall of war. They were brought together by friends when they were vacationing on the beautiful Island of Amrum in the North Sea. Those carefree, exhilarating moments of happiness were sobered by the bugles of battle—Germany marched into Poland.

Stranded on the island for days, they were unable to return to the mainland until the ship *Queen Louise* suddenly put into port. The word went out —only those with identification papers would be permitted to board. Inge had none with her. Krafft insisted that she pack and come to the ship anyway and trust to him to get her on board.

As they climbed the gangplank, officers were stationed on either side to inspect the papers. Krafft nudged her. "Here, you take my dog, and just go ahead. Don't turn around, just go through, and let me do the talking." In a few moments, he joined her on deck. Their friends—who had been watching the incident—laughed with joy and drank a toast to the success of getting Inge on board. Though she was baffled by it all, they were in on the ruse he had used to get her through; he had turned the family ring he wore so that it looked like a wedding ring and passed Inge off as his wife.

The next day after their return to Berlin Krafft came calling, armed with a massive bouquet. The handsome, twenty-three-year-old man was not only charming; he was studious. He remained until dawn, talking philosophy with her father. Then, as now, the word which friends and associates most often used to describe him was "gentlemanly."

Only when Inge received word that Krafft had been drafted did she realize that she loved him. Through long separations during the War their engagement persisted; for one dreadful year Inge did not even hear from her fiancé. Battles, bombs, separations—all are the scourge of war.

Finally it ended. Krafft and Inge were reunited—though in a distraught Berlin—and their life together might at last begin. It was here in Berlin that their first daughter was born, and they chose the name Krista, spelled with a hard K, to ever remind them of the hard days they were experiencing at the time. Krafft's father presented to the baby a family ring like the one Krafft had used to get Inge aboard the boat in 1939. The ring had become a treasured family tradition, with its Arabic inscription, "In faithful memory."

Suddenly, now, memories were mingled with promises. In early December, 1946, Major Sternberg approached Krafft with a contract to work in the United States.

Ehricke can still relive his first impression. "My arrival in this country, especially the trip from New York to El Paso, was almost like a dream. It was as if I had gotten on another planet. I had come out of a Europe that was war-devastated and in need; but, even if it hadn't been that way, the Continent is relatively heavily populated—there you are accustomed to having people everywhere and every square inch of ground being utilized. You never see great stretches of endless plains, deserts, or mountains.

"Of course, New York had impressed me tremendously. But my greatest experience was on my arrival at El Paso. Our plane touched down in the morning—about five-thirty—and it was just sunrise over the desert. It was breathtakingly beautiful. The dry, transparent air is something Northern Europeans see very rarely. And the whole layout of the city was unbelievable. Here was a little modern downtown district—with skyscrapers even—in the middle of nowhere! It was surrounded by miles and miles, endless miles of desert. I fell completely in love with the country. I could have stayed in El Paso forever.

"In the months following, I explored the city and got accustomed to such things as supermarkets—and to the fact that I could really go in and buy ten pounds of cheese or twenty pounds of butter if I wanted. This was certainly quite a contrast to conditions in Europe toward the end of the war.

"I walked out into the desert and climbed the mountains that are directly to the west of El Paso, staying out from sunup to dark. Europe, the War, those terrible experiences, the great need—as if by magic, they completely disappeared. I suddenly felt that life could be something different—something much more beautiful, much more exciting."

Two assignments were given Ehricke in his new post with our Army at El Paso: first, he was to familiarize the military and industry with various aspects of the V-2 rocket, and second, to perform theoretical work. In this new land with its foreign language, he found he could resume his scientific endeavors without difficulty. But the thing that defeated him was his efforts to read the funny papers. As he attempted to understand the slang and colloquialisms of "Blondie" or "Bringing Up Father," he realized that his schoolbook study of classic English would never enable him to speak and read "American." He hit upon a plan to learn quickly!

"Mr. Birney," asked Ehricke of the editor of the camp reports, "would you have the kindness to read over what I have written here, go over it with a red pencil, and tell me what is wrong with it? You can't hurt me. Tell me even if there is not a single thing right." Hoffman A. Birney, who had authored books about the Indian country and was a former book critic for *The New York Times,* generously agreed to help him.

Ehricke had evolved a method of teaching himself common usage, slang, and application of the language of this country that he had adopted. He wrote little stories—themes. Birney, with the patience and perseverance of a true scholar, read, marked, and made suggestions. The first writings were laced with red pencil. Again and again they were written—rewritten. Birney's comments guided Ehricke on an ever improving path.

The man with a weak leg exercises until he becomes a physical specimen; the boy who has known hunger grows up to become a tycoon; the shy girl becomes an aggressive woman—overcompensation. A handicap reaches into the spirit of a person and drives him into a frenzy of action. In Ehricke's case the effort was toward overcoming the barrier of the English language. His intelligent approach and slavish application brought him to such a high standard that his writings are among the finest in the field. The help of Hoffman A. Birney shall never be forgotten, for it continues to pay dividends.

Recently James Dempsey commented, "One of the interesting sidelights about Krafft, I think, is that he uses the English language perhaps more precisely than anybody else around here. Also, he has great descriptive powers. For instance, we had been trying for eight or ten months to get an answer from the Air Force on a particular question; in reporting the current status Krafft said, 'I think we now are gradually drifting toward a decision.' That summed up the situation better than anything I've ever heard."

The path of progress led Ehricke from El Paso to Huntsville, Alabama, and the Army's Redstone Arsenal, where he became Chief of the Gasdynamics Section and worked with ram jets, as well as heat transfer research. Here his principal attention was devoted to the development of supersonic diffusers for high-speed ram jet engines.

The diffuser is a system of inlets, or a single inlet, into which streams supersonic air in a ram jet engine. To control shock waves, Ehricke introduced a scheme of alternate shock waves and expansion waves in such a fashion that the boundary layer of air could be smoothed out between the various compressions of the air. As he explains it, "Every time you compress a boundary layer, it gets excited and wants to separate; so then you run it through an expansion fan and sort of calm it down again by relieving the adverse pressure before the next compression."

In 1952 the ponderings of this imaginative brain also moved in the direction of two types of rocket launchings into space—one for men, one for cargo. Previously it had always been assumed that the crew would carry with it the required equipment for its orbit. But, reasoned Ehricke, this is rather inefficient. With men aboard, a winged vehicle is necessary, and many safety provisions must be incorporated. These extra safety provisions can be eliminated in cargo rockets—thereby allowing great reduction in weight. Thus was first stated the plan for initially firing cargo ships into orbit to be followed by rockets that would carry men.

With proliferation the ideas continued to flow. Ehricke introduced the principle of very, very low orbits. Always before, orbits of a thousand nautical miles or even more had been proposed. A long series of calculations convinced Ehricke that this was an unnecessary and expensive plan. Why not orbit as closely as possible to the earth as the ship is assembled to go from this orbit into space? Now, the parking orbit—or perigee orbit—is a generally adopted approach.

From this grew the conviction that another wrong theory was being followed—that of the massive space station as a point of departure into many areas of space. Ehricke deduced that this space station might be in a completely wrong plane and would thus require great expenditure of power to change the flight vector of the departing vehicle to adjust for this error. This would be an even greater problem with vehicles returning to the space station after a probe into deep space; on a self-arbitrary orbit, which had neither the same inclination nor the same distance from the earth as the orbiting space station, the rendezvous would indeed be difficult.

Therefore there should not be just one space station from which to do all exploration. In the scientific paper which Ehricke delivered at the Fifth International Astronautical Federation Congress in 1954 at Innsbruck, he suggested that the approach be in terms of smaller stations—several of them —and that these stations have specific tasks. A "lumber camp" approach should be used: go to the proper orbit, do the job, then forget about that space station and launch another to accomplish the next mission.

"After twenty years with Krafft, I'm still flabbergasted at his knowledge. I don't know how he acquires it when he is working night and day, but he keeps up with everything. There is nothing in this world that cannot be discussed with him. It doesn't matter who comes to visit and what subject is brought up, even if it has nothing whatever to do with Krafft's work, he has read all about it and is able to speak about it and give his opinion. There is never a dull moment," says Inge with wifely devotion.

How does he accomplish this? "He never spoils a minute," she says. "He's figuring out integrals and mathematical problems even when he's watching detective programs on television or playing with the children."

The second daughter, born in Buffalo after Krafft had joined Bell Aircraft Corporation, was given the lyrical name Astrid, derived from the Latin word *astrum* meaning star, constellation, or height. Her eyes are still like beautiful blue stars in the heavens. Doris made her debut in San Diego, fulfilling a dream Krafft had long held to have a child born by the ocean; to remember that, she was given this name of the Goddess of the Sea.

San Diego was to have been but a stopover to visit old friends; but, when Ehricke was approached by Convair to join their staff and work on the Atlas intercontinental ballistic missile, he remained to make it his home.

Ehricke's decision to join the San Diego company was influenced greatly by Karel (Charley) Bossart—who was then technical director of the Atlas and had contributed several innovations in its design. There was found in this association an attitude of understanding for his far-range thinking; the executive personnel encouraged Ehricke in his important studies—one study that emerged concluded that the Atlas had the capability of firing itself into orbit carrying a small orbital research and test vehicle as pay load.

This proposal answered an urgent need exactly three years later, when Mr. Roy Johnson—then head of the Advanced Research Projects Agency —asked Convair for some spectacular feat which this country could perform to offset the impact of the Russian launched Sputnik. Project Score was the result—the 822-pound "talking satellite" which broadcast President Eisenhower's Christmas message to the world. This shot helped restore to America some of its crumbling scientific prestige!

Design Specialist Freeman D'Vincent recalled that "Krafft would come up with a configuration—perhaps from his broad background, perhaps just intuition—and I would think maybe he might be mistaken so I would begin trying to prove him wrong. I'd go around in a big circle and end up with his original design. After all I specialize in structure, and his basic work is in flight mechanics. But, doggone it, he's always a jump ahead of me in my own specialty."

D'Vincent asked the question that recurs from all who know this dynamic scientist: "Where does he get all this knowledge—and all the enthusiasm and energy—even when he works fourteen-hour days? He never has time to meet with the vendors, yet he seems to have a thorough knowledge of everything that is going on. A very sharp representative of one of the largest propulsion companies came in one day and described a new design. Krafft told him it wasn't right, and they got into such a discussion that each was betting his pay check. Two days later the propulsion expert came back and conceded that Krafft was correct. Now I've just given up —I automatically assume he's right."

The key to performance of rockets, to extension of range, to more reliable guidance, to heavier pay loads, all lay in one word—propulsion. Propellants are like a family of daughters—some are reliable and easy to get along with, some will wait patiently, others must be tended constantly, and some are tempestuous and unpredictable. One of the wildest and most difficult of them all is a half-caste—liquid hydrogen-liquid oxygen, O_2/H_2. With a nature approaching absolute zero—423°F—there were rewards awaiting the man who had the intrepidity to tangle with her, for she promised far greater energy than any of her faithful sisters. Ehricke was not the first to undertake to tame her.

The "hydrogen story" dates from the theoretical pioneer Konstantin Tsiolkovsky. For the film, "The Girl in the Moon," in 1929, Oberth designed a model of an oxygen/hydrogen upper stage for the final portion of the journey. In the following years hydrogen offered so many practical difficulties that efforts toward its use in early rocket projects had to be abandoned. Hydrogen slipped into the category of a very energetic but also very impractical rocket fuel.

In 1947 von Braun assigned Ehricke to study the feasibility of using liquid hydrogen for missiles after a technical report had been written by another scientist advocating it. Ehricke verified von Braun's contention that hydrogen was not right for missiles, but as Ehricke extended the study to space vehicles he could confirm Oberth's belief that for upper stages and very high energy requirements O_2/H_2 and comparable high-energy propellants were most attractive. Ehricke continued his studies and published a report in the September-October, 1953, *ARS Journal* of the American Rocket Society, concluding that for space operations O_2/H_2 for chemical rockets and H_2 for nuclear rockets of high mission energy requirements were most attractive. His conclusions have been verified.

There were others who sporadically investigated this fuel—Dr. Johnson of the University of Ohio, John Sloop, and Abe Silverstein of NACA (National Advisory Committee on Aeronautics)—but the general feeling remained that H_2 was at best a far-in-the-future proposition for rockets. In fact, some most emphatic reports were issued against it.

As is usually true with advanced work, Ehricke's efforts during 1956 and 1957 were highly classified; he was giving countless presentations to ARDC (Air Research and Development Command) in Baltimore and also in the Pentagon on strategic high-altitude satellites and the O_2/H_2 upper stage for the Atlas to get them into orbit. From among numerous proposals submitted to the military this vehicle concept was selected. The Centaur principle set the pattern for the latest and final versions (C-1 and C-2) of von Braun's Saturn rocket.

His colleagues readily admit that it was "Ehricke's bulldoggedness" that put through the acceptance of this important "next step" in propellants. He not only had the scientific acumen to reach a correct conclusion; he had the conviction to fight for it. Could such have happened if this man had not had what he terms an "ultimate refuge" within himself? That inner recess of his mind stood up against the trend. Such a character trait offers protection, for, since the day of Pontius Pilate, the lesson has been monotonously repeated with both large and small matters—majority opinion can be wrong.

Krista, now attending high school, and Astrid and Doris, occupied alternately with romping as cowgirls and twirling as ballerinas, are receiving strong paternal encouragement toward independence. "The strength to stand alone if necessary is—in my opinion—one of the most important things in life," reasons Ehricke. "I see young people driven into a panic when they are excluded from a fraternity or sorority. This obsession to conform is one of the worst things possible. And in time there must come a change in the penchant some youngsters have of calling any serious student a 'square.' They must see how ridiculous it is, for the world of tomorrow—more than ever before—will be controlled by people of intelligence.

"From boyhood I've studied and read the stories of the lives of pioneer scientists; so I early learned this—physics and mathematics are the best places to start a science education. Today a thorough grounding in these subjects is like 'ready cash.' They are actually the currency with which you can buy yourself into any field."

The extensive background which Ehricke has in science, combined with his tremendous enthusiasm, has prompted him to turn many a twenty-minute briefing into a much, much longer session. These briefings—which he delivers to important government people and visiting dignitaries, such as the Aga Khan—became the object of some needling by friends and associates. With his usual spirit of determination Ehricke decided to take corrective measures. Now he pointedly looks at his watch as he begins and as he ends a briefing. When he has come close to the allotted time, a smile of triumph frames his face!

Freeman D'Vincent explains one reason for Krafft's being such a favorite with others at Convair—he has an ever present habit of seeing the better side of everybody. Once as they walked through the plant together a fellow worker was far away from his desk. To most it would seem apparent that the man was "goofing off," but Krafft's reaction was, "There's a fine fellow. He's been down at the library studying I imagine." (Such faith has remarkable influence—next time the man probably went to the library!)

The hum of activity has risen to a high pitch at Convair with the Centaur project. In the scramble of late 1957, when Sputnik I triggered frenzied reaction and quick proposals on every side, Convair had the advantage of studies on which Ehricke had spent years.

As he mentions, "I kept expecting James Dempsey to look at my various studies and say, 'You're way too fast. Stop that kind of planning.' But instead he always urged me to continue."

So when the atmosphere in Washington changed, when there was receptivity to daring proposals, Ehricke was well prepared. In 1958 Project Centaur was created. In the upper stages of this first real space vehicle, there will be utilized liquid oxygen-liquid hydrogen—the high-energy propellant that has been Ehricke's big crusade. This mighty vehicle will be capable of orbiting pay loads of 9200 pounds at 100 miles altitude—or it can land a 700-pound cargo of delicate instruments on the moon—or it can perform by sending between 1000 and 2000 pounds in a close probe of Venus or Mars!

The Centaur upper stage can start itself in zero gravity after it has left the earth's atmosphere. This fact is important for the reason that Ehricke explains in this way, "If you enter an orbit in the vicinity of the earth and want them to climb into a very high orbit, it is necessary to give yourself another kick to go farther! Then it is necessary to close up the ends when you arrive at the higher destination to prevent falling back. After floating around weightless for hours, in order to start powered flight again there must be extra engines with monergolic fuel. Monergolic fuel is one that does not have a separate oxidizer and a fuel; both are combined as in the case of hydrogen peroxide, which through decomposition from the cartridge becomes oxygen and steam—extremely hot and expanding to produce thrust. By employing the oxygen/hydrogen concept, Centaur actually blazes a trail for all the chemical space vehicles to come."

There is an aspect to activating a space project that must rate almost as much attention as the technical feasibility—and that is the economic battle to present it, get the proper support, and finally the decision to go ahead with it. Dempsey comments that "Krafft sometimes underestimates these latter obstacles. As a result, he has an enthusiasm which is not always felt in more cynical circles. I think his perseverance at a time when nobody else was interested or permitted to talk about space was one of the things that gave us here at Convair Astronautics a very good position and the ability to develop projects like Centaur."

Scientifically, Ehricke's imagination and finely trained mind can conjure and solve the problems of how to travel about in space. But to understand the real motivation behind his outpourings, a relationship must be established to his philosophical reasoning of why man shall investigate space. In the November, 1957, issue of the American Rocket Society's publication, *Astronautics,* he writes:[2]

"It is part of our heritage as children of this planet to seek out other worlds, to grow and to mature with our expanded capabilities into degrees of freedom and independence which would make present-day societies appear like the incredible confinements of medieval communities or African tribal regulations. It is a historical fact that man's mind and spirit grow with the space in which he is allowed to operate. . . .

"We today are merely the shipbuilders for the men and women who will enter the new era of discoveries and lay the foundations for those after them who will develop planetary technologies and create cosmic civilization."

Since 1929, when he was twelve, Krafft Ehricke has lived, dreamed, and thought space. So precious to him were his rocket models that he took them to a remote farm and buried them, lest the battles of World War II damage them in his home in Berlin. (The home was not touched; the farm was overrun by Russian occupation forces and the models never retrieved.) Over thirty years of such concentration on the topic of space has produced a man whose commonplace thoughts naturally extend to the universe; the most startling concepts will flow from his conversation as the accepted, while his vision is racing into the next challenging area. George Whitney, Vice-President and General Manager of KFMB-TV, thanked Krafft for a guest appearance with these words, "San Diego must consider itself fortunate in having in its scientific community one of the world's foremost apostles of space travel."

Ehricke is equally at home with a conference room of scientific giants or at a P.T.A. meeting. Dorothy Schiefer, secretary of the Farnum group, wrote thanking him for "one of the most exciting experiences we have ever had. We are honored that you would give of your valuable time to help us understand our future in space." To emphasize how thoroughly he captivated an audience of mothers and fifth graders (who pelleted him with questions), she adds, "We would cheerfully have purchased a vacuum cleaner if you had requested it!" Ehricke's appeal is equally great among his colleagues as is indicated by this Christmas message he received: "You were voted the most popular lecturer of the Space Technology Institute! Congratulations on this and on your 'talking Atlas.'"

Fellow scientists further evidenced their respect for Ehricke when they honored him in 1955 with the first Gunther Loeser Medal for presentation of the best paper at the Sixth Congress of the International Astronautical Federation. In 1957 for "outstanding contribution to the advancement of space flight," the American Rocket Society bestowed upon him their Astronautics Award.

Thomas G. Lanphier, Jr., the crusading former Vice-President of Convair, relates that Ehricke is a "scientist's scientist." In meetings when controversy arises, one or another of them will turn to Ehricke for verification of technical points. To be so accepted by this exclusive and objective fraternity of men—and to have done it in such a short time—is a remarkable attainment. Lanphier adds, "Ehricke is a tremendous thinker—and he thinks such 'nice' thoughts. There is a great, gentle quality about him."

Such tributes are testimony to many qualities in the man Ehricke; the most outstanding among them, perhaps, would be creativeness. The artisan reproduces or adapts; the artist creates. This elusive spark that a kindly fate grants to some answers to another name also—inspiration.

This is the common denominator that links Ehricke to the ages. For whatever has been the tongue that was spoken—whether the garments have been togas, silken breeches, or blue serge—whether the fields of activity have been music or mathematics—all who create are bound together with an indestructible mortar. The provocation is always the same; only the forms of manifestation vary. When this potential rests within a soul, it bubbles to the surface, like oil that gushes from the ground, refusing the confines of a hundred million pounds of earthly pressure.

The beings who create are allotted a force that surpasses in magnitude the power that is mightiest in most—that of self-preservation. Indeed personal well-being is generally an object of neglect to the creative person.

Insatiable curiosity emerges as another shared quality. These creative ones display the courage to probe into the vast areas of the unknown; their probing extends also into the mountains of accepted beliefs, searching for that possible crevasse of error.

Just as no fetters can bind the scope of their thoughts, obstacles appear but as tenpins to be tumbled. Those with purpose fashion opportunity from the tools at hand. Ehricke cut his pattern from the historical biographies he devoured as a boy: Sir Isaac Newton, cast from his home at the age of three when his mother remarried, was taken back only when she needed him to work on her farm. Though removed from school Newton still persevered in his study of mathematics and eventually set forth laws and theories that multiplied man's store of knowledge; Galileo Galilei's father sheltered him from the subject of mathematics, fearing it would distract him from the study of medicine but, when the boy overheard a discussion of geometry, so passionate was the response in his mind that he plunged into a study of mathematics.

Why do such men heed a call? Not for applause—a monastery or a lonely laboratory has allowed no witness to some of civilization's greatest forward strides. Even threat of imprisonment and torture has not deterred the conviction of great scientific minds. The sustenance of faith has a core no despot can comprehend. Our progress to date as a civilization has one interesting means of measure—we have grown more understanding of scientists. But true maturity will come only when we take the next step and extend greater encouragement and support for their perpetual efforts to better the world.

Today there are discernible the glimmerings of a change in the general attitude toward the forward thinkers. If these small indications were to develop into a trend, what an age of promise could emerge! The history of rocketry is still so fresh that we can almost hear the plaintive unheeded

call sounded by Dr. Robert H. Goddard in the Twenties and the Thirties, urging serious consideration of this new art. Whether or not we listen, science, in an inevitable way, will always progress. But if rapport can be established between the great and the less great, how much acceleration can be added to the pace! This Space Age demands it. We cannot fail to use the full potential of all our creative minds.

Krafft Ehricke believes, "A very great event of our time is the integration of technology and science into our way of life. It has increased our capability to communicate with each other and has increased our capacity of reasoning. However, communication is a very dangerous two-sided sword. It also can be used to whip up mass hysteria.

"But since a human being has the capability of learning, exposure to an unfortunate situation teaches him to resist it. Like someone who has been ill, he becomes immune to the same disease. There are exceptions, of course, and oscillations up and down. But speaking of major trends, whenever man has gone through an experience, he has learned from it. In my opinion, the term 'history repeats itself' is not correct. Trends repeat themselves, but history, as such, shows always an inclination toward gradual improvement.

"To me the worst thing that could happen to man would be confinement to certain mental conditions and a way of life from which he could never break out. This would bar him from experiences, which in turn would prevent him from maturing. You must go through these things. You don't mature abstractly by thinking about them—at least the human race is not yet of that high caliber.

"So the best way of developing man, I feel, is by exposing him to new challenges. This brings about an interaction between knowledge and experience. With knowledge you create something new that can be used for good or bad. That's where knowledge stops. Man's reaction is one of emotion—he's still the animal who threw himself on the ground 10,000 years ago when lightning struck. Man doesn't throw himself on the ground anymore, but he still has the tendency of being on the defensive at first. So he misuses the experience. Then, in the final phase, he understands it, incorporates it into his wealth, and uses it correctly. It's the only way to grow. Anything that holds us back, 'fences us in,' is bad for us in the long run."

There are no fences sufficiently high to restrict Ehricke's thinking. The individual problems that lie ahead on each project he recognizes in an embryonic state and drops each into his mind, like seed in the good earth. Then, in constant rotation, this crop is tilled by his conscious and his subconscious. He searches out cross-connections with other problems in other fields until the matter at hand is gradually assimilated. He says, "In this manner, I am able to combine strict scientific methods with intuition. If my work is in the conceptual fields, I need this intuition. If a proposal is right or wrong depends on more than just whether it is technically feasible. With too much concentration on the technical aspects, a good idea could be aborted."

Space Flight: Environment and Celestial Mechanics is an imposing work published in 1959, the first of three volumes which Krafft Ehricke is writing. These textbooks are the efforts of decades. They will stand as monumental contributions to this science and shed new rays of knowledge on the still dark areas of space.

In this branch of science progress is outdistancing expectation—reality is in a headlong race with Buck Rogers, and we're gaining on him with every lap. "He used to be 2000 years ahead of us—now he's no more than 500," is a favorite quip around the Pentagon. Nothing is more remarkable actually than the drastic change in our attitude about this. To the average person, fantasy became reality overnight. On October 3, 1957, America's attention was focused on the World Series. On October 4, 1957, a much larger ball was orbiting through the sky, with the universe as its ball park. Facing the stark reality of Sputnik, we quickly "came of space age."

What's ahead? Tomorrow? Next year? Ten years? The pondering of these questions has produced one of the most fascinating documents ever compiled, *The Next Ten Years in Space*. It is a lengthy report prepared by the Select Committee on Astronautics and Space Exploration of the House of Representatives and contains myriad visionary predictions by those who are considered among the world's leading authorities on space.

The Committee chose well in inviting Krafft Ehricke to participate in this report, for no scientist has demonstrated greater vision combined with the technical genius to turn dreams into workable hardware. His projections are poised on the launching pad we call "today" and stand ready to blast off into the long trajectory of time, aimed for that "tomorrow" a decade away.

With carefully prepared tables, Ehricke has set a schedule for our most daring exploits; he has reduced the vastness of space exploration to a lucid outline which logically progresses from the existing "state of the art." With his customary deft handling of words, he conveys his expansive thinking in "Plateaus of Achievement." The final page of his report summarizes in this manner:

"By the end of the next ten years we can thus expect the following state of development in astronautics:

"1. Communication and television relay satellites at very great altitudes, probably as high as 22,000 miles (twenty-four-hour orbit) in equatorial and inclined orbits.

"2. Global weather monitoring on a routine basis from optical satellites circling the globe in polar or highly inclined orbits some 4000 to 8000 miles high.

"3. Radio-navigation satellites some 1000 miles high, serving the ships on seas in equatorial and inclined orbits.

"4. One or more relatively small manned space stations some 300 miles high in the equator plane for orbital flight training, life-support systems development, and man-conducted research in space.

"5. All or many of these satellites and space stations will be equipped with nuclear auxiliary power supply systems.

"6. Satellites of the Moon will have been established and landings with instrumented probes on the Moon will have been accomplished. Probably the first landings by man will have been achieved.

"7. Man will have circumnavigated the Moon using vehicles launched directly from the Earth's surface without orbital assembly or fueling.

"8. Interplanetary probes will have covered the entire inner solar system from inside the orbit of Mercury to the asteroid belt beyond Mars. Encounter probes will have been sent to Venus and Mars and instrumented satellites of these planets will have been established. Probes may have been sent out as far as to the planet Jupiter.

"9. All these projects will have been carried out essentially on the basis of chemical rockets, such as ICBM boosters with advanced chemical upper stages and the 1.5 million pound thrust booster with chemical upper stages. However, at the end of the decade nuclear powered upper stages, boosted beyond the atmosphere by chemical first stages, will be available.

"10. Research in auxiliary power systems, energy conversion, materials, and electrical propulsion systems will have made great strides.

"11. Close international cooperation in the scientific and practical usage of satellites, as well as in monitoring and tracking of space vehicles and in control of transmission frequencies, will have been established. At least one new launching complex for space vehicles will have been built, located in the Mid-Pacific on or near the Equator.

"12. Man will have sufficient information to decide for or against a permanent lunar base and will begin to look to the planets Venus and Mars as his goals for the decade to come."

To perform these feats he has outlined, advancements must occur. Just as Ehricke crusaded for the adoption of liquid hydrogen-liquid oxygen fuel, he now is urging the next decisive progression, nuclear propulsion. To travel the almost incomprehensive distances in space in a time span that is reasonable, propulsion of this magnitude will be required. "Specific impulse" is the gage by which propellants are measured. RP-1, liquid oxygen fuel commonly used in today's launchings, has a specific impulse of approximately 260 seconds; a nuclear propellant would have a specific impulse of at least 800 seconds. (This means that one pound of propellant expelled per second will deliver that many pounds of thrust.)

In recent testimony before a Congressional committee, Ehricke explained:

"The universe is run by nuclear energy. Space will be conquered only by manned nuclear powered vehicles. Planning anything else for the late Sixties is, in my opinion, flirting with obsolescence almost from the start. At the risk of being repetitious, I would like to express again my strong conviction that *the nuclear engine is for astronautics what the combustion engine is for aeronautics,* namely the basis for true superiority and utility in atmospheric flight. The chemical rocket engine is a carry-over into the space age from the missile phase, just like the balloon helped bring about the air age. Like the balloon, the chemical rocket will retain indefinitely its usefulness for special applications. However, true astronautics and nuclear power are inseparably connected. I am firmly convinced that the surest way to cripple the United States space capability of the Seventies is to cripple the nuclear engine development now in the critical years ahead."

Ehricke's hopes are not limited to these leaps outward into the universe. He hopes, also, to reach inward, into the minds of men and to exhort them to work together. Only with international co-operation can effective interplanetary experiments be conducted. Probes to the moon and to the planets demand a world-wide net of tracking stations. By sharing one system and by jointly evaluating scientific data, enormous benefits could accrue to all nations. The location of launching sites also stresses the necessity of agreement—some orbits can be achieved from the equator; others must be gained from launchings far to the north or south.

But, as he said in the March 28, 1958, issue of *Aviation Week,*[3] this can be realized only "if reason can prevail in these matters over hostile pride." He repeatedly voices the hope for an International Astrophysical Decade from 1965 to 1975—a plan which he feels could have even greater potential than the tremendous achievements of the International Geophysical Year.

With the wisdom of a philosopher, Ehricke has opened the vistas of thought with three Laws of Astronautics—a trilogy expressing an inspired faith, which first appeared in an article he wrote for the November, 1957, issue of *Astronautics:*[2]

> "I. Nobody and nothing under the natural laws of this universe imposes any limitations on man except man himself.
>
> "II. Not only the earth, but the entire solar system, and as much of the universe as he can reach under the laws of nature, are man's rightful field of activity.
>
> "III. By expanding through the universe, man fulfills his destiny as an element of life, endowed with the power of reason and the wisdom of the moral law within himself."

To achieve the almost incomprehensible distance to the moon and planets is triumph in itself, but there the story only begins for Ehricke. As the final climax builds in this space adventure, he foresees "the opportunity of utilizing the vastness of space for real purpose. For instance, in the long space between earth and moon, we will conduct superexperiments—in which we simulate cosmic processes by means of very large thermonuclear bombs, which we would never like to explode on the earth. It's like being able to move with nitroglycerin experiments out of a basement and into a laboratory which is explosion-proof. I believe that by means of experiments of this type which we can conduct in earth-moon space, and perhaps even farther out, we will get new experience and new knowledge of the nature of matter and the nature of gravity; and finally, the third objective, we will achieve the capability of operating on the surface of other worlds—the moon, Mars, Venus—to study whatever life exists there. If a planet has not been able to develop life by itself, it may be able to sustain life which we could implant."

Earnestly Ehricke savors the prospect. "With these gigantic laboratories, we will experiment on a scale unknown to us at this time!" The dream in his heart has changed but little. At twelve he was creating the universe with a glass of water, a glob of oil, and his mother's knitting needle. Now his remarkable mind by its great expansion has shrunk the universe until he grasps it as easily as a glass of water and speaks of "superexperiments" that stagger imagination!

Krafft Ehricke is the embodiment of his belief—the only limitations are those man places on himself, and the universe is man's rightful field of activity!

REFERENCES

1. *San Diego Evening Tribune,* March 24, 1958.
2. *Astronautics,* American Rocket Society, November, 1957.
3. *Aviation Week,* March 28, 1958.

Father of modern rocketry,
the first to prove his theories
with actual tests

ROBERT H. GODDARD

"There is one thing stronger than all the armies in the world; and that is an idea whose time has come."[1]

The time had not come for Robert H. Goddard's idea. All the armies of the world could not have forced it. Still, he waged a valiant, lifelong fight for a mighty dream. Had we listened, his dream could have changed history.

The great depression of 1929 might have been eased—or averted—by a budding astronautics industry sociologists have speculated. World War II could likely have been deterred had the United States possessed the might of military rockets. And most importantly, this country could have introduced the Age of Space twenty years before Sputnik had we supported Goddard's work. Such was the potential of this man's dream.

Springtime in Boston is an invitation to activity—running, jumping, rough-and-tumble games that boys enjoy. But frail Bob Goddard didn't usually do those things. With skinny legs tucked up under him he'd sit for hours with Jules Verne's *From the Earth to the Moon,* creating his own adventures. Excitement would surge through Bob as he read of preparations for three characters to be shot from a long cannon toward their lunar destination; then he would study each passage, this time applying the analytical reasoning of a scientist. Writer Verne had taken disturbing liberties with fact, and Bob methodically noted these errors in the margins of the book.

The *Boston Post* sowed added seeds of interest when they devoted many months to the daily feature "Fighters from Mars or The War of the Worlds, In and Near Boston." Perhaps the newspaper's "local" treatment of the invasion heightened the drama. Bob Goddard set himself to figuring out how such space flight could actually be accomplished. (Years later he wrote to H. G. Wells, relating what a source of inspiration his work had proved, and he received a kindly answer from the great author.)

The basics of science, which Bob learned from such books as Cassell's *Popular Educator,* set his guidelines; an inherited bent toward mechanics, plus his father's encouragement, molded these inclinations into a life's purpose. The experiments started early. When only four or five years old, Bob obtained a zinc rod from a Leclanche battery and scuffed his feet along a gravel walk, endeavoring to produce enough electric sparks to bounce him into the air. A wise mother, fearing a skinned knee from the antics, put a stop to it by warning him that his experiment might succeed and send him off into space!

But this experiment was merely replaced by others. A few years later the windows of his "laboratory" were shattered as he made the explosive discovery that a mixture of hydrogen and oxygen must be handled with care!

The habits of a true scientist being instinctive, Bob methodically recorded all his searchings—even the ones that ended in "failior." (His knowledge of spelling was then somewhat less than his understanding of Newton's laws.)

One failure, which he duly noted, occurred in the spring of 1898 when he attempted to probe the blue skies of New England with a balloon. This was fashioned of 1/100 sheet aluminum, was oblong shaped, and the edges were sealed with litharge and glycerine. The local druggist was impressed with young Bob's seriousness of purpose and agreed to fill the balloon with hydrogen. Unfortunately the man's only reward was a severe cold (since the trial took place on a rainy morning) for, although Bob possessed a soaring enthusiasm, he could not budge the too-heavy balloon.

From that early time until the last test he ever conducted, one attitude characterized his reaction to failure—"let's pick up the pieces and start again." For all his imagination, his ability in rocketry, which amounted to genius, he could never have realized such accomplishment in his lifetime had it not been for this spirit. "Failior crowns enterprise" he recorded in his boyhood notebook.

Rockets were first crude weapons of the Chinese nine centuries ago.

Sporadically, they burst upon history's revolving kaleidoscope with one of two purposes—to kill or to amuse. While some monarchs used them on the battleline, the more aesthetic rulers gleefully shot them off as elaborate displays, illuminating dark skies.

Dotted throughout the chronicle are such legends as those of the foolhardy Wan-Hu, who lashed himself to a contrivance with forty-seven oversized firecrackers, or of the glib promoters who vaguely associated rockets with the moon and generously offered others the chance to purchase an interest in the venture.

Rocketry was a haphazard pseudoscience at best when young Bob Goddard latched on to a vision. Unaided, he put into motion an incredible transformation, which in time stimulated efforts from others. Within Goddard's productive lifetime rocketry assumed the status of a science, to be approached with all of the resources of physics, chemistry, astronomy, and various branches of engineering. Today the giant, named Astronautics, towers over the earth and reaches into the universe, exerting an influence, in one manner or another, on almost every being.

To have effected this evolution, Robert Goddard had to draw on more than his own physical strength, which was never adequate. The constant pattern of disappointment and frustration he ignored, to concentrate on the larger design of purpose. He was confident that the source of his dream would also be the fountain of fulfilment.

Though he relished the study of physics, mathematics proved to be a chore. Finally two things spurred him to great effort—a need of math in the career he'd chosen, and the keen competition offered by a gifted girl classmate. The result was that he spent time outside school, making—and proving—a book of original geometric propositions. By the end of the term he led his class.

During these years he devised many novel methods of propulsion into space. Goddard recalled, "By the time I graduated from high school, I had a set of models which would not work and a number of suggestions which, from the physics I had learned, I now knew were erroneous. Accordingly, one day I gathered together all the notes I could find and burned them in the little wood stove in the dining room."[2]

But Goddard's nature was underscored with resiliency. The dream of rockets returned with added forcefulness. As a gesture of willing concession to the impulse, he bought many new notebooks with numbered pages and started systematic entries in ink. This habit he continued throughout all of his years of work, leaving a tremendous store of valuable data.* Just before New Year's Day, 1910, he entered in these notebooks twenty-six

* Mrs. Robert H. Goddard has compiled this report of his fifty years of research into twenty-seven indexed volumes; when work on them is completed, they will be presented to the Library of Congress.

items on propulsion and guidance; this determination to achieve flight into space was likely the most unique New Year's resolution in the country.

As a freshman in Worcester Polytechnic Institute he was assigned to write an essay on "Traveling in 1950." The resultant work, "The High-Speed Bet," outlined a remarkable vacuum tube railway from Boston to New York which would reduce commuting time to ten minutes! The airtight cars would be supported electromagnetically so that they would not rest on the roadbed; thus, eliminating friction, they could be accelerated during the first half of the journey at the rate of 11.6 feet per second each second until they attained a speed of 3500 feet per second.

Midway in the journey the chairs in the train would pivot around, and a deceleration of a corresponding rate would occur. The unique conveyance was to be propelled by electromagnets in the sides and roof of the tube. The imaginative essay contained an important principle, as is stated here in Goddard's words: ". . . the continued acceleration of a body by forces which changed from attraction and repulsion as the body passed by the source of the force."[2]

Goddard's nose was not always buried in science books. He evidenced creativity in another line when he wrote the words and music for the school song "Old Tech." Some of his underlying philosophy seems revealed in a line of the lyrics—"men throughout the land, whose highest aim is usefulness."[3]

His quiet friendliness won him the honor of being elected class president and editor-in-chief of the school paper *Aftermath*. When fellow students evaluated the members of the senior class in a poll, Goddard received the highest possible number of votes in the category headed "Brightest," and a very large number of votes for "Most Versatile," "Most Broad-Minded," and "Most Benefited by Worcester Polytechnic Institute."

It is doubtful that any member of the class received a more complimentary total evaluation. If further evidence of his standing were needed, it was forthcoming when he was invited to teach at the Institute after graduation. The students who studied under Goddard had a unique opportunity, for they were constantly being exposed to thinking that leaped beyond their textbooks. And here, among eager minds that had not yet dwelled upon restrictions, there was ready acceptance.

This retiring American scientist was to figure in many lives. Wernher von Braun has remarked that Goddard was his "boyhood hero." As the activities of this New Englander became known, his influence was also felt in the realm of science-fiction writing. In this popular revival of the art, typewriters spewed forth an abundant stream of adventures, using Mars or the moon as a jumping-off place.

It must have seemed disheartening to Goddard that these writings could have been snatched up so eagerly by editors when a work such as his own advanced essay on propulsion into interplanetary space by means of heat from radio-active materials was rejected in turn by *Scientific American, Popular Science Monthly,* and *Popular Astronomy.*

Dr. G. Edward Pendray, another pioneer in the field, speaks of the "ironic twist" in rocketry: "During the period when for the first time it was really undergoing something like genuine scientific development, the rocket was to become, to many unthinking people, a symbol of impractical ideas and fantastic schemes. Everyone who had to do with rockets during the next two decades was to be branded as 'queer'; and rocketors were to inherit the mantle of ridicule previously worn by airplane pioneers."[4]

Goddard won his Ph.D. from Clark University in 1911, then went to Princeton University on a one-year research fellowship. While days were occupied with producing the first laboratory demonstration of mechanical force from a "displacement current" in a magnetic field, his evenings were confined within a labyrinth of calculations. His small-scale experiments conducted in the basement of Worcester Polytechnic Institute had been mere warm-ups. Now he was ready for the main event!

Relates Goddard in his autobiographical notes: "In the fall of 1914, while teaching part time at Clark, I worked out the theory and calculations for smokeless powder and hydrogen and oxygen completely and began experiments on the efficiency of ordinary rockets. Curiously enough, the initial mass needed to send 1 lb. to infinity for hydrogen and oxygen at 50 per cent efficiency, namely 43.5 lbs., was close to that estimated roughly at 45 lbs. on January 31, 1909."[2]

It was as if he had been trudging a winding road for years when suddenly a broad and well marked highway appeared to lead him toward his goal! He raced with fervor along its broad lanes in a frantic race toward the destiny that he had chosen. The days in the Princeton lab could not pass swiftly enough—the nights he treasured, when he could concentrate solely upon rocket plans and calculations. Hours grew late. Dawn came early. Time was evanescent. Only the excitement of his progress seemed real to Goddard, for he was proving on paper that reasonably small amounts of fuel could lift scientific instruments above the veil called atmosphere!

Just when the race was about to bring results, it was brought to a grinding halt. Goddard would work no more for a long while. The mental stimulation had driven his body beyond its limits. The weakness of his boyhood had developed into pulmonary tuberculosis.

Treatment. Quiet. Rest.

Snatched as he was from a peak of activity and plunged into the confines of a prolonged illness, the experience could have embittered him. But Goddard, the student, learned even from this. He mastered fortitude, which he was to apply to every subsequent disappointment in his life. And during this trial he discovered the deep sources of spirit that lie within a man, providing courage in the face of defeat.

In that twilight between sickness and health—convalescence—he asked permission to resume work. The flow of his creativeness had been dammed up too long. If only as a trickle, it had to resume its surge toward the ocean of knowledge. Out of this setting was produced the material which constituted the basic Goddard rocket.

On July 7 and July 14, 1914, patents were granted to Goddard. Three general principles were covered: the utilization of a combustion chamber and nozzle, the feeding of either liquid or solid propellant into the chamber to give either a steady or discontinuous propulsive force, and the discarding of individual stages of a rocket as they were burned (the step rocket idea).

Fundamentals. How elementary they seem once they have been established. After the first man hacks and beats his way through jungle thickets, then the path is clear and marked for all to follow. But that first trail blazer has to explore the way, intelligently plan a method of reaching the goal, and possess the perseverance to stay with the rigorous journey.

Though Goddard was now recovered, the doctor issued him stern warning that he would fall easy victim to illness should he overwork. What stern self-discipline he had to muster to follow such a dictate, for he was smoldering with the fire that burns within the soul of every gifted man—so much to do, so little time!

Back in the familiar surroundings of Clark University, his position as an honorary fellow and part-time instructor in physics allowed hours for experimenting. The most readily available rocket was the kind used in signaling, but Goddard found this too inefficient for his tests. (It has been reported that these rockets had an exhaust velocity of approximately 1000 feet per second, operating with as poor an efficiency rate as two per cent.) So he devised a steel chamber on a static test stand, fitted it with different sizes of nozzles, and chose as propellant, smokeless powder—an innovation at that time.

Not only were there new ideas to be built, there were old fallacies to be destroyed before the rocket would be generally accepted. Methodically, Goddard developed a case, much as a good attorney plans a defense of his client. He wanted no weak spots which the prosecution could question. So he set out to gather conclusive evidence on a widely disputed point of whether a rocket would operate, would have thrust, once it had left the earth's atmosphere and had reached the altitude of space. The opposition —which included some of the soundest scientific names in the world—contended that it would not, for without the atmosphere the rocket would have nothing to "push against."

In theory, Goddard knew them to be wrong, as had the early theorist Tsiolkovsky. They both understood that a rocket is self-contained in its function. The gases it expels provide the driving force, making it the perfect example of Newton's Third Law of Motion: For every action there is an equal and opposite reaction. Goddard illustrated it in this manner. "The phenomenon is easily understood if one thinks of the ejected gas as a charge of fine shot moving with a very high velocity. The chamber will react or 'kick' when this charge is fired, exactly as a shotgun 'kicks' when firing a charge of ordinary shot."[3]

Though such reasoning could be entered as prima-facie evidence, Goddard strengthened his point by running a series of tests in a vacuum. The rocket performed, as he knew it would, but a most amazing revelation was made as he checked his figures—it not only operated, but actually delivered greater thrust than when it operated in atmosphere! Excitement welled within Goddard. It was as if he'd discovered a law of nature that was on his side to partially balance that opposing law of gravity which his rockets must battle in their ascent from the earth.

Had this professor been a research scientist only, perhaps the development of a rocket engine would have proved sufficient end in itself. But he was also an idealist. His immediate aim was the gathering of meteorological data; for this he must reach into the vastness of the upper atmosphere and the rocket was the means—the only means—of sending delicate apparatus to great heights. He deemed ten to twenty miles as most desirable for beginning high altitude studies of pressure, temperature, and wind velocity—those vital adjuncts to weather forecasting. So these were the objectives of the timid first probe. Then as increased fuel supplies would open the universe to scrutiny, he planned examinations of the aurora and the radiations of the sun. And even this would be but the beginning.

The test results of this period were carefully written up as a monograph, illustrated with photographs, bound into book form, and given the title *A Method of Reaching Extreme Altitudes*. Having depleted his small savings by 1916, Goddard needed financial assistance for further research; so he sent this report in turn to three institutions which made grants for such study. Goddard wrote asking two of the organizations to disregard his appeal when the Smithsonian Institution replied promptly. They were very much interested.

Founded in 1846 by Englishman James Smithson for "the increase and diffusion of knowledge among men," the Smithsonian Institution saw in the small document by an unknown professor the key to unlock a mighty force. The Hodgkins Fund, which they administered, was instituted to "encourage explorations of the upper air," and had once given a grant for three miles of silk string for a kite. Goddard's monograph outlined a much more likely means of reaching the upper atmosphere, so the Institution replied to his request for assistance, asking the amount of money he would require.

Their reply proved a dilemma to the scientist. He had managed to conduct the tests for less than $1000. But now his aim was to build a rocket. His estimate totaled $10,000, but, fearing this would cool their interest, he cut the figure in half.

The grant was forthcoming, as was great support in other ways from the Smithsonian Institution. The secretary, Dr. Charles D. Walcott, admired the report, and the writer as well. He thought of Goddard as a "lone wolf," and said, "He knew precisely what he was doing. I have never seen so much confidence."[5]

The word was well chosen. As a man, he was modest. As a scientist, he knew his goal. The magnitude of it prompted him to remark, "I'm just a little dog with a great big bone."[5] So though his approach was humble, he also had a supreme confidence in what he was doing, and this gave a singleness of purpose that filled every day and guided every step.

When America finally became involved in World War I, Goddard—so acutely aware of the vital role rockets could play in warfare—wrote to General Dunwoody with the open offer of assistance. By this time the Smithsonian Institution had seen the professor at work and was convinced that its grant was well placed; so it made a strong recommendation to the Army Signal Corps to take advantage of the man's talents. Goddard visited the bustling capital to complete arrangements and in January, 1918, started two projects: first, a rocket was to be developed which would fly a trajectory course, being propelled by solid fuel charges injected into the combustion chamber in a repeater-rifle type of operation and having a motor capable of intermittent operation. Had work on this proposal been started in time, it might well have been the answer to the German's destructive Paris Gun (Big Bertha). The second project Goddard undertook exhibited its enormous worth some twenty years later, for it was the parent of the fire-lashing Bazooka of World War II.

In his urgent wartime work, Goddard had the assistance of two bright and resourceful graduate students of Clark University, H. S. Parker and C. N. Hickman. Until June the feverishly paced endeavor was carried on in Worcester at the Polytechnic Institute.

Then with the availability of better facilities, the operation was moved to the shops of Mount Wilson Observatory in Pasadena. Within relatively few months Goddard had readied test models; representatives of the Signal Corps invited members of the Ordnance Corps and Air Service to attend the closely guarded demonstration.

At Aberdeen Proving Ground in Maryland the gathering witnessed a seeming marvel—great explosive force without recoil! Hickman held a tube from which was fired one of the seventeen-pound Bazooka-type rockets—a vivid example of its feasibility in the hands of infantrymen.

Much later, in 1936, details of the secret demonstration were released by International News Service in an interview with Dr. Charles C. Abbot, who had succeeded Walcott as Secretary of the Smithsonian Institution:

"Dr. Goddard brought with him a projectile which looked like a regular three-inch artillery shell, brass cartridge and all. It was comparatively light in weight. There was no gun, no carriage; simply this strange-looking shell —a rocket.

"Carefully, Dr. Goddard laid this shell on a wooden table, which was resting on the ground. There was no bracing, no base against which the shell would recoil. A slender wire was attached.

"Before the table was a bulwark of sandbags, used in the best trench defenses, capable of stopping machine gun and Army rifle bullets before two of the bags were penetrated.

"All were quiet.

" 'Are you ready, gentlemen?' asked Dr. Goddard. They were.

"There was a low crackle of electricity, a loud swish. The brass shell of the rocket trembled, spurted fire, and the projectile hurled outward, into the sandbags.

"An examination revealed the rocket had penetrated three sandbags, and the light brass shell didn't even fall off the table."

A number of other tests then conducted were of great interest to the group, particularly the Air Corps. But however rich was the satisfaction of that successful demonstration, it was superseded four days later by the news that an Armistice was announced! Goddard gave thanks, as did all the nation, that World War I had ended. All military interest in rockets was dropped for then—and for too many years to come as later events taught us.

Returning to Worcester, Goddard plunged into his effort of preparing a test model designed for peaceful purposes. He resumed his usual pattern of application—his work being conducted in the privacy of the laboratory, his theories and results of his tests being recorded only in his meticulously compiled notebooks. This became a matter of concern to his colleague and friend, Dr. Webster, Director of the Physical Laboratories at Clark University.

Webster felt these important pioneering efforts should be made a matter of public record, so that in the phylogeny of the modern rocket Goddard would be justly credited with his contributions. Further, he felt there was an obligation to apprise the scientific world of these vital data. Goddard's approach was more conservative; he felt such an announcement was premature. Only when Webster said that he would publish a report if Goddard did not was the professor euchred into making the arrangements. He asked the Smithsonian Institution to publish the monograph he had submitted to them in 1916; this he updated with reports on the use of hydrogen and oxygen, the probability of a collision with meteors, and other items.

Thus did *A Method of Reaching Extreme Altitudes,* by Robert H. Goddard appear in the *Smithsonian Miscellaneous Collection,* Volume 71, Number 2, dated 1919. Quietly it emerged in January, 1920, and from the total printing numbering 1750 Goddard sent a few copies to friends. No one took any particular notice.

Time passed. Then headlines hit like a bolt of lightning, Goddard was spun in a tornado of comment and engulfed by a tidal wave of public interest! This eruption came not from the scientific circles, where he had expected some degree of interest in his treatise; rather, it burst from the daily newspapers, editors seizing the possibilities for sensationalizing the last pages of his report. The Smithsonian Institution's own press representative had ferreted out this conjecture, which involved sending a rocket to the moon! Further, Goddard had suggested a pay load of flash powder so that the rocket's arrival on the surface of the new moon might be heralded with a mighty signal visible through telescopes from the earth!

Stunned by such wild reaction, Goddard well recalled why he had described this moon rocket in his paper. He had desired to point out the limitless future possibilities of using the rocket for interplanetary travel but felt such a broad suggestion might be too advanced in its concept. So he had selected the illustration of a moon shot as a compromise. Had he proceeded with his first impulse instead and had written about a trip to Mars, it would have seemed so preposterous that it would have passed without being seriously regarded. Hence, his "conservative" reference backfired into a furor!

A front page story in the January 12, 1920, edition of *The New York Times* was headlined "Believes Rocket Can Reach Moon." The following day an editorial accused him of deliberately making the same "mistake" as Jules Verne—that of assuming a rocket could operate in a vacuum. Goddard felt a certain futility in making rebuttal—the erroneous assumption that a rocket needed the atmosphere to "push against" seemed too firmly established.

So instead of going into specifics, he made a general statement, endeavoring to put the situation back into proper perspective: "Too much emphasis has been concentrated on the flash powder experiment and too little on the atmosphere. . . . Whatever interesting possibilities there may be for the method that has been proposed other than the purpose for which it was intended, no one of them could be undertaken without first exploring the atmosphere. Any rocket apparatus for great elevation must first be tested at various moderate altitudes. Also a knowledge of the densities at high levels is essential. Hence, from any point of view, an investigation of the atmosphere is the work that lies ahead."[6]

But public fancy would not be dampened. It rallied to what seemed the challenge of the age. On April 1, 1920, the *Baltimore Sun* announced "Woman May Join Flight to Mars" and named Miss Ruth Phillips as an enthusiastic Kansas City girl who was willing to outdo the suffragettes and demonstrate the ultimate in woman's independence. In her ardor she had extended the hypothetical journey thirty-five million miles farther to the planet. The following September 21st the *New York World* carried the story of Captain Charles N. Fitzgerald who wanted to be "the first visitor to say 'Hello' to the man in the moon." Fitzgerald, a member of the New York Air Police, was described as a daredevil who had stood on the wings of an airplane while it looped the loop! (However, it is assumed that he did not expect to cling to the rocket's nose for the lunar trip.) By February, 1921, it would have taken a rocket the height of the Eiffel Tower to accommodate all the volunteers—the count had mounted to eighteen!

All of this happened despite Goddard's repeated statement that such a rocket, if ever constructed, would not carry human cargo. In a strong plea to try to dispel the clamor Goddard made a statement while in Chicago explaining something of the extremes of temperature on the moon and the presence of possibly lethal radiation in space. But a scientist's language is often dull from a reporter's point of view. So what got into print under Goddard's name was considerably more flamboyant (and less accurate): "Moon Beams Would Cremate Human Rockets!"[7]

This set off another round of news items. Seeing his every word thus dramatized and colored, Goddard stopped granting interviews and refused comment on his activities. But there was no winning this battle against a stirred imagination, for then the Sunday supplement sections termed him a "Mystery Professor" and gave vividly illustrated accounts of fantastic preparations for his "Moon Journey." It was highly incongruous that these stories of the scholarly, retiring man appeared nestled between tales of the romances of the daring "flappers" of the Roaring Twenties and somewhat gory narratives of notorious murder cases.

Even the cartoons caught the spirit; a drawing showed "Boob McNutt" being led to a complicated-looking contraption as two eccentric scientists generously informed him, "Listen, we've invented a rocket that can travel all the way up to Mars—it will hold one man and we want you to be the first man to make the trip."[8]

It is a curious fact that while the United States played on the sensational aspect of Goddard's effort, the reaction in Europe was generally quite different. The scientific aspect of his Smithsonian report received much more attention, even though in some instances it was critical. F. G. Morrell, in an article appearing in the London paper, *The Graphic,* enumerated several items which he judged technical inaccuracies. Goddard felt such an attack should be answered, point by point. So he detailed how in his proposed upper-atmosphere experiments the instruments in the pay load would not be damaged in the fall because they would *fall from rest* (at the peak of the trajectory) and would be further protected by a small parachute and possibly a few charges left in the rocket, which could be fired to check the descent. (Thus even today's concept of retrorockets was presented in the report.) Next, Goddard would not concede that the velocity of his rocket would cause it to "vanish in an incandescent wisp of flame and smoke," as Mr. Morrell contended. Until the rocket was out of the earth's atmosphere, Goddard planned to keep the speed below a level that would generate such heat. Finally, the English writer averred that a hit at the destination would be impossible, since the earth and the moon are traveling in different directions at high speed. Goddard replied that the speeds of the two bodies were known with great precision since accurate predictions could be made years in advance.

But, however lucid the reply, the voices of criticism can never be stilled when a new idea is the target. Man has lived in the same groove for eons. It is comfortable and familiar. Every effort to change it is opposed with a fury inspired by fear. Those who venture into the morass of the unknown and open the way to progress must be possessed of a mighty courage, for they will be condemned for their efforts and resisted every step of the way toward betterment. Therefore it seems necessary, in the pattern of life, that when the Almighty endows an individual with the capabilities of expanding the store of knowledge He must also link with that the quality of supreme understanding. Goddard exemplified that quality. If he failed in his effort to enlighten critics, he certainly felt no bitterness; he simply realized that in time they would come to accept the ideas he set forth.

As foreign scientists were apprised of the novel report through headlines such as the one in the *Corriere D'Italia,* on 13 Giugno, 1920, which proclaimed *"Nel Mondo Della Luna, In America Si Parla Di Un Viaggio Nel Nostro Satellite,"* the spark was lit. For the serious ones, the report was available in larger European libraries, to which the Smithsonian Institution customarily distributed its publications. But one young student in Heidelberg made a request for a copy on May 3, 1922, by sending this letter to Goddard at Worcester, Massachusetts:

"Dear Sir:

"Already many years I work at the problem to pass over the atmosphere of our earth by means of a rocket. When I was now publishing the result of my examinations and calculations, I learned by the newspaper that I am not alone in my inquiry and that you, dear Sir, have already done much important works at this sphere. In spite of my efforts, I did not succeed in getting your books about this object. Therefore I beg you, dear Sir, to let them have me. At once after coming out of my work I will be honored to send it to you, for I think that only by common work of the scholars of all nations can be solved this great problem.

"Yours very truly,

"Hermann Oberth, stud.math.Heidelberg."[4]

In 1923, a booklet appeared under the title, *Die Rakete zu den Palnetenräumen (The Rocket into Interplanetary Space),* by H. Oberth. A Transylvanian who became a German citizen, Oberth emerged in later years as one of the leaders in rocket development. His profound respect for the concepts which Goddard had set forth were evidenced by the statement that he could find but one flaw in the Smithsonian report and that was not in the rocket but in Goddard's estimate regarding the flash: "Professor Oberth, stressing that this was the only mistake he had been able to find in Goddard's work (the first Smithsonian Report), said that Goddard had greatly underestimated the amount of flash powder needed."[9] Other indications of the knowledge the German scientists received from Goddard's rocket were to be revealed in 1945, when the V-2 burst upon the world.

There was the stir of interest in other places. As Mrs. Goddard recalls, "Many foreign nations, including Russia, Japan, Germany, and Italy wrote to my husband asking for his services, but he turned them all down even though he received little support from his own government after World War I."[10]

The interest from abroad disturbed Goddard, especially in view of the lethargy which existed toward the new advancement in this country. As with all thinking people, his sense of responsibility extended far beyond his immediate circle of family, friends, colleagues. He knew that part of everything in the world was in his keeping—not only from the broad sense of Christian principles, but in a very specific manner that related to his rockets. He had conducted small tests of their destructive power. He did not need to see tests of great scale to be acutely aware of expanded possibilities. Calculations with pencil and paper illustrated to him the gigantic proportions that rocket weapons could assume.

Yet, even with constant efforts, he could not interest the United States in the military aspects of this new science. This being the situation, he most certainly would not encourage developments leading to rocket weapons by nations which might threaten this country. So Goddard withdrew, hoping that the United States acceptance would soon come.

This prudence on his part has brought forth criticism from some, who term him "secretive" regarding his efforts. In view of his conscientiousness about the military potential of his findings, it is understandable that he felt no moral obligation beyond keeping those sponsoring him fully apprised of his progress. In detail, he reported on his experiments, devices, and results to the Smithsonian Institution, Clark University, and The Daniel and Florence Guggenheim Foundation. The release of information was always the responsibility of the sponsors.

"She shut out the world that pounded at him." The insulation of his scientific activities extended to his personal life when Esther Kisk Goddard read that sentence from *Arrowsmith* and suddenly felt as though Sinclair Lewis might have directed the words to her instead of describing the young wife in the novel. Esther had worked with Robert Goddard in the compiling of his notes since 1918—even during the years she had returned to college—so she knew him well before their marriage in 1924. But she had not crystallized her own role in the life they were sharing until that descriptive sentence jarred her.

With the mighty power that rests within words—to influence, to change minds, to affect lives, to alter the face of the world—Esther's dedication took form. She could screen some of the correspondence that burdened him, try to stretch his modest salary to cover equipment purchases, keep the records of his experiments in order, remove petty distractions that would intrude upon his studies, provide the warmth of a happy home, give constant reassurance that she believed in his dream, and listen when he needed to talk. Singled out, each element might be appraised as a small bit of clay; but, fired with devotion, they built a protective fortress of sturdy bricks.

Mrs. Goddard, being an honor student, absorbed a superficial knowledge of his activity and came to hold many titles in his unofficial corporation—she was the vice-president in charge of putting out the small grass fires that his experiments ignited; she was chief motion-picture photographer (often ruining stockings as she knelt down to follow the rocket's path); she was head seamstress, sewing parachutes to float the rockets back to earth (a saving device when the 'chutes did not snap loose or split open); and she was manager of the special fuel department (not fuel for the rockets, but rich soup and homemade cookies to propel her husband and his assistants who were all absorbed in technical activity). Thus was the function of Mrs. Goddard a many-sided one, bringing her the reward of participating in a development that ushered in the Space Age.

Danger dogged Goddard from his first handling of explosive materials. He was careful, as an experimenter knows he must be if he intends to complete his work, but the very nature of rocketry posed endless threats, whether his work was with powder rockets or with the liquid fuel to which he inevitably turned. Even when conducting the tests with powder rockets which were reported in his paper, *A Method of Reaching Extreme Altitudes,* he knew the limitations of solid fuel—its inefficient burning and incontrollability; but, with only his own funds to draw from, it was expedient. By 1920, with the help of the Smithsonian Institution, he could turn his full attention to the research with liquid fuel. The starting point was zero, for though they recognized its possibilities no scientist had ever ventured the handling of this highly volatile and difficult fuel.

What mixture was most suitable? After experimentation, Goddard decided upon liquid oxygen and gasoline. With this advance, the rocket also started its progression toward the enormously complex mechanism that exists today. With liquid, it ceased to be a simple firework. Tanks, valves, pipelines, and other elements of a rocket engine were added. He built two vehicles which were restricted to static testing. Then came the third, which made history!

A layer of snow covered the Massachusetts countryside on the morning of March 16, 1926. But enthusiasm warmed Goddard and his companions —his wife, Henry Sachs, of the University instrument lab, and Dr. P. M. Roope, assistant professor of physics, as they drove the car and trailer to the Auburn farm of "Aunt" Effie Ward (a prefix which did not denote her kinship but merely her gregariousness).

When the rocket was unloaded and erected on the launcher, it appeared a mere skeleton. The combustion chamber and nozzle were located at the top and connected by two long pipes to the tanks of liquid oxygen and gasoline—this separation removed the flame from the proximity of the tanks. After a thorough last-minute check, Mrs. Goddard readied her camera, and Sachs wielded a blow torch on the end of a pole to ignite the engine. For an instant it seemed to hang suspended in midair. Then with a burst of flame and a proud roar, the world's first liquid fueled rocket shot 184 feet in two and a half seconds!

This event has been termed as epochal as the Wright Brothers' flight at Kitty Hawk. Though the contrivance landed ingloriously in a snow-covered cabbage patch, it shaped the destiny of the future development of the rocket and added one more triumph to Goddard's store of accomplishments. The momentous event was revealed to the public in a statement contained in an article in *The New York Times* on December 15, 1929, and in numerous other newspaper accounts of the event. Some have contended that there was no report of this work until 1936. The facts are these: It was related in the Smithsonian Institution *Annual Report* for the year ending June, 1930, as a part of the Report of the Secretary of the Institution, C. G. Abbot.* On page 10 it states:

"After much experimenting with a rocket equipped with a device for feeding small charges of high explosive, Doctor Goddard turned finally to the scheme of a steady combustion of hydrocarbon in liquid oxygen. After further modifying the design of the rocket itself to adapt it to the use of this

---

* This was published between September and December of 1931 the Institution states. As to the availability of its *Reports,* it confirms that they are mailed to all of the larger libraries, including all depository libraries; and they are also sent without charge, as long as in print, to interested individuals who request copies.

means of propulsion, Doctor Goddard was ready at the close of the fiscal year for an actual field trial of the device.

"It may be said that on July 17, 1929, a trial of the liquid-propelled rocket was made at Worcester, Mass., the device functioning satisfactorily as regards the flow of liquid, the ascent of the rocket, and its rapid motion in air."

This was followed in 1936 by what is generally termed his second report, entitled *Liquid-Propellant Rocket Development*.

"Terrific Explosion as Professor Goddard of Clark Shoots His 'Moon Rocket,' " the headline of the *Worcester Evening Post* screamed on the afternoon of July 17, 1929. Wild-eyed spectators told a variety of colorful accounts of the launching from the Auburn farm. First reports had brought a police ambulance to the area with the information that a plane had crashed in flames. An airplane was dispatched to search for the wreckage.

The rocket Goddard had launched was but eleven and a half feet long, but it assumed the proportions of a fire-breathing monster endangering the lives of all residents in the area before the alarmed citizenry could be calmed. Though it had risen but ninety feet, there were solemn accounts of its soaring thousands of feet into the sky.

"Nell,"* as the little group had affectionately come to call each of their rockets, had kicked up no more fuss than her predecessors, but perhaps the still, summer air had carried the sound farther. The rocket had performed as expected, parachuting back a small barometer and a camera. In spite of this, a newspaper chose to misinterpret her mission and write this caustic banner line, "Moon Rocket Misses Target by 238,799½ Miles."[11]

So was the entire matter reopened in the press. The relative peace which Goddard had enjoyed for the past few years was shattered as each reporter rehashed the account of the "Mystery Professor" and his activities. Dr. Abbot of the Smithsonian Institution issued the statement that no such "wild thing" as going to the moon had been attempted and that the shoot was merely in the interest of gathering meteorological data.

It was difficult to dispel the idea that dangerous explosions were being set off, especially since Goddard was reticent to discuss any of the details of his project. The President of Clark University stated that "German and U.S. scientists are in a rocket race," and further elaborated that "They are using the principle Dr. Goddard has worked out and which has been published. . . . Military men all over the world are watching the experiments. . . ."[11]

When further distraction appeared in the person of George C. Neal, the

---

* The morning after the July 17, 1929, flight, Lawrence C. ("Larry") Mansur, a graduate student who had helped with the test, came into the Clark Laboratory and deplored, "They ain't done right by our Nell." Forever after, every rocket shot was "Nell."

State Fire Marshall, to investigate the possibility that Goddard might set forest fires, it became apparent that his test area would have to be moved. Dr. Abbot appealed to the War Department and received permission for Goddard to continue his work in an isolated area of the Fort Devens, Massachusetts, artillery range. From "Aunt" Effie's farm, Goddard moved his "mail-order" launching tower—an ingeniously converted windmill which he'd selected from the pages of a Sears Roebuck catalogue. The meager installation was completed with the building of an observation post, constructed of scrap wood and covered with metal.

The new location was hardly the essence of comfort or convenience. Mrs. Goddard recalls the drive there over roads which were most difficult in winter. Headquarters were set up in an abandoned henhouse where a potbellied stove provided the only means of preparing hot food for the men. All in all, the necessity of moving the testing to Fort Devens had made things much more difficult.

A wise teaching states that it isn't what happens to a man that is important—it is his reaction to it. Goddard's reaction was predetermined, because he faced truth. He accepted the proportions of his undertaking, never deluding himself that there would be any "short cuts." The gravest problem he faced with the reasoning, "If it were easy, someone would have done it long ago."[12] Such determination overrode his state of health, his limited funds, the constant ridicule and skepticism, and enabled him always to "pick up the pieces and start again" (which he and his men did, literally, after the rockets exploded).

Though every little cloud doesn't have that silver lining, the storm brewed by the 1929 commotion produced one that did. The flurry in the press served an excellent purpose, for the items were read with intense interest by the man who had grown to be America's hero, Colonel Charles A. Lindbergh.

Whatever else Goddard did for the town of Worcester, he certainly kept the people supplied with conversational tidbits. When the famous flier arrived, unannounced, on the campus of Clark University and asked to be directed to the laboratory of the scientist, the word spread fast. Goddard merely stimulated the speculation when he made the noncommittal statement that it was just a "friendly call" and that the Colonel would prefer not to have it known he was in town.

That visit, on November 23, 1929, brought together two kindred minds. Each had a love of the air and vision of what the future held as man was enabled to rob space of some of its secrets. Goddard took the tall flier to his home at One Talawanda Drive where he might view some of the film Mrs. Goddard had shot of the test launchings. "I can remember serving Col. Lindbergh chocolate cake and coffee by the fireside here," Mrs. Goddard recalls.[13]

But the purpose of the visit was not just conversation or encouragement. The nation's hero was a thoughtful man, who pondered where aviation's future lay and what was beyond the science of aviation as it was then known. As he spoke with the Worcester scientist, his hopes were confirmed. Here he saw a man who linked vision with technical brilliance; who could dream, then transform hopes into hardware. He deserved more substantial backing and understanding. To continue to withhold such support was not just robbing Goddard—it was depriving mankind of the benefits of progress.

Lindbergh conveyed his convictions to Harry Guggenheim, the son of Florence and Daniel Guggenheim. This family's deep interest in the potential of flight had been generously evidenced in their Fund for the Promotion of Aeronautics, established January 16, 1926, with a grant of $2,500,000. The Fund had almost all been expended by 1929; however, when the Lone Eagle brought them word of the remarkable work being done in Worcester, there was a personal grant that Daniel Guggenheim made to Goddard through Clark University in the amount of $50,000 for two years of research and experimentation! An additional grant was contributed by the Carnegie Institution to aid in the establishment of adequate facilities.

The Roswell, New Mexico, area is a prairie—not a desert—the Goddards were soon to learn. This was a drastic change for two people who had always called New England home, but it provided ideal conditions for rocket testing—sparse population, level country, moderate winds, and few storms, year-round outdoor working conditions (no New England winters!). The Mescalero Ranch which they chose also had adequate roads and an abundant power supply. Useful equipment was brought from the laboratory at Clark University, and the launching tower was once more dismantled and moved.

Four loyal assistants made the move west with Goddard—Henry Sachs of Clark's instrument lab, employed by Goddard since 1924; Albert Kisk, Mrs. Goddard's brother, employed since 1928; Lawrence Mansur, graduate student, volunteer helper at tests from 1929–30; and Charles Mansur, Lawrence's brother, employed just before the departure for New Mexico.

They first plunged into the task of building a shop, a 30′ x 55′ frame structure. In it was installed necessary pieces of machinery which had just been purchased, including a lathe. As an auxiliary item, the Smithsonian Institution had also loaned them the nine-inch lathe which had belonged to Samuel Pierpont Langley; he had used it to fashion "Langley's Folly," the airplane that failed.

Within Goddard there was a feeling of deep joy. He was able to work full time on his project! Previously it had been a snatched, after-school, weekend, and summer kind of operation, leaving a constant feeling of frustration and yearning. Now he accepted the crude conditions of his Roswell facility with only thankfulness for the privilege of being able to work all day every day on his experiments.

On the morning of December 30, 1930, the dawn light revealed "Nell"—confined to her trailer—being gently towed along the fifteen miles of road that led from the shop to the launching facility. This was the big day! The group was unusually keyed up as they started their routine duties of preparing for a launch. Through the hours they worked, completely absorbed with the preparations at this, the world's largest rocket range! (Of course, there was little competition in the exclusive category at that time.) At 3 P.M. all was in readiness.

The seconds before launch were tense ones. After a heartbreaking struggle of years, "Nell" now had a real home. She blasted her approval by rising 2000 feet into the vivid blue sky! The test was a marked success.

The faithful group watched, silently. No one dared to speak. There was too much to say.

The striving for dependability of performance of a rocket or missile—the aim of today's top experts—had its beginning with Goddard. At best rockets are temperamental beasts. Goddard also concentrated on the stabilization problem. The flight of December 30th had demonstrated the need by the rocket's yawing and swerving in its course. But, persistently, the work continued, and by 1932 gyroscopically controlled stabilization of a rocket had been evolved. In this, vanes were articulated in the blast by means of pressure, which was controlled by a gyroscope. The April 19th test proved the theory, though the vanes were too small to make sufficient correction.

An advisory committee* had been formed at the time of the Guggenheim grant to appraise results and determine further support. In May, 1932, Goddard made a report on his Roswell progress. Members of the scientific body drew from their combined knowledge and offered suggestions on possible solutions to problems he outlined. They commended Goddard on his results and recommended a two-year extension of the grant. However, the depression years made it impossible for the Foundation to continue support at that time.

This was indeed a blow.

With the establishment of the Roswell facility it had seemed that there might be the opportunity, at last, to bring rocketry to an advanced state. The distraction of part-time teaching had been removed as Goddard had concentrated on his great effort. Now the honeymoon was over. He would

* The committee was comprised of: Dr. John C. Merriam, Chairman; Dr. C. G. Abbot; Dr. Walter S. Adams; Dr. Wallace W. Atwood; Col. Henry Breckinridge; Dr. John A. Fleming; Col. Charles A. Lindbergh; Dr. C. F. Marvin; Dr. Robert A. Millikan.

return to Worcester, resume his teaching, and do what little research he could on a small grant from the Smithsonian Institution.

There were other sides to Goddard's nature that had the chance to emerge during periods of lessened activity such as the two years that ensued. He was highly sensitive to the beauties of nature and had a true appreciation of her "workings." Photography was a useful adjunct in his work, but it also gave him pleasure on weekends when spring had clothed the countryside in green or during autumn when oranges and yellows tinged the trees. An affinity for color guided the strokes of his brush when he took occasional hours to paint. His professional-like canvasses still grace the homes of many friends.

Out of the precision of his thinking was an instinctive knowledge of harmony. Though never trained, he had the ability to play elaborate compositions "by ear" on the piano. This taste extended from concert music into the area of musical comedy.

He whistled and hummed the songs of Victor Herbert, or one of his later favorites, the melodies from a stage show. He always conveyed a cheerful air, as Mrs. Goddard was forcibly reminded recently when compiling his voluminous notes. In these detailed accounts of all his years of striving, there was but one sign of discouragement, when he wrote. "A bad day." He could accept the other days with equanimity because he knew what his job in life should be and, somehow, he would do it. The opportunity to resume full-scale work came again in 1934 with another grant.

Though Daniel Guggenheim had passed away four years before, the spirit of his interest was carried forward by his son, Harry, acting in his capacity as President of The Daniel and Florence Guggenheim Foundation. This financial support reactivated the Roswell facilities. During October, 1935, Harry Guggenheim and Lindbergh visited Goddard and viewed his installation, to learn firsthand of his further work with stabilization. March 8th and May 31st of that year marked important tests of that series. In writing of these tests he made a descriptive comment quite out of the ordinary for his reports, "The first few hundred feet of the flight reminded one of a fish swimming in a vertical direction."[14] Perhaps this was in answer to his wife's chiding that with his scrupulously accurate scientific reporting, so devoid of hyperbole, he had a talent for making the most interesting things seem dull.

Liquid-Propellant Rocket Development, his second Smithsonian Institution report, covered this period of experiments. Both this document and his original report were reprinted in 1945 by the American Rocket Society. They were out of print at the Smithsonian; so the ARS, recognizing their very great importance, published them in a small book with a new foreword written by Goddard. He commented that the general precepts which he set forth in the works remained sound, a most modest way of acknowledging that his principles—which he not only theorized but tested—have emerged as the fundamentals of rocketry.

At the closing of the second Smithsonian report, Goddard headed a brief paragraph, "Further Development," and spoke of the necessity for the reduction in weight and noted that progress in that direction had been made. His thoughts and plans stretched much farther into the future than this statement indicated. Many of his calculations on space flight he put for safekeeping in a locked file, with the instructions that they were to be "opened only by an optimist." In 1922, in a newspaper interview, Goddard was speaking of his faith in the possibilities of the rocket "as a means of exploration."[15] Though his own rockets never soared above eight or nine thousand feet, real use of his vision and his know-how could have hurled a mighty challenge into the universe long ago.

October 13, 1936, was a day of excitement on the Mescalero Ranch, for a special visitor had come from Washington! Lieutenant Colonel (later Major General, now deceased) Oliver Echols, Chief of Engineering Division, Air Materiel Command, Army Air Corps, had heard of the work going on in New Mexico and sent Lieutenant (now Major General, Ret.) John W. Sessums, Jr. to investigate. Goddard was overjoyed at this indication of interest from a member of the military services. As Sessums recently recalled, "Goddard was so absorbed in telling me about the status of his work, and the future possibilities of it, that he drove in first gear the entire fifteen miles from the launch tower back to the shop."

That night Goddard recorded in his journal, "Lieutenant Sessums came in A.M. Showed him the shop, had lunch, talked over rockets for gliders for targets and took him out to the tower in P.M." The entry ended there, on an expectant note. He knew the intelligent young officer had been interested and impressed. He waited for further word. Somewhere in the circuitous route between recommendation and action, the report had bogged down.

There is a curious, inescapable question that always frames itself when hindsight is employed: Why couldn't more people have realized what Goddard was trying to accomplish? The situation has parallel through all recorded history, but even that does not ease the frustration for any of the individuals involved.

In 1940 Harry Guggenheim was so strongly convinced that the United States military forces should avail themselves of Goddard's genius that he arranged a meeting with the chiefs of Army Ordnance, the Army Air Corps, and the Navy Bureau of Aeronautics, offering to place at their disposal all research, data, facilities, and patents.

"After a sympathetic reception," Mr. Guggenheim recalls, "we were asked to present our project in detail to their representatives at a joint conference on May 28, 1940. On hearing our story, the representative of Army

Ordnance said: 'All very interesting, but we don't think rockets will play any part in this war; we believe this war is going to be fought with the trench mortar.'

"However, the representatives of naval aviation and the Army Air Corps said they thought there might be a specialized field in which Dr. Goddard's work could be useful—jet-assisted take offs."[12] But nothing materialized. Goddard returned to Roswell.

Considering the grave position of the world and feeling the inevitability that the United States would become embroiled in the war, Dr. C. N. Hickman wrote Goddard in 1940, referring to the work on rocket weapons in which he had participated with the scientist during World War I and indicating that he wanted to try to arouse the interest of Dr. F. B. Jewett. Jewett was president of Bell Telephone Laboratories where Hickman worked as an engineer and had just been appointed to the NDRC, the National Defense Research Committee. Goddard urged Hickman to try. The effort brought results. Within record time, the invaluable weapon of the infantryman, the Bazooka, was produced.

Goddard received both help and encouragement from the visit of Lieutenant General James H. Doolittle (Ret.). The distinguished officer recently recalled, "I was a Major in the Air Corps Reserve when, at Mr. Guggenheim's request, I went to see Dr. Goddard at Roswell, New Mexico. He was, at the time, interested in special fuels, so I had the Shell Oil Company mix up a high vapor pressure petroleum blend which worked perfectly and obviated the need for a fuel pump. This greatly simplified the apparatus required for this particular test."

Guggenheim and Doolittle were not the only "believers" who persisted in efforts to get a full-scale rocket research program underway; two other members of this relatively small circle were Captain (now Brigadier General) Homer Boushey of the Air Corps and Lieutenant (now Commander, Ret.) Charles Fink Fischer of the Navy. By odd coincidence, after the years of waiting, both services came through with requests for Goddard's assistance just before Pearl Harbor. The Navy offer reached him first, and he accepted immediately. Quickly, preparations were made for the move. Goddard had acquired many pieces of fine machinery which were packed for shipment to the East; these were the machines that made the parts that General Boushey referred to as "exquisite little devices." At Annapolis Goddard became Director of Research on Jet Propulsion for the Bureau of Aeronautics.

Ever the sleeping giant, this nation may rouse slowly, but its scope is tremendous once it gets underway. When we were plunged into war on December 7, 1941, we possessed no rocket weapons. When hostilities ended, the Army and Navy were budgeting rockets at about thirteen million a year.

When a test model of the German V-2 fell on Swedish soil in 1944, the twisted fragments were shipped to the Aberdeen Proving Ground for inspection. In jigsaw fashion the pieces were assembled; though vastly more complex, the result bore a sickening similarity to the basic Goddard rocket. Here was the weapon, developed by an enemy nation, that could have been in the hands of the United States!

Dr. Wernher von Braun has commented that Goddard was "ahead of us all," and continues, "In light of what has happened since his untimely death, we can only wonder what might have been if America realized earlier the implications of his work. I have not the slightest doubt that the United States today would enjoy unchallenged leadership in space exploration had adequate support and recognition been provided to him."[16] At von Braun's suggestion, the American Rocket Society has erected a tablet and marker commemorating the 1926 launching of the world's first liquid propellant rocket; the years have transformed the site on Pakachoag Road in Auburn, Massachusetts from "Aunt" Effie's farm into a golf course.

This is but one of the flood of tributes that America has bestowed upon Goddard. Unfortunately most of them have come since his death on August 10, 1945, following surgery for throat cancer.

The United States Congress voted him a posthumous Congressional Medal in 1959 and the Smithsonian Institution awarded him the famous Langley Medal in 1960 (previously awarded to only eight men). He was the recipient of the first Louis W. Hill Space Transportation Award of the Institute of the Aeronautical Sciences in 1959. Clark University granted him an Honorary Doctor of Science degree in 1945.

There are fascinating Goddard exhibits at the Smithsonian Institution, the Institute of the Aeronautical Sciences, the Roswell Museum, Clark University, and Worcester Polytechnic Institute. The exhibit at the latter institution was created by The Daniel and Florence Guggenheim Foundation which has further honored the scientist by creating the Robert Hutchings Goddard Professorships at the California Institute of Technology and at Princeton University.

The National Aeronautics and Space Administration has named its Space Flight Center for him; the American Rocket Society and other organizations give awards in Goddard's name. The present and future generations of young men of the Air Force Academy are reminded of the important heritage by the Goddard Award, presented each year to the student with the highest grades in mathematics.

But of all the honors and tributes, perhaps the one that would most please the warm and very human scientist was the comment made recently by one of his former assistants who is now at the White Sands Proving Ground in New Mexico. He wrote to Mrs. Goddard, saying, "We have great big rockets and lots of things to work with down here, but it isn't half as much fun as it was working with Dr. Goddard!"

If one truth were demonstrated by all of this history, it would be the inescapable lesson: Great things are not always done in great-seeming ways!

REFERENCES

1. Stevenson, Burton: *The Home Book of Quotations,* ed. 9, p. 2298, New York, Dodd, Mead, 1956.
2. *Astronautics,* 4:4 pt. 1:24–27+, April, 1959.
3. *Tech. News,* XLIX:14:1–6, April 29, 1959.
4. Pendray, G. Edward: *The Coming Age of Rocket Power,* New York, Harper, 1947.
5. *Reader's Digest,* 67:147–152, November, 1955.
6. *Space Age,* 1:11–13+, May, 1959.
7. *Milwaukee Journal,* Milwaukee, Wis., April 4, 1920.
8. *Boston Sunday Advertiser,* Boston, Mass., April 18, 1920.
9. Ley, Willy: *Rockets, Missiles, and Space Travel,* New York, Viking, 1957.
10. *Columbus, Ohio, Dispatch,* Columbus, Ohio, October 11, 1957.
11. *World-Telegram & Sun,* New York, N. Y., July 5, 1958.
12. *Boston American,* Boston, Mass., July 18, 1929.
13. *Sunday Telegram,* Worcester, Mass., April 18, 1948.
14. Goddard, Robert H.: *Rockets,* New York, American Rocket Society, 1946.
15. *Philadelphia Public Ledger,* Philadelphia, Pa., July 11, 1922.
16. *Astronautics,* 4:6:36, June, 1959.

Lieutenant General, United States Air Force. Forceful leader who gave America its first intercontinental ballistic missile in record time

BERNARD A. SCHRIEVER

The Juggler had six items. They all had to be kept in motion simultaneously in an act that had never been tried before. He was working at double tempo, attempting an unheard-of speed-up. Though no one questioned his skill, there were still wagers that he wouldn't make it—he couldn't. But if he didn't the consequences were too grave to consider. There were bobbles, near-slips; strain was taking its toll; yet he never dared to relax for a split second. Outwardly he remained composed, though pressures mounted to the bursting point. As the climax neared, the performer drew upon all of the support of his backstage crew and staged a finale that surpassed every hope! The greatest juggling act in history was a triumph!

The "performer" was Lieutenant General Bernard A. Schriever, and the "juggling act" he performed was more properly known as the "concept of concurrency," the daring new weapons systems concept which produced the United States' first mighty missile, the Atlas, in half the previously required time for projects of only one-tenth the complexity. The development of this ballistic missile program will go down in history as one of the greatest calculated risks ever undertaken. There was only one risk greater—trying to survive in the world without it. When Schriever drew the assignment, he knew the preservation of this country could well hinge on his ability to make the "impossible" program succeed. How he did it, and why he did it, are as complex and intriguing as the inner workings of the "bird" he delivered!

In 1953, when most Americans were listening to "How Much Is That Doggie in the Window?", and reading Hemingway's Pulitzer Prize novel *The Old Man and the Sea* a responsible few in Washington, D. C., were reading sobering top-secret reports with ominous overtones. A great scientific advancement had occurred in atomic development—the thermonuclear breakthrough. In simple terms this meant that fantastically high-yield H-bombs, even more devastating than the A-bombs dropped on Hiroshima or Nagasaki, could soon be reduced to a size which could become the warhead of a missile! At that instant there was born the potential of retaliating to the front door of anyone, anywhere!

All prior reports and evaluations became archaic overnight. The world's future could be projected only through the eyes of experts. Trevor Gardner, Air Force Assistant Secretary for Research and Development, sped into action by establishing the Teapot Committee. This mundane code name was applied to the Air Force Strategic Missiles Evaluation Committee,* and brought together ten of the finest scientific minds in the country under the chairmanship of the mathematician, the late Dr. John von Neumann (who was with the Princeton Institute for Advanced Study). The Teapot Committee's function was to evaluate the feasibility and practicability of developing an intercontinental ballistic missile, an ICBM, weapons system—a complete new concept in warhead delivery.

These were days when the atmosphere hanging over Washington—from the Pentagon, across the bridge, up the mall to Capitol Hill—was one of budget-cutting; and a preconditioned negative reaction greeted any proposal that dealt with space (a word snatched from the fanciful pages of science fiction).

Despite this, Gardner—armed with his own strong convictions, plus the urgent recommendation of the Von Neumann committee, the support of General Nathan F. Twining, Air Force Chief of Staff, and Secretary of the Air Force Harold E. Talbott—managed to slice through channels, override stringent objections, and set up a project to develop an intercontinental ballistic missile. Schriever, whom Gardner dubbed "vice-president in charge of getting things done," became the boss.

* Other members were: Prof. Clark B. Millikan, Prof. Charles C. Lauritsen, and Dr. Louis G. Dunn, California Institute of Technology; Dr. Hendrik W. Bode, Bell Telephone Laboratories; Dr. Allen E. Puckett, Hughes Aircraft Co.; Dr. George B. Kistiakowsky, Harvard University; Prof. J. B. Wiesner, Massachusetts Institute of Technology; Mr. Lawrence A. Hyland, Bendix Aviation Corp.; Dr. Simon Ramo and Dr. Dean Wooldridge, Ramo-Wooldridge Corp.

"You have the responsibility of getting into operation an ICBM, an intercontinental ballistic missile, at the earliest possible date; it must be the best possible weapon, built for the least possible budget. Those are your only boundary conditions. Get to work, now, and don't let it worry you that the existence of the United States could be in dire peril if you should fail. Good luck!"

That, in essence, was the assignment. Why was he selected for this vital mission? Lieutenant General Donald Putt (Ret.) could give a ready answer. "Schriever is a natural. He was born for the job." Putt, as Deputy Chief of Staff for Research and Development, had had ample opportunity to formulate an opinion, for Schriever served under him as Assistant for Development Planning. In those Pentagon days, Schriever was a colonel, but this did not prompt prudence where principle was involved. He had stood up against high ranking officers, including four-star generals when his convictions dictated. And he had frequently made himself unpopular by beating the drums for an ICBM and other equally advanced weapons systems.

Schriever was not given to snap judgments; he gave careful consideration to issues. Once he had reached a decision he was willing to stand by it. Should the opposition persist, he was infinitely patient to outwait them. Never forcing, but logically leading, he was victor in many a skirmish within the Pentagon corridors. He could be termed neither rebel nor nonconformist—rather, an individual with complete integrity and sound judgment. In the purest sense, such men are few.

But this in itself could not account for his record of accomplishment. A believer may donate his life to crusading yet never enlist one follower—however right may be his mission. Ideas must be brought alive—be made to work. Schriever could deliver; he was an officer who could stimulate action. There was a "let's get things done" feeling about his efforts.

So there was both wisdom and logic employed when Schriever was named Assistant to the Commander, Air Research and Development Command, and Commander, Western Development Division, and given what has been termed "the most important job in the country." Paradoxically, the project which he headed was given the highest priority in the Air Force and in the nation; yet it was—and is—for military weapons that we pray will never be used.

So was initiated a new concept, that of push-button warfare; but the man who was then the chairman of the Joint Congressional Committee on Atomic Energy, the late Senator Brien MacMahon, pointedly remarked, "All we have now are the push-buttons."[1] Thus were three minds goaded by dire necessity into forging the bold "concept of concurrency." Gardner, von Neumann, and Schriever all joined to formulate the plans, though perhaps the latter deserves the most credit.

They dovetailed their separate abilities into a mighty triumvirate. Von

Neumann, the genius, could think through the existing knowledge to a far-reaching conclusion; in consultation with the entire committee but ever the leading force, he projected the problems that would confront development. His group had to determine that it was technically possible to build such a weapon.

Gardner utilized all his knowledge of governmental functioning to rush through the program in record time. He was able to bring to bear the resources of the nation, secure priorities, and break down red tape.

Schriever closed the circle with his magnetism to gather the right kind of military people and to engender the confidence in the plan so that people were anxious to work on it. He also added a rare understanding of the ins and outs of the industrial jungle.

One of the first tasks in organization was that of gathering his staff. Says the General, "The one overriding qualification in my opinion is a man's loyalty. If he has a deficiency in his loyalty, I don't care how smart he is or what he can do, I won't have him around. This doesn't mean I want a lot of 'yes' men; because I try to give all of my key staff people adequate opportunity to state their cases in any major issue. But if you don't have loyalty in an organization, you don't have anything. And I like people who are smart, who have the attribute of wisdom as well as intelligence—particularly in the key spots. Also, I want to see initiative. I like aggressive people."

From his years in the service, from his wide exposure through various commands and locales, Schriever hand-picked a nucleus* who measured up to these stringent requirements—plus a half hundred more—to fly to Inglewood, California, in July, 1954, to set up the Western Development Division, later renamed the Air Force Ballistic Missile Division and known as BMD.

They wore only civilian clothes. They met in a small building which was formerly a chapel. They moved in a vacuum of total secrecy. They toiled to the absolute, utter breaking point—and they'd hardly started the task. On one of those nights when Schriever got home very late—as usual—dropped his briefcase on a table and slumped into a chair, he heard a stir from the bedroom. Dodie, like most teen-agers, usually slept too soundly to be roused easily but that night she had heard him come in. Sleepily she crept into the living room. "Wanted to tell you good night, Daddy." She gave him a loving hug. Was there something on her mind Schriever inquired—any-

---

* The following comprised this group (rank indicated was that held as of December 2, 1954): Brig. Gen. Bernard A. Schriever, Col. Harold T. Morris, Col. Harold W. Norton, Col. William A. Sheppard, Col. Charles H. Terhune, Jr., Lt. Col. Benjamin P. Blasingame, Lt. Col. Beryl L. Boatman, Lt. Col. Philip C. Calhoun, Lt. Col. Roy L. Ferguson, Lt. Col. Otto J. Glasser, Lt. Col. Edward N. Hall, Lt. Col. Joseph D. Heck, Jr., Lt. Col. John B. Hudson, Lt. Col. Norman J. Keefer, and Lt. Col. Edwin A. Swanke.

thing that had happened to disturb her since the last time they had had any chance to visit? She reassured him there was nothing.

This girl was the granddaughter of General Brett and the daughter of a dedicated officer; even if there had been some minor disturbance in her life she had too much the spirit of the soldier to let him know. She and the other children knew nothing of what Daddy was doing, but they could sense an urgency about it. "You're sure there's nothing you want to talk about, Dodie?" She shook her tousled head and buried it against his rough tweed. "Not a thing, Daddy." It helped to hear her say that. When the job is so pressing, the hours so all-demanding, every man has the nagging realization that he is neglecting those he loves. There was no escaping the fact that Dora would have to be father as well as mother much of the time, for this assignment would be little better than a wartime rigor for his family. His schedule would allow no letup until the job was done. (For the next three years he was to work even on New Year's Day.) It all added up to one thing—his children would be growing up virtually without a father, just as he had done.

Fear dominated the entire crossing of the Atlantic. There was great agitation from Mother Schriever over the possibility that the British might intercept the Dutch ship and all of those fleeing Europe's plight in the dreadful days of 1917 would be interned in England. There was also talk that the United States would enter the War and that as soon as the ship docked in New York all the Germans aboard would be returned via the Red Cross. It was a long voyage—they had not dared to go through the English Channel but had had to circle the British Isles.

To further complicate the trip, both of her sons, Bennie and Gerry, were terribly ill with mumps. She couldn't get proper care for them on the crowded ship, where everything was so strange and frightening to the children anyway.

How Mother Schriever wished that their introduction to America could be as happy as hers had been! She was just thirteen when she caught her first glimpse of the Statue of Liberty. It was clothed in the rosy tint of dawn and characterized her nine-year stay in Long Island. There she had met Father Schriever and had returned to her homeland after their marriage.

Father would be waiting for them at Ellis Island. Since the Hamburg American Lines vessel on which he served as an engineer had been caught in an American harbor when War was declared, he had not been able to return to Germany. Now Mother could almost count the hours until the family would be reunited—providing none of her fears materialized.

She pleaded with Bennie. She knew the mumps had led to dreadful earache. But he mustn't cry as they left the ship—else they might never make it past the health officer. His little mouth drew down in pain, but there would be no more tears. After all he was seven, and his brother was just five. He'd have to be a man. But his ears did hurt so much. Then he saw Father, and everything was so much better.

Once they were settled in New Braunfelds, Texas, Father seemed to want to spend every evening with a son on each knee. He'd been at sea so constantly that there had never been time for many of the things that boys and fathers share. Father would light up his pipe, take a few long puffs, then embark on a session of storytelling about his travels.

There was fun in the household—the fun of being together! As Mother hummed and busied about the kitchen, Father was occupied with making gifts for Bennie and Gerry; from empty red cans of Prince Albert Tobacco he fashioned piggy banks! How they all laughed as pennies clanked to the bottom of the cans—and what treasures those gifts became such a short time later when Father was killed in an industrial accident! (The tin box has been kept through all the years, through all the moving that Schriever has done in his military service.)

Mother had instilled discipline in her boys. She applied the same stern lesson to herself. Alone in a strange country, with two sons to support, she transformed her grief into determination. They would have a good and full life. She would give her sons all the things her earnings could buy and make up shortages with love. And they would get good educations—she would see to that.

What a blessing that they had moved to this German community of New Braunfelds, thirty-five miles northeast of San Antonio. The chance for adjustment to their new country was so much better. Even language proved no problem, for the children in Bennie's school spoke German; he was not ostracized during the period until he learned English. Yet it seemed the boy's nature to stay somewhat apart from the rest of the students.

Did the loss of his Father, the period of readjustment in his boyhood, leave a serious mark? Were there memories of grave disappointment? He says, "No, I have little recollection of discouragements. I have never had the willingness to be disappointed." What a meaningful statement! Such dominion over his reactions has served Schriever well in the exceeding trials of his adult life.

An interest in sports supplanted his social activities and was heightened when he was twelve, for his Mother became housekeeper to a well-known San Antonio philanthropist, Mr. E. B. Chandler. Schriever recalls, "He was active in youth programs, so he gave Gerry and me golf lessons. The game became a very important phase of my life for a few years. It was something at which I wanted to excel, and I think I did. My score has deteriorated in recent years, of course, because I've had no time for golf. But the point is that as a boy I had a feeling of wanting to compete and not liking disappointment or loss. You might say I was always a pretty poor loser." A more accurate interpretation would be that Schriever was determined to win!

Bennie and Gerry found a way of helping with the burden of responsibility that their Mother was carrying—they operated a cold-drink stand at the golf club; their backyard fence line was opposite the twelfth green. Reversing the usual procedure, when a parent builds up a business for the sons, they were the ones to start this stand, which their Mother subsequently took over and ran for thirty years.

Among the qualities she instilled in her sons was a strong desire for an education. Schriever recalls, "I was very addicted to study, and I definitely wanted a college degree. I chose engineering because my father had been an engineer, and also because I was quite good in mathematics—not a genius by any means, but it was a subject I enjoyed.

"Financial reasons narrowed my choice to a state university, but aside from that Texas A & M appealed to me—it was a military school, not co-educational, which I liked. I was still antisocial at that time," he smilingly admits.

The depression had slashed away job opportunities in 1931. Classed among the "least-wanted" applicants were young men with a fresh degree tucked in their pockets, trying to offset lack of experience with high hopes. When he could find no position, Schriever had an ace in the hole, or at least a ball on the green. He turned hobby into profit by playing in golf tournaments and winning more money in prizes than a job would have paid!

R.O.T.C. training at college had earned him a reserve commission in the Field Artillery. The military he liked; but service on the ground he yearned to trade for service in the skies. No boy growing up in San Antonio, the cradle of Army Air Corps flying, remained untouched by its fascination. Hours spent hanging over the fence at Kelly Field conjured up visions of what it would be like to zoom down a runway, climb to an altitude where the city appeared below in an orderly pattern, then test skill and courage with turns and banks and inverted loops! Flying was a husky youngster in those days, filled with promise! Unlike the large and highly professional organization that the Air Force is today, it was a closely knit and very glamorous group in the early Thirties. Goggles and helmets and long white scarves conveyed a devil-may-care attitude that set these men apart from the rest. Bennie Schriever wanted to be one of them.

July of 1932 and the first step into the skies was taken; he became a cadet at Randolph Field in Texas. The event was not without its interesting ramifications. He had just won the San Antonio City Golf Championship, and he won it from an instructor at Randolph Field. The reception that awaited him hit where it hurt most—at his retiring disposition. The upper classmen had collected all the newspaper accounts of his golf victory, and he was obliged to read the glowing accounts before the assembled cadets—not just once but on a regular basis. That he could be a good sport, as well as a sportsman, saved the day. He accepted the hazing in stride.

Fellowship has been one of the basic desires of men throughout time. Whether designated by the beads and feathers of a special tribe, the insignia of a particular religious group, or the sign of a fraternity, there is reward in "belonging." It is an unspoken testimony to something shared, a recitation of kindred beliefs and customs. Conditions may break the chain, or force may dissolve a group, but soon the regrouping begins to build another class, clique, clan, or assembly.

A military career proffers deep gratification of this need. There is satisfaction in being a member of one of our services; broken down into one of its subdivisions the reward becomes increasingly important. To be a member of one class at one field of one branch of the Air Corps was a special privilege. The cadets at Randolph Field in Schriever's class numbered but eighty-eight. He says, "You form close friendships going through flight training. We were a small class—then a few were killed, and this heightened the bonds between the rest of us—and we lived together for one year under considerable discipline. I don't see many of them now—one of the men, William Hudnell, has become a Major General in the Air Materiel Command; and another, Beirne Lay, Jr., is an author of excellent books and screenplays about the Air Force. But if any one of those men were to walk into the room today, though that group began in 1933, I know we would immediately resume the feeling we had for one another."

One phrase tells the story—esprit de corps!

Discipline was a lesson early learned in the Schriever household—not by means of a "hickory stick," but by the intelligent realization that discipline is the best habit to form. So cadet training offered no problem of adjustment to Schriever in that regard. Discipline, of self or of others, asks its price but becomes one of the real bargains in living, for it returns manyfold in benefits and productivity.

The early morning air was still and humid, as it usually is in Panama. The Matson liner, *Pennsylvania,* had just docked and Schriever scanned the rails in search of a lady. On the top deck, a blonde head appeared for a moment, then vanished. Wearily, he climbed the gangplank and started the search.

Military service in Panama was more like a vacation than work. He would jokingly say he suspected there were two reasons why Lieutenant General George H. Brett had selected him as aide: first, he was a bachelor to escort the many single girls to the social activities at Albrook Field, and second, he was a golfer, so he could keep the General company on the links. But this particular mission, to come to the other side of the Isthmus to pick up the General's daughter, had not appealed to him. (It wasn't that his boyhood disinterest in girls still persisted, but rather the fact that the 5 A.M. docking had allowed him no sleep!)

Within an hour, as he finished ham and eggs in the ship's dining saloon, his drowsiness had vanished. Miss Dora Brett was a charming breakfast companion—so charming, in fact, that he soon made up his mind to seek a permanent arrangement.

By the fall of 1937 he was flying for Northwest Airlines, a position that offered more salary and better security than had his Air Corps active reserve status—important considerations for a man about to be married. But within a year competitive examinations brought Schriever the commission in the Regular Army that he had long sought, and he returned to the service.

"When I was assigned to Wright Field as a test pilot in 1939, the matter of research and development really became a matter of high interest to me. The whole aviation business was in its infancy; I could see we had a long way to go, and that R & D [Research and Development] would be the vehicle to take us." Better to face the job ahead he attended the Aeronautical Engineering School at Wright Field, then attended Stanford University to earn his Master's Degree in Mechanical Engineering (Aeronautical) in June of 1942. A month later he left for the South Pacific area.

In those early days of the War, the tide was moving against our forces— it was rough going for the 19th Bomb Group. Efforts to increase effectiveness, such as rigging handmade flare-dropping devices, proved futile as the forces participated in campaigns from the Bismarck Archipelago to Ryukyu. Schriever flew sixty-three missions before being transferred to logistics.

"I left the States as a captain in June of 1942," he recalls, "and in December of 1943, I was a full colonel. That's a very quick build-up of responsibility, which happened not only to me but to a lot of other men too. I think this is one of the reasons why young men have been able to do a very creditable job of running the Air Force. In wartime you can cram almost the experience of a lifetime into a few years. In many respects there is much to be gained by having this level of responsibility suddenly thrust upon you. Either you can accept it and do the job, or you can't. The ones who can't fall by the wayside like flies. It just happens."

Is there any way of duplicating this process in peacetime? Says Schriever, "No, we have too many checks and balances in our system. We, unfortunately, reduce things to the lowest common denominator too often. It is one of the problems of a democracy that within our governmental structure there are administrative rules and regulations which are aimed at the most incompetent individual, rather than rules that permit the most competent to exercise judgment in running the show. Only in wartime can we provide the flexibility to allow the right people to get in and do the job expeditiously." Adds Schriever significantly from his position in 1960 as

Commanding General of the Air Research and Development Command, ARDC, "This flexibility of which I speak is never granted in normal times —except all should realize these are not normal times. If only something would convey this sufficiently to the American people, so that provisions could be made to allow the top people in the government to get the job done!" The job at hand—the protection of the United States through an arsenal of missiles—was foreseen many years ago.

Air Power and the Future was a remarkable document written by General H. H. "Hap" Arnold in 1945. Though peace had just returned, he conveyed the thought that future airpower would obviously include destructive missiles. Though Dr. Robert H. Goddard was not heeded when he led the way toward military rockets, the German V-2s—an outgrowth of Goddard's principles—proved the mighty destructiveness of such weaponry.

When General Carl Spaatz became Chief of Staff, he furthered the thought of missiles in Air Force requirements, spelling out that efforts should be directed toward a 5000-mile-range supersonic speed vehicle that could carry an atomic warhead. But in those days, before the technological breakthrough that signaled the advent of the H-bomb, it would have taken a missile weighing 500 tons to deliver such a punch.

K. T. Keller, forceful former president of the Chrysler Corporation, became Director of Guided Missiles in the Office of the Secretary of Defense in 1950 and ordered full speed ahead on the production of smaller missiles: the Matador, Nike, Corporal, and the Terrier.

The road called Research and Development had many turns. When viewed from above, it can clearly be seen how it wandered from the direct path, how roadblocks were erected by divergent opinion, how paths often but led to blind alleys. A study contract on the MX-774 was given in April of 1946 during one of the broad stretches of the road; this forerunner to the Atlas quickly took form in the plans of Karel "Charlie" Bossart and his team at Convair, but in fifteen months the contract was cancelled—on the eve of completing the first test missile. Another project that died aborning, however, ultimately served good purpose toward the development of an ICBM; had it not been for the ill-fated Navaho missile project, North American Aviation, Inc., would not have had the ready capability to produce the giant rocket engines for the Atlas.

That was history, prologue, overture. Now the real show was beginning. Of absolutely colossal proportions, it was the greatest concentration of men, money, and materiel ever assembled! Schriever's function was similar to that of Lieutenant General Leslie R. Groves who bossed the development of the A-bomb, except that the BMD expenditures for the first five years quadrupled the amount spent on the Manhattan Project.

The assignment was first for an ICBM, the Atlas. Then, it was discovered that by a 10 per cent increase in the over-all cost, a second missile could be put together. This was possible because the subsystems of the Atlas—propulsion, guidance, nose cone—each had "backups." The "back-up philosophy" provided necessary protection during the development stage—a kind of insurance against the failure of any one of the systems to meet the schedule. By this method separate contractors developed alternate (not parallel) technical approaches to each system.

Instead of allowing these to remain as backups for the Atlas, the subsystems were realigned into a new ICBM weapon, the Titan. The 10 per cent additional cost was required for the airframe—for there had been no backup for this. Thus emerged the second ICBM, the Titan, with a completely different technical approach.

Then a need arose for an IRBM, an intermediate range ballistic missile. Employing the same basic subsystems, the Thor was born out of the Atlas. So the project mushroomed, and the already huge task assumed even greater proportions. Since a similar project had never before been attempted, since the rules had yet to be written, how was it to be approached?

If this had been happening in a novel or a motion picture, the hero would have plunged in single-handed, employed a bank of telephones, an IBM machine, drawn upon his own mental magic, and solved the problem. One of the greatest departures of fiction from fact is in the "single-handed-ness" with which such an endeavor can be accomplished.

Particularly in this era complexity is commonplace. One man must lead, to be sure, but he stands on the shoulders of giants. At his right hand Schriever had the Guided Missile Research Division of the Ramo-Wooldridge Corporation serving in a unique capacity. This team had been retained by contract with the Air Force to provide technical direction and weapon systems engineering. The term "systems engineering" denotes a remarkable method of co-ordinating many different elements—airframe, propulsion system, guidance system, etc.—that were being built by separate corporations scattered throughout the country. As Colonel Otto Glasser, project officer on the Atlas, explains, "It is patent as you go through the design of a system that, if you were to build the best possible propulsion system, you would probably accrue constraints on the guidance system. Conversely, if you say, 'I'm going to make the guidance system the best that it can possibly be,' the flight profile of the mission might be such that you would get excessive aerodynamic heating. Compromise of each element is the answer. But this compromise or adjustment would not be feasible should the program be segmented and fragmented through a series of offices. This is only possible when you have an integrated systems-engineering technical-direction group which has all the pieces under its control." Such was the duty of the Ramo-Wooldridge Corporation as the scientific member of the team. Its staff of about 400 experts formed a link between the Air Force and industry—primarily the eighteen prime contractors for the major subsystems.

At the time of the project's organization the California Institute of Technology and the Massachusetts Institute of Technology were approached to function in this capacity; both declined because of the heavy load of government work they already carried. The Air Force felt that the Ramo-Wooldridge Corporation was best set up to get the job done, but questions were raised as to the advisability of having one corporation in the position of giving technical direction to other corporations. The truly remarkable results of their efforts stand as the best testimony to the wisdom of the choice. Dr. Simon Ramo has been termed the "architect of the Thor, Atlas, and Titan," lending a scientific wizardry which he had earlier demonstrated in the development of the Hughes Aircraft Company's air-to-air missile, the Falcon.

Among the major responsibilities in the BMD operation was that of contracting and procurement. Major General Ben I. Funk headed this division and in working with his special plant representatives kept close touch with the companies who delivered the components and subsystems. Funk praises the support of industry, saying that its investment in highly specialized facilities has been substantial "in spite of the fact that the work to date has been principally developmental and that no contractor has complete assurance he will be given a contract for quantity production."[2]

In keeping with the concept of concurrency—that all phases of the program be developed on parallel tracks and simultaneous time schedules—the logistics of keeping the operational missile bases supplied was also under Funk's command. A dramatic innovation in this procedure is explained by the General: "A fully integrated electronic data-processing system, along with a communications system, will link the ballistic missiles manager, the operating squadrons, a storage site for common items of supply, and the applicable contractor. . . . The ability to react instantaneously to a requirement, coupled with the close inventory control this system will permit, will save countless millions of dollars usually expended to stock larger quantities of spares."[2]

Lieutenant Colonel Donald L. Perry was given a strange assignment at BMD. As public information officer his duties ordinarily would have been to disseminate information by means of press conferences, news releases, and other coverage; but with this supersecret project his full energy was given to the suppression of any leak of their activities. This news blackout persisted for a year and a half. Mrs. Schriever recalls, "The first I knew of what my husband was doing was when I read of the project in *Newsweek* in January of 1956. Before that, I'd had no idea what was happening—except that it was vitally important."

Her greatest concern during the long years was for the other officers' wives, ones who had not grown up in the military as she had and had difficulty understanding the stringent demands that were being made upon their husbands. Since they were not operating from a base and the families lived in widely separated districts of the sprawling Los Angeles area, it was difficult for her to form the wives' club (as the wife of a commanding officer customarily does). But they managed to meet in one another's homes, or at centrally located restaurants for coffee or luncheon. She even called upon Colonel Perry to give the women occasional briefings. He could only talk in cryptic terms, however, telling them that the officers were engaged in the greatest undertaking the Air Force had ever attempted and that their long hours of work and reluctant silence could be lightened by blind understanding and confidence from the families. There were no switches installed at the Ballistic Missile Division offices in Inglewood, for the lights were never off: crews worked around the clock. There was no normal home life, no rest on Saturdays and Sundays. Much was demanded of, and given by, the wives of the officers, and also of the civilians who were occupied with the giant effort.

Perry added, "The Boss expected exceptional results from some fairly ordinary individuals—and got them. But there weren't too many 'ordinary' people around; BMD had the highest educational level of any military organization before or since—more than one third of the hand-picked officers held Ph.D.'s and Master's degrees."

General Schriever avers with conviction that this Space Age necessitates the development of mind power if our nation is to survive: "In my view it is a national disgrace that the term 'egghead' as a synonym for intellectual excellence has become a derogatory expression. Let me tell you that it is the 'eggheads' who are saving us—just as it was the 'eggheads' who wrote the Constitution of the United States. It is the 'eggheads' in the realm of science and technology, in industry, in statecraft, as well as in other fields who form the first line of freedom's defense."[3]

The skill which Schriever lent to the program was primarily managerial; though holding degrees in engineering, he never regarded himself on this assignment as purely a technical man. The broad view, rather than a specialization in any technical field, provides a leveling effect and a truer perspective of the entire objective. That such nontechnical leadership is highly desirable is demonstrated by the appointment of such men as Brigadier General Charles A. Lindbergh to the Air Force Scientific Advisory Board.

At staff meetings Schriever would bring up some of the knottiest problems and lay them on the table for discussion. Several specialists in the particular area would in turn voice opinions, and the conflicting ideas on solution would bring the discussion to what appeared to be an almost uncontrollable point. Schriever would suddenly interrupt. "OK. I think we've had enough discussion. This is the way we'll do it," he'd say and proceed to outline the answer. Dumbfounded, the experts would sit back and exclaim, "Of course. Why didn't we think of that!" What Schriever had done while the discussion was proceeding was to summarize the technical ideas presented with the practical management approach and come forth with a solution based on his own technical background and experience.

Fellow officers were also astounded, and sometimes dismayed, at Schriever's unbelievable memory. He can seemingly file away every bit of information he has ever gathered and call it up at will. In briefings his project officers would quote budget figures which they had carefully studied, only to have Schriever pick up an error that had crept in or to compare them with figures quoted some years back. Also any unresolved question always got answered—though possibly as much as a year later when he had to refresh the memory of the man who had initially posed it. Considering the magnitude of the missile project, this capacity unquestionably aided him in staying "on top" of all phases of the work.

Linked with this unique talent to store information, he possessed an insatiable desire to acquire it. He wanted to know—and did know—every detail of every phase of every division of the ballistic missile evolvement. He tore rapidly through stacks of reports; he scrawled his initials on more pages and in more places than did the ever present Kilroy of World War II. No instant was wasted. Mornings he was picked up from the five-room apartment he and his family occupied in Santa Monica; the driving time to Inglewood was utilized for discussion of the most pressing matters.

At one time he was spending two thirds of his time traveling—to the headquarters of Strategic Air Command in Nebraska, to Washington, D. C., to Cape Canaveral, and to the major companies involved in production. An extremely able pilot, he would stay at the controls until cruising altitude was reached, then he'd turn the airplane over to his copilot and take a seat in the rear for conferences or study. "He reminded me of a college student cramming for finals," commented one of his men. Added another, "I've been on many of those twelve-hour cross-country hops— this was in the days before jets cut down our time—and the General would start discussions soon after take-off. Before we'd finally touch down at Andrews AFB in Washington, he would have wrung out five or six top staff officers, but he would be fresh and bright—ready to go do battle at the Pentagon or on the Hill."

Catnaps! This was Schriever's secret weapon! He could sleep at will, shedding all problems. Often on trips he'd glance at his watch and interrupt a discussion of some difficult matter by saying, "I think I'd better get an hour's nap before we arrive." Then he'd put his head back and completely relax. Such absolute control of his mind gave his body a chance to replenish itself and undoubtedly contributed to his remarkable physical stamina. He could wear down successive teams of younger associates. (The average age at BMD was thirty-two, and Schriever was forty-four when assigned.)

"He drives his people." That is a simple fact. It has been whispered. It has been shouted. It has been said with understanding of the urgency that he felt, and it has been said almost as a curse. But no one has ever failed to admit that he drives himself hardest of all. And, equally important, he makes every effort to reward his people; in every manner under his control he sees that they are compensated for the almost merciless demands that have been made upon them.

A demeanor that is controlled should not be mistaken for one that is cold. The deep regard that Schriever has for his friends and fellow officers is revealed in countless instances. When a man falls seriously ill or is injured, the General is the first to visit him, to comfort and ask what he might do to help. Staunchness is characteristic of his loyalty.

There is a faithful and fierce pride among the inner group of BMD that refers to itself as "The Tong." Officers who've worked for him don't want to leave his command. Those who are unwillingly transferred on to other assignments will continue an allegiance that never seems to waiver. They faithfully pass on tips, "scuttlebutt," information, that may aid in support of his effort because our government is, in one sense, like a giant family. And part of the game is in knowing how "to get along" with the other members.

As Colonel Beryl Boatman phrased it, "General Schriever has always been way out in front of the crowd, but not so far out that he would ever permit himself to get cut off. I think this is the very difficult thing that any leader has to do—whether he is leading men at a battle front, in an industrial organization, or in the forefront of government. He must blend boldness with caution. Schriever will never allow his lines of communication to be severed so that he doesn't know what other people are thinking.

"Still, he will not hesitate to commit himself. He realizes full well that this new situation in the world brought about by the exploding technology is something that is going to move forward. Some people just stand up in front and holler that we are going the wrong way. Then there are others who try to get hold of the string to steer it the right way—because it's going to go. Those who just sit are likely to be steam-rollered. I've never seen Schriever sit."

The top priority that the ballistic missile program has had accounts for only part of its outstanding progress. Schriever's facility for imparting his own deep conviction has been a material aid in its success. The time he has spent on Capitol Hill counts from days into weeks into months—months of his time devoted to telling committees and Congress what has happened, what will happen, and what could happen with regard to the defense of this country. He is regarded as one of the most reliable witnesses ever to testify before those who govern.

But from the standpoint of the public it will be said that Schriever is not a good speaker. In a news conference he will deliberate before giving a reply to a vital question; this is somehow considered a failing in a society accustomed to "no pauses," the split-second timing of carefully rehearsed television dramas, and fast-paced comedy routines. It is a curious fact that a fast answer is considered by some to be preferred over a thoughtful one.

Positive thinking is a characteristic of Schriever's staff meetings relates Boatman. "If someone comes in with an idea that sounds like a good one, Schriever wants to know how to bring it into being. If a thing is worthwhile, he feels there must be a way to make it live. Of course, he will objectively consider the problems, but not let them become so great that we can't put a handle on them." The General has his creed for handling problems: "Don't look back to worry about a thing; just learn from it. Organize your time so that you can devote your major energies to the big things." What a simple, evident approach! Results with this project have told their own story.

The backup philosophy is a revolutionary approach. Another innovation is the "test philosophy" created from the requirements and restrictions of missile production. When it is considered that each Atlas has 300,000 individual parts and that the failure of any one of these parts might cause the failure of a launching, it is miraculous that the vehicle not only flies but has achieved a high degree of dependability. The thorough test program begins with the testing of each part, leads to the testing of components, subsystems, assemblies, then finally to a "captive" test—where the missile is restrained and "idled" (as the father of rocketry, Dr. Robert H. Goddard, termed it). The culmination is the flight test, where the countdown at Cape Canaveral gives the real verdict on the missile's capability.

From the time of receiving Department of Defense approval to develop an intermediate range ballistic missile, the first Thor missile came off the production line in eleven months—an unbelievable eleven months, compared with the normal time cycle of approximately eight years for development and manufacture of a complex new aircraft! Exuberance over the achievement was high as the moment for the first test flight approached. The "brass" was all gathered in the blockhouse awaiting the countdown. As it progressed, tension mounted. Remembers one officer who was present, "Confidence for the success of the test was high, though no one would outwardly state it for fear it would upset the delicate balance of man and machine. The moment came. It was an appalling sight to see the Thor hang almost in midair for an instant, then only seconds after the launch command had been given to see a massive fireball engulf the launching pad. There was stunned, utter disbelief painted on the faces of those who had labored so hard to bring the Thor into being. It was almost as if they had lost their first-born child.

"This terrible, deep dejection was not just self-pity. Mostly they were unhappy for the Boss, who had worked so hard. They really expected him to sound off. In a forlorn little group we all trudged back to the motel. We waited. In a little while he came in. 'When is the next one?' he asked!"

The "next one" flew—like a good bird should. Before the end of 1957, the Thor had redeemed itself with a shot traveling 2400 miles, sixty per cent farther than its designed range!

But the bitter disappointment of that first Thor incident, plus the failure of the birds to leave their nests on the next two occasions that he visited the Cape, set up a sensitivity in Schriever. He feels that his people try too hard when he's around and that this may actually affect the launch. So now, it's said, he thinks it best if he's not around, especially when it is an important shoot.

Three sad Chinamen played important roles in the missile effort. After a particularly rough week of disappointments Schriever was in San Francisco on business and wandered into Chinatown late Saturday night to try to divert his mind from problems for a few hours. But thoughts of meetings and reports kept him preoccupied. Distractedly, he paused in front of a gift-shop window, glancing absently at kimonos, pieces of jade, and brass nicknacks, when suddenly he laughed out loud. He saw before him the dejected faces of his three project officers in the form of little carved wooden figures! Early Monday morning he called in the three project directors, Colonel Otto Glasser on the Atlas, Colonel Richard K. Jacobson on the Thor, and Colonel Benjamin P. Blasingame on the Titan, and he gave the figures to the three men with the admonition, "I don't want to see these figures again until you each have a successful launch. Put these sad little men on your desks to remind you that we have a schedule to meet."

As success came to the projects in turn, the officers entered into a bit of collusion—the figures were returned to Schriever wearing tiny silver halos.

Like a proud father watching his children perform, Schriever can now pause in the work on his next projects at ARDC Headquarters, Washington, D. C., to note progress such as that evidenced on May 20, 1960, when the Atlas flew 9000 miles! And in *Newsweek* of April 11, 1960, it was revealed that the Atlas had averaged hitting within seven tenths of a mile of the bull's-eye on 6000 mile shots! Great performance, indeed, for a weapon that started such a short time ago as just an idea in the minds of the Pentagon's persistent ones!

As a friend remarked about the BMD period, "The General must have felt terribly alone, for there was no place he could turn, actually, for the answers. All the major decisions he had to pull out of his own head, and he was controlling the spending of three million dollars a day!" Under the heading "Air Force Research," *Ordnance Magazine,* publication of the American Ordnance Association, Washington, D. C., in the September-October, 1959, issue sums it up in this manner: "Within the space of five years, the Air Force Ballistic Missile Division has built and test-flown Atlas, Thor and Titan missiles.

"Test stands, check-out facilities, launchers, and masses of analytical equipment have been developed and put into use. Construction has begun on bases for operational Atlas and Titan missiles. Two ocean-spanning missile ranges have been implemented, and tracking stations have been placed in globally strategic areas. The dynamic and brilliant leadership given by General Schriever in the Ballistic Missile Division will find its proper focus in the even broader aspects of the entire Air Force Research and Development Command."

What are the projects upon which Schriever is expending his limitless energies today? This we won't learn until a much later date. He terms survival "everybody's business," and we can be confident that he is applying greatest vision and determination toward seeing that our defenses will meet the ever-mushrooming requirements. He points out, "On the clock of national security, we must be able to tell time not just by the minute hand, but also by the hour hand. This means long-term planning. This means that 1968 has to be as real in our thinking as 1958 or '59 or '60."[4] As Senator Leverett Saltonstall said to Schriever during his appearance before the Senate Preparedness Investigating Subcommittee on January 2, 1958, "Certainly it is comforting to have men like you around."

To the joy of his family, he is "around" a little more often these days, although son Brett and daughters Dodie and Barbara still refer to him as "our star boarder." Living on the base at Andrews in Maryland, he is able to bring his work home more often. Almost every day that he's not traveling, he now brings along at noontime a group for discussions; the vivacious and capable Mrs. Schriever is geared to serve luncheon to one or to ten—however many walk through the front door. Weekdays, dinners are also usually devoted to business, but he now has tried to keep weekends for his family—making a happy ritual of cooking breakfast on Saturday mornings for his mother and stepfather, Hans Betzlmann, who live in a small house adjoining his.

There is a deep bond between Mother and Son, for he is well aware that it was her high standards and selfless efforts to give him the proper education that laid the foundation on which he has been able to build his life and career. One of the few times Schriever ever openly displayed the emotions that are so deeply felt within him was in Austin, Texas, on May 5, 1959. He had been invited to address the Texas State Legislature regarding his Ballistic Missile Program. At the conclusion he was delighted to be made a member of the Texas Navy! Then, as a complete surprise to him, his mother was brought out, in a wheel chair, and paid great tribute by the assembly.

Of the many awards, decorations, and honorary degrees which line the walls of his den, the one of especial meaning is his life membership in the "88 Club." He is proud to have been one of the only eighty-eight men who planned and executed Project Score, our Atlas "talking satellite." Considered to be one of the finest of our space achievements, this secret was so well guarded that even the man who pressed the button for launch did not know what he was sending up!

Dora Brett Schriever makes the somewhat surprising statement, "I don't consider my husband a typical military man." Then she clarifies it by saying, "Particularly in the past, military men always seemed to think of their service first. My husband always puts his country first—in all ways. He has a very active and abiding patriotism."

Speaking of his country, Schriever says, "Love and loyalty demand from all of us not only an understanding of the challenges which beset us, but also a heightening sense of personal involvement—that attitude of 'what can I do to pitch in and help?' It seems to me that each of us should search his own conscience and act upon the obligation that each of us has to return to our country some small portion of what it has given to us.

"This kind of patriotism is a rational and thoughtful awareness that, at this point in time, with its troubles and its tensions, with its perils and its promises, we have the responsibility of helping to determine whether the next few years will mark freedom's most magnificent period or freedom's slow decline to be a footnote only in whatever history books may be written in the future."[3]

The favorite diversion Bernard A. Schriever seeks is the reading of early American history, especially the study of Lincoln and his generals. From the writings of the great President, the belief which guides the General's life can be well stated:

"Let us have faith that right makes might; and in that faith let us to the end, dare to do our duty as we understand it."[5]

REFERENCES

1. *Time*, 67:53, January 30, 1956.
2. Gantz, Lt. Col. Kenneth F., ed.: *The United States Air Force Report on the Ballistic Missile*, Garden City, N. Y., Doubleday, 1958.
3. *Space Age*, 2:36–38, November, 1959.
4. Schriever, Bernard A.: *Equation for Survival: Lead Time Equals Leadership*, address before Economic Club of New York, January 21, 1958.
5. Lincoln, Abraham: Address, Cooper Union, New York, February 27, 1860.

Colonel, United States Air Force (MC).
Dedicated and courageous doctor famed
for his rocket-sled test rides

JOHN PAUL STAPP

As a child he protested against taking an afternoon nap by shouting Biblical quotations in Portuguese. As a boy he got up off the mat twenty times, until finally his boxing opponent didn't have the heart to knock him down again and broke off the match. As a medical student, he cooked and ate the remains of the guinea pigs he used in the laboratory because of his meager budget. As a doctor in the United States Air Force, he subjected his body to lethal tests of deceleration that caused it to weigh 7751 pounds for a fraction of a second!

Those who work with him proffer fanatical devotion. Those who know him are constantly amazed by the diversity of his interests and the sparkling humor that peppers his conversations. Those who reported on his rocket-sled tests termed him "the bravest man on earth." All agree that he is one of the most dedicated and complex of men. His intellectuality is balanced by a good measure of horse sense. His scientific brain is linked to a poetic soul. John Paul Stapp is a complete individual.

Among his "Stappisms," is one that reflects his humorous, indulgent appraisal of mankind, "The Ironical Paradox: The universal aptitude for ineptitude makes any human accomplishment an incredible miracle." He extends to others more tolerance than to himself. His self-demands have been gigantic.

A startling evaluation comes from one of the men who knows Stapp best Dr. Charles Lombard, "His determination was almost a hate in his life. He hated the fact that not enough was known about acceleration to save the lives of jet pilots in bail-outs, so he went to great extremes to learn more, then educate the world. I think this hate is one component of the true Stapp. How else would he have the gumption to keep going against the odds he has faced?" This unusual application of the word "hate" assumes validity when one searches for motivation strong enough to permit a man to challenge and conquer the seemingly insurmountable—the pattern of Stapp's life.

Says motion picture producer William Bloom, "It's the biggest piece of miscasting I've ever seen. He doesn't fit the real life role he plays." Bloom depicted Stapp's rocket-sled work in the film "On the Threshold of Space," but he admits the true drama of the experiment was more powerful than any he ever captured on the screen. "On the late afternoon before his big run a few of us visited the track to check over the sled. As we turned to go back to the car, we beheld one of those glorious New Mexico sunsets. Stapp lingered a few steps behind. Not a word was said, but the moment crackled with significance as he seemed to be memorizing that sight, for he was well aware that of all the threats posed by his sled run the next morning the greatest danger was to his eyes. He might never see another sunset."

Such fiber was inherited from a mother whom Stapp describes as "carrying on her conscience the conviction that she was responsible for the conversion to Christianity of every native in South America" and a father who courageously took over a "haunted" castle in Bahia, Brazil, for his missionary college—then was aghast when he found that the nocturnal "ghosts" skittering over the roof were opossums, drunk from nibbling mash at a near-by rum factory.

Young Stapp viewed the tipsy animals as he did every living thing—with profound curiosity. Among his favorite animals was the blind cecoecilian, which he described as "a relative to the frog, legless, no identifiable tail, and called blind because all that can be distinguished as eyes are two little purplish spots like powder burns."

On a television tribute, Ralph Edwards reminded Stapp of his early lesson about gravity—that force he later defied in twenty-nine runs on his rocket sled: It seems the boy John Paul sawed off the limb of a tree while he was on the limb, so got to the ground in a most unscientific manner which resulted in a broken arm. Stapp added, "and that's not the only time I've been out on a limb."[1]

Responsibility has never been a stranger to Stapp. At four years of age his mother assigned him the care of her thirty flowerpots and the sweeping of the long walkways surrounding the castle. Soon there was more precious duty, for along came three younger brothers to love and help care for.

A great adventure was lived within the Stapp household—the seeking of knowledge from their library of books. Education was a game, and John Paul scored high. The Bible was his ever constant companion—his special favorites being The Book of Job and The Proverbs—which he read in the Portuguese translation.

But the son of American parents should learn his native tongue; so when the family visited the United States the six-year-old was taught English by a somewhat drastic means—he wasn't fed until he asked for food in the new language! With a growing boy's appetite, he was an apt student.

Upon returning to South America, the family with its missionary dedication was led from Bahia to Araçaju, the city whose name is a lilting combination of the Portuguese words for guava and cashew nuts. At Araçaju there was excitement in the yearly pageant of Lambesuja—a vivid reenactment of a Negro jungle community being attacked by Indians. Half the townspeople dress as Negroes, half as Indians, and comically portray the battle; the event ends in a friendly free-for-all. This colorful celebration stimulated young John Paul, arousing an ability that later prompted one of his drama instructors in university to say that he could have become an outstanding actor.

But other interests were foremost—his pursuit of science and mechanics took more of his attention, even as a child. He would ingeniously carve little wooden boats, propel them with rubber bands, arm them with thirty caliber empty shells filled with match heads, then attach a fuse, and sail his battlewagons downstream, firing charges of rocks at the fern-lined banks.

The routine of life drastically changed for John Paul in his twelfth year. The family paid another visit to the United States and reluctantly made the decision that their eldest son must stay behind when they returned to South America. The boy should continue his education in American schools; his tutoring to date had been at the hands of his gifted mother.

In making arrangements for enrollment, unexpected complications faced Reverend Stapp and his son at the Brownwood, Texas, High School. John Paul lacked the usual background and was younger than any of the other 800 students, so the principal was unwilling to accept him. Resourcefully the boy Stapp proved his scholastic capability by giving the startled school official a comprehensive summary of the theory of evolution. And at the end of the first year, he further evidenced his ability by ranking fourth in his class.

Then Stapp switched to the San Marcos Baptist Academy to complete his high school training; he found the institution a place made up in large degree of "displaced hellions."[2] The students quickly adopted Stapp as their special prey; with a scrawny frame stretching only to four feet nine inches and with a nature quite apart from the usual pattern, he gathered a host of "vociferous enemies." Further, his meager eighty-one pounds of weight was pitted against the school routine. "We drilled every day with twelve-pound 1917 model English Enfield rifles. In a special competition a student had to drop back each time he made a mistake. Penalty for this poor drilling was 'going through the gauntlet'—a ritual where the whole company formed two facing ranks and pulled off their belts; then the ones of us being disciplined had to run through with arms folded. When it came my turn, I tried a little psychology—I walked through. That spoiled their fun; nobody would hit a walking target. After three times they gave up."

In his struggle to survive and supply himself with the basics, Stapp worked as waiter, janitor, and gardener. Summers he picked cotton and delivered ice. Most important, these earnings bought him more than food and clothing. They purchased a lifetime supply of determination and established an open account for perseverance. Stapp budgeted more than money; he learned to treasure time and squeezed full value from it. School and work did not prevent him from studying music and gaining a place in the school band as bassoonist.

A year of business courses bridged his completion of high school and his entrance into Baylor University—marking time until he was fifteen. Like many another American student, he sold pots and pans to work his way through university! But it was not enough to peddle the utensils of the Wear-Ever Company—he must also demonstrate their capabilities. His buddy, Dennis Sullivan, still moans when he recalls, "Those of us who lived through that cooking session got the best stomach aches of our lives."[1] The "us" that Dennis referred to included the younger brothers whom John Paul constantly looked after in fatherly fashion.

Not daunted by the personal load he carried he was always ready to assume responsibility to help those around him. When his friend Dan Hampton lost all his possessions in a fire, Stapp took him in, fed him, and each of the Stapp brothers gave him an article of clothing. Celso Stapp says, "When it wound up, Dan was the best dressed of any of the four of us."

Stapp had held the dream of becoming a writer until his sophomore year in Baylor. During the Christmas holidays, he visited his Aunt Verna and Uncle Hansford in Burnet, Texas. There, fire transformed the festive holiday spirit into one of tragedy. The couple's two-year-old boy threw newspapers over the fire screen and set his clothing on fire.

For sixty-two hours Stapp nursed the child, only to have him die in his arms. At that instant seeds planted in Stapp's boyhood blossomed into the desire—the obsession—to become a medical doctor. His snatched reading of "forbidden" medical books in Brazil had first spawned it; an ever present urge to help others had nurtured it; the example set by his revered uncle, Dr. Hall Shannon, had defined it. Now the decision was clear. Only the means were clouded, and that cloud persisted into an eleven-year storm of struggle.

First, there was his brother Celso to consider. He had long planned a medical career. Since it was not possible to earn enough for them to attend medical school at the same time, John Paul kept his desire secret so that Celso might go first.

Consequently a frustrating period followed Stapp's graduation from Baylor. To finance his graduate study and to help Celso, he acquired a job as field representative for a biological supply house, searching for snakes and scorpions. During this period, pigeons and an odd assortment of other creatures ended up on his dinner plate. "If it breathed, it had protein, and if it had protein, I ate it."[2]

After earning a Master's Degree in Zoology, Stapp saw the prospect of financial gain by teaching at Decatur Baptist College in Decatur, Texas. The hope was short lived. The depression forced payment in students' notes —not in cash.

Undaunted, he applied to himself one of his axioms, "The gift of do is worth a thousand times more than the gift of gab." He went to the University of Texas as a teaching assistant and to work for his Ph.D.

Boundless patience, coupled with endless work, spanned the eight years until he had saved enough money for entrance into medical school. Then, sending out twenty-nine inquiries for a combination teaching-student arrangement, he received five favorable replies. The University of Minnesota was his choice.

Stapp left Austin, Texas, at a temperature of 102° and rode a bus for forty-eight hours to reach Austin, Minnesota—temperature 26°. The trek allowed time for a quiet review of the cavalcade of his life. The drowning man may see this in an instant; Stapp had monotonous hours to review the path that he had chosen.

In objective appraisal he looked upon a fiercely determined personality. He had set a goal. But every uphill road has side paths. Why must the climb be continued to the absolute summit? Weren't some of the tangents along the way good enough? And when the necessities for his own existence would have been a heavy enough burden to carry, why did he assume responsibility for friends in need, for a world whose cry of misery had sounded for millenniums?

The answers came hard upon the nagging questions. This path must be followed because Stapp knew that ultimately his compensation would surpass the riches heaped upon the scales of an oriental potentate. His coffer would glitter with the smiles of children he had healed; through some research at his hands, the stone of knowledge might yet have another facet chiseled upon it.

Was it part of the master plan that fate was to deal miserly with Stapp from her storehouse of opportunity? Perhaps. The richer material grants she saved for those less determined—those who otherwise might be dissuaded against attaining their goal. For she knew that John Paul Stapp would win, whatever the odds.

Thus the trip to medical school was not a forty-eight hour bus ride. It was a twenty-nine year march, with only temporary stopovers along the route of his life.

A quadruple effort punctuated his freshman year of medical school. Stapp had his thesis to write to complete his Ph.D. degree in Biophysics at the University of Texas, so he worked with two research problems, taught three classes, and attended his own classes and studies. It was something of an experiment in human stamina since he averaged but two-and-a-half hours sleep a night for the entire year.

"The University of Minnesota had an excellent medical course in that we started in our sophomore year doing histories and physicals on patients. We were always very proud to put on our white coats and pick up our little hammers and work on these frightened patients. I can now realize why they were frightened." Stapp viewed the memory with amusement.

In his senior year the Army Student Training Program was instituted. With this support Stapp gave up his extra jobs and started searching for something to fill the breach. He found it. He served as substitute for vacationing interns—which gave him a schedule of classes all day and hospital duty all night. This term of bonus internship he labeled "tremendous experience."

The only valid promises are those a man makes to himself. When Stapp pledged his life to medicine in 1931, he vowed that he would practice medicine and do research in a charity hospital for the rest of his life without monetary compensation if only he could achieve that aspiration.

On New Year's Eve in 1943 the dream was fulfilled. He was a full-fledged doctor, ready to receive his first patient. He began his regular service as intern at St. Mary's Hospital in Duluth. The police brought in his first patient, a man found lying unconscious in the snow. This was a significant moment for Stapp, who had envisioned his life as dedicated to helping the poor. But at that instant his preconceived thought about his patient's financial status was shattered—the nurses found the man's wallet bulging with $4900 in cash!

The important part of Stapp's vow has always been kept—he has never taken one cent for medical services. His pay as an Army and Air Force officer has been for research; he has never taken money for the endless hours of effort he has expended to serve, well beyond the call, the intent of the Hippocratic oath.

A succession of special Army medical training assignments followed, which included the flight surgeon's course at the School of Aviation Medicine in Texas, the place jokingly dubbed "the Worst Point of the Air." Stapp drew such duties as examining the eyes, ears, noses and throats of 600 men in a single day during demobilization—a chore which he recalls as "a nightmare relieved only by the thought that I might have been a proctologist."[2]

Now his Army service was ending. Freely, wisely, he must choose. He searched, but destiny would not reveal her plan for his future. He made a trip to Rochester, Minnesota, to seek a fellowship at the Mayo Clinic, but too many applicants returning from the war were ahead of him. Then, like an artist possessed with a vision which he must capture with brush and oil, Stapp realized that an elusive promise was mistily forming in his consciousness. The dawning came when he reasoned that the Mayo Brothers did not have a Mayo Clinic to which they could go—they were the ones who founded it. Perhaps he could begin an original project. But what? Where?

He groped within the recesses of his memory, probed the open avenues of possibility, yet no vista opened before him. To complicate the turmoil of his search, a transfer in orders came through—he was to report to the Wright Field Air Medical Laboratory to complete his military tour.

Dutifully he began fulfilling the obligation, believing that he would be marking time until his military service ended; then he would be free to shape this malleable aim into a pattern for his life. Suddenly a blinding realization stunned him.

This was it! Aero medical research!

With aviation, as with other areas of progress, retrospect proved the true evaluator. Charting its advent, the curve was strikingly flat in the early years—then advancements sent the graph into a steep upward climb. Wartime brought about the acceleration.

Since that momentous day at Kitty Hawk when Orville Wright first nursed his frail craft to the altitude of eight to ten feet and traveled at the "dizzying" speed of thirty miles per hour, a twin aim had consumed every man who proudly bore a pilot's wings—to go higher and faster!

Famed aerodynamicists like Dr. Theodore von Kármán helped free airplanes from capricious currents that tugged at the backs of their wings. The triplane gave way to the biplane, which was soon replaced by the monoplane—so there would be less area for drag. Surfaces were slanted and smoothed, the landing gear was tucked inside the fuselage to allow the airplane to slip through the air smoothly in defiance of mischievous eddies and vortices.

Whereas this airflow was ethereal and often unpredictable, gravity was a plodding constant force, battering man with its downward pull. So larger engines were needed to complement design and thus become the key to unlocking gravity's chains. The ratio was fixed: more speed and altitude—more power.

Twelve horsepower had allowed the Wright Brothers to make history. Soon, twelve times twelve, times twelve, times twelve would be required! The might of 20,000 horses would be called into play before one slender test plane would pierce the barrier of sound. But this was still theory in 1944.

A dilemma had seized the planners in their assault on the air. They knew more about their craft than they knew about the men who sat at their controls.

The year before brilliant and courageous flight surgeon, Colonel William Randolph Lovelace II, had climbed out of a bomb bay into temperatures of 50° below zero to determine what would happen to the human body when subjected to bail-out at 40,000 feet. Miraculously he lived—though not without serious injury—through the ghastly jolt of his chute opening in the thin upper atmosphere. This jump proved the lifesaving ability of the small, portable oxygen bottle for emergency bail-out which was developed in 1939 by Colonel Rudolph Fink, Dr. Manley Pessman, and Mr. Sydney Winton.

Now the crusade for understanding how to protect men in this threatening upper-atmosphere environment had an eager new zealot. John Paul Stapp, M.D., extended his military service so that he might probe into these multiple threats.

How does a doctor's skill outwit the bends and chokes of high altitudes? Must gas pains and dehydrations be endured? How reliable was a liquid-oxygen emergency breathing system? How does a warm body cope with the frigid stratosphere? The submerged poet crowded his way into the academic doctor's report when Stapp penned this description of his first stratospheric flight: "The landscape flattens out into geography, where the stars cease to twinkle, where shadows are darker and sunlight more burning, where at dusk it somehow looks as if a solar eclipse is about to begin."[2]

His reports were a remarkable contrast to the one on file by the only American pilot to have then used an ejection seat. It was terse and direct: "Jeez, whatta whoomp!"[2]

Completing that area of research, Stapp was called into the office of Colonel Mike Sweeney and informed in routine manner of his next assignment. On a dry sandy bed at Muroc Lake in a desolate, desert region of California, a 2000-foot stretch of track beckoned him. A rocket test sled would ride that track. Stapp responded with alacrity. He had made the rules in his bargain with life, and he was collecting the reward he stipulated—the chance to apply his knowledge.

With customary sparkle Stapp adds, "I was a bachelor, so I could appropriately be shanghaied to the desert. I was called the 'Ghost of Muroc,' for I was listed in only three places—the post office, the paymaster's office, and the flight record office. Otherwise, not being listed anywhere else on the base, I was left to my own initiative."

This meant there was a track, a sled, and a mountain of unsolved problems. John Northrop, then president of the aviation corporation that bears his name, had this idea to test linear deceleration and assigned the skillful and meticulous George Nichols as track project engineer. With the whirling of the giant centrifuges a man's tolerance to the force of gravity had been explored in a cursory manner. But only with the jarring stops of the rocket sled at the end of its track could the real forces of airplane crashes be duplicated.

What protection would save lives of pilots caught in this dreaded emergency? The increase in the speed of aircraft did not simply multiply the problems in proportionate ratio—they were compounded as the critical upper limits of tolerance were approached. What helmet would protect the human skull, frail when pitted against the extreme forces of accidents? What harness would hold the body in position to suffer least damage when frightful jolts tug at bones and tissue? The Air Force termed this project "Grand Slam." But they didn't expect the "slamming" to be against Stapp's own body—this was his idea.

The idealistic doctor dreamed of building something. Here was the chance—to an even greater degree than he might have expected—for there was nothing beyond the sled and the two railroad tracks patterned after the tracks that had launched the German Buzz Bomb of World War II. Ingenuity, charm, resourcefulness, and his own barter system of exchanging his medical services for equipment, supplies, and manpower, eventually created adequate test facilities.

After this begging, scrounging, and "moonlight requisitioning" finally got him the equipment needed for his testing, he did not stop his lifelong habit of helping people. This had been established during his early days as an intern, and at Muroc it grew to such a practice that his clientele dignified it with a name—the Curbstone Clinic. After his day's work was ended, Stapp made his rounds as faithfully and earnestly as any devoted doctor. Usually he did not reach his quarters until bedtime; but, when he did, he could sleep with the knowledge that others who had been in need of his help would spend an easier night.

The facilities Stapp had gathered included a shed for test animals and abandoned buildings that had been dragged across the dry lake and converted into a laboratory and stocked with discarded equipment from the salvage yard. The inclusion of running water was among their "luxuries." At last all was in readiness. The sled itself had assumed such personality that the team christened it the Gee Whizz. Spirits were high as the seven men from Northrop and their Air Force doctor-officer-in-charge loaded Oscar aboard for the first momentous ride. It proved routine, uneventful.

Their plans grew bolder with each run. More rockets, more speed. Oscar obediently took his ride, day by day. Then came the frightful moment when the unexpected happened. Malfunction in the brakes caused them to grab. Oscar snapped his harness and slammed forward with the force of a battering ram—his 185 pounds splintering the inch-thick plank that served as his windshield—then tumbling over 700 feet down the tracks.

No ambulance was rushed to Oscar. No need. Only a good metalworker could determine if this anthropomorphic dummy would ever ride again. That day's events gained him the nickname of Oscar Eight Ball, but Stapp was not a man to become wary because of the possibility of accidents.

After thirty-two runs with Oscar, chimpanzees were supposed to have been used in the next stage of testing, but the Air Force flies on a foundation of paper. Every order, decision, or requisition builds its own tower of forms—in decuplicate—before realization is achieved. Somewhere in this morass of papyrus the channels grew clogged. Impatiently the men at Muroc tended their idle track, and no chimps were forthcoming.

The delays of his lifetime had been maddening. With the beginning of research and tests for the Air Force Stapp had realized a sense of fulfillment. Now he was again confronted with the terrible ordeal of waiting.

All other commodities may be gathered, stored, rationed. Only time is perishable, irreplaceable. And John Paul Stapp had used up far too much of his store to again allow such squandering. He made the decision. There would be no further tests with Oscar. There would be no waiting for animals to arrive. A test run would be made the following morning with a suitable "subject."

Stapp is a warm man, a witty and charming man, but the impersonality of which he is capable—when he regards his own activities—is infinite. There was never the thought nor conversation that "he" would be riding the sled that had spilled Oscar in a shattering accident; always, it was "the subject" who was readying for the first experiment involving a human being.

This trait persisted through all reports, all lectures, regarding the hazardous activity. Those hearing his speeches on the Human Tolerance to High Deceleration would hear only that "the subject" had undergone and survived stress of high magnitude. Any in the audience who might lack prior knowledge of the research program would never know that the lecturer and the subject were the same.

A single rocket propelled Stapp on that first introduction to sled riding. His eagerness whetted, he increased the power to three rockets the following day. Bruises and strains were no deterrent. He was a man with a mission, and at last there was thrust in the direction of progress, speed that he could feel in every muscle and every tissue, symbolically propelling him toward a predetermined goal.

Many an officer has been assigned to hazards of varying degrees, but few have ever reached out with such zeal for the difficult areas of living. Stapp recalls, "When I first entered the Armed Forces, I learned two fundamentals very early: You are what they tell you to be; you do what they tell you to do. The complication begins when you start volunteering for things. At one base I had nine separate duty assignments. When I looked at the long list of duties on my orders I was reminded of the second lieutenant's epitaph: 'In addition to all his other duties, he died.' Many months later I was given the opportunity to volunteer for a tour at the Aero Medical Laboratory at Wright Air Development Center, Ohio, and I have been volunteering with reckless abandon ever since."[3]

With true detachment Stapp could view the larger picture into which his activities fitted. It was the quiet stampede of progress which changed aviation from a spectacle to a science. As he says, "Early hero worship of pilots as something more than human probably relates to the attitudes built around the strenuous selection procedures. Today the scene has changed. Mental and psychological factors take precedence over physical attributes in choosing fliers. We are now by-passing the football squads and raiding the graduate schools for candidates. The art and science of flying has progressed from the seat of the pants to higher centers at the other end of the spinal cord."[3]

But as the rocket-sled tests continued, there was certain blending of the mental and physical. Stapp had to outwit the inherent dangers—to "think" his way into staying alive. Systematic increase in speeds was planned with progressive rides, adding forces in increments of five. One g—that ever constant pull of the earth's gravity—was being multiplied into strong forces fast approaching the 18 g limit that had arbitrarily been accepted as man's limit.

Excitement grew within the circle of men on the Grand Slam project. They were about to witness the crumbling of an accepted law that put a ceiling on a pilot's capability. If the tolerance to greater g's could be proved, new areas of possibility would spread before those who plan the conquest of the skies. The vastness of space, unknown and forbidding, would come closer to human grasp. Without tolerance to high g forces, the dream of a man in space could never become reality.

In the desolate surroundings of a tiny section of the Mojave desert with disinterested jackrabbits as the only spectators, seven technicians and a doctor were about to participate in experiments which would prove that blast-off in a rocket destined for space could become reality. These findings could presage the soaring of a human body into terrestrial space—that beckoning area beginning with the edge of the earth's atmosphere and reaching out for 40,000 miles.

The g forces mounted, and still the sled rides continued—each bringing more bruises and more enthusiasm to participant Stapp. The crew was wildly jubilant when the previously established barrier of 18 g's crumbled under the onslaught!

But the power of old wives' tales have governed varying phases of man's behavior and habits for centuries. Implanted with each repetition, these superstitions attach to the mortal consciousness and become the Siamese twin of truth. Inseparably they are passed along to succeeding generations, until a brave and curious soul pauses in the headlong race of living and asks, "Is this really so?" Stapp had been such an inquisitor.

However officers who bore the responsibility for his well-being, gleaned piecemeal reports of the activity on the faraway desert stretch and made a decision: Stapp would not continue his rides. He must first test these high g runs with animals.

Disinclined to accept the edict, Stapp journeyed to Wright Field to present his case for continuing the experiments. His scientific approach, eminently successful in countering the objectives of unfriendly bacteria or defeating the fury of windblast, met stoic resistance from his commanding officers. He dealt with projected facts—they traded in a share of human reactions. This highly trained and gifted doctor was not to continue risking his life. The only concession they made was to allow him to ride the sled to 18 g's, reverting to the old accepted limit of human endurance.

So, alternating with animal experiments, the routine of his own sledriding was resumed. After evenings spent calling on patients of his Curbstone Clinic, Stapp worked until midnight on complicated calculations and projections. Then his days started at four-thirty when he breakfasted on coffee and fruit, saving his real appetite for the work he relished. The clothing he donned was regulation Air Force flying equipment, and the preparations included a check of his heart and blood pressure.

From the Northrop team led by George Nichols, absolute efficiency prevailed. Jake Superata, chief mechanic, checked and rechecked the sled against malfunction which would endanger its human cargo. All other members carried through their assigned tasks with precision. There was but one startling exception to this orderly procedure—an exception which Stapp recalls with a twinkle: For all their ability to make elaborate calculations, somehow they just couldn't add! Somewhere they always got confused with the number of g's he was taking on these rides. Most certainly no one would be party to disregarding the limit set by the command at Wright Field, but, as Stapp says, "the Northrop people were, shall we say, having trouble with instrumentation. They were obtaining readings of half value. I managed to get up to 40 g's before the error was corrected."[4]

The wise and prudent man would have exercised a measure of caution before even considering the procedure that Stapp had undertaken. He would have recognized that such disregard of orders was open invitation to court martial. But then it is questionable that he would ever have been faced with the situation, for a wise and prudent man would not have been seated aboard the Gee Whizz in the first place. This special seat had the marking of "reserved for a dedicated soul who ranks the saving of other lives more important than his own."

If Stapp had written a new lesson in physiology, his superiors learned a lesson about individuals. Regimentation is the order for any military force. Disobedience must be disciplined. But now and then a quiet individual appears, fittingly garbed in the usual uniform, respectfully giving the proper salute, but so powerfully motivated that his actions do not fit channels. Such a man was this doctor, and the realization prevailed among his superiors that greatness does not always conform to a pattern. During this period Stapp "learned to be casual about casualties," as he says. For fillings popped from his teeth, ribs snapped under the horrendous jar, and hemorrhages occurred in his eyes. But another Air Force doctor recalls the incident that pleased detached-scientist Stapp the most: That was the fact that since he broke his wrist twice, he could compare two different methods of healing his injuries. (The second break he set himself, while being driven to the hospital.) But there was another side also.

The sentimentality of the doctor was never more in evidence than on the occasion of the termination of his experiments at Muroc. As a remembrance of their joint effort, he carved a small rectangular medal showing rocket sled MX 981; from this he made a mold and cast a gold medal for George Nichols and silver medals for the other six men of his crew. These medals have become treasured souvenirs of the group who helped explore a new dimension in human tolerance.

When Stapp's Muroc experiments ended in 1951, he harbored the intention of returning to more drastic and hazardous rocket-sled tests at a later time. Meanwhile he applied his findings to a wider area of benefit than just fighter airplane crashes. His suggestions for air transport safety brought about the rear-facing of seats in Air Force transports. He had proved conclusively that passengers facing to the rear have a greatly increased chance for survival in crash. Yet, strangely, this has never been adopted by the airlines; they are seemingly more influenced by tradition and appearances instead of the factor that should be of paramount consideration—passenger safety.

The effects of those desert sled rides have even been felt on the nation's highways. This came about when the Air Force tallied fatalities and came up with the horrifying statistic that during a peacetime year they lost almost as many men in auto crashes as in plane crashes! Stapp organized a study program, which sent old autos and their dummy occupants smashing into concrete walls. Applying much of his prior research work to this new area, he defined many ways in which automobiles can be made less deadly: Equip doors with safety locks that will not spring open during crashes, pad dashboards, install safety belts, remove the shelves from the rear of cars, because any items put there can well shoot forward to hit the heads of occupants in event of crash.

Many of Stapp's findings have been noted and utilized by the Automobile Manufacturers Association in the production of today's models. In July of 1959 Stapp testified before the Subcommittee on Health and Safety of the House Committee on Interstate and Foreign Commerce to report in detail on his experiments so that his findings might be translated into laws regarding crash safety.

A mountain of briefs and reports testify to Stapp's medical development. But what of the personality, the characteristics, and fundamental nature of the man? What kind of thinking has the struggle of his lifetime produced? His contemplative thoughts provide deep insight.

"Courage for living comes from the realization that every difficulty overcome brings increased equanimity toward lesser distresses that daily beset us. The worst one could be called upon to bear can be no more than what has already been borne and, having survived that, why succumb to lesser ills? From the totality of events, let good experience be refined and accumulated as a memory of happiness and a beginning of wisdom."

Though at work Stapp possesses the ability of complete objectivity and detachment of self—a characteristic which George Nichols terms a blessing to work with—the alert, alive individual personality of the doctor blossoms forth in interim moments.

His friend Dr. Charles Lombard asked, "Have you ever seen a left-handed person (which Stapp is) learn to fish with a right-handed reel? Years ago we took Stapp for his first deep-sea fishing experience. Not knowing anything about fishing in the first place, and the right-handed reel being very awkward for him, he threw his bait over and forgot about his fish line and started thinking about one of his research problems. Soon everybody on the boat had his line tangled up with a bite on Stapp's line. We spent thirty minutes getting them unwound and finally threw Stapp's dead mackerel back into the ocean. He felt this jerk on his line, and excitedly cried, 'Oh, look, everybody, I have a bite!'"

Though such "absent-minded professor" lapses occasionally occur, producer William Bloom colorfully describes Stapp as a wonderful host. "He is never so unintelligent as to run on one track. He enjoys people tremendously and never gives you the feeling that he wishes you would leave so he could get back to the laboratory and cut up a dead mouse."

However, those who do not share his scientific objectivity should be wary of his speeches. At a banquet of an exclusive group of surgeons, he was asked to deliver the address. He chose the topic of crashes—properly illustrated with slides, in color, the better to show the physical injuries. A few of the wives of the surgeons did not find this compatible with their demitasse and promptly fainted.

During the period at Muroc many friends were concerned that he lacked proper companionship, but Stapp remained a bachelor, pointing out that he "wasn't a very good risk" for any wife.

With great maturity, he was a "father" to all those with whom he worked. Extending limitless patience to any man who was doing his best, he had a resolute, constructive means of dealing with a slacker. He would first plot how to motivate such a person into greater productivity. If this failed, he then turned to the second phase of his scheme, which involved trying to get the person into a place he would like better. By seeking out another assignment, he helped both the person, and the rocket-sled project. This substitution of intelligence for annoyance served good ends.

Though "space" was, in 1951, and for three years thereafter, still relegated to the vocabulary of the science-fiction writer and rarely voiced in serious circles, the visionary ones were planning. The theory of rocketry had been laid down by pioneers Tsiolkovsky, Goddard, and Oberth. But what would happen when you merged a man to this rocket for travel into space? If jet aircraft taxed the upper limits of his capability, how could he ever survive the high number of g's to achieve escape velocity of about 25,000 miles per hour?

Time magazine, in the September 12, 1955, issue, observed in a profile on the rocket-sled hero, "Not the machine but man himself appeared to be limiting man's conquest of the jet age. However the engineers tried, they could not evade, as Stapp puts it, 'that one stubbornly unchanging item peeping forlornly from among the titanium rivets: man, M-1, the same yesterday, today, and forever; fallible, vulnerable, incurably addicted to errors, and above all, pathetically mortal.' "

But for all of his recognition of the frailty of a human body—with the ever present reminders of treating the sick about him—Stapp was most dubious of the evaluation of man's limits that existed at that time. His work at Muroc had explored the area of crash. But this was not the entire problem. In high speed ejection, could man tolerate ejection in a seat or would a bulky capsule be necessary to protect him? There were other limits to be tested. The answers were to be found aboard the rocket sled, at higher speed, quicker stops, and involving even greater personal danger for Stapp. In slave days the eternal dream was to escape the dreaded flail of the whip. Now deliberate calculations were being made to determine the exact amount of wind-whip man could endure and live. This was the fickle nature of progress.

The experiment must be done. It would be done.

The Northrop team was gathered. A sled, the son of the Gee Whizz, which answered to the more dignified name of Sonic Wind, was born. This sled was to receive a fast education as to its duties along a 3500 foot stretch of track at Holloman Air Force Base in New Mexico.

To those who lacked the understanding of what Stapp was doing and merely labeled him a crazy fool he would counter, "If I really wanted to kill myself, I've been doing a pretty sloppy job. I already had twenty-six chances at Muroc. And I'm likely the only doctor who ever put his life in the hands of an engineer for that number of times and has come out alive."[1]

The engineer, Nichols, was busy with his slide rule. No more than a 1 per cent margin for error could be tolerated. This was to become a five-year project, sixty long months of checking, rechecking, planning, and proving the mechanical phases of the operation. Stapp made the most of individual tests, learning something from every one conducted with anthropomorphic dummies or animals. If the brakes didn't function properly or the instrumentation didn't prove out, the crew appeared much more upset and frustrated than the doctor.

This tour of duty produced a certain "settling down" in his personal life. Stapp bought a home at 300 Lovers Lane—prophetic in view of later developments—and delighted friends with his dinners, a remnant of his association with Wear-Ever cooking utensils. His culinary talents had continued to develop from student days. Feminine guests shuddered at the abandon with which he compounded a stew combining recipes garnered from East Indian and Scandinavian friends. But, after a taste, these skeptical guests were begging him for the recipe. Said Nichols, "I've never eaten anything like Paul's cooking—before or after—which sounds like an insult, but it isn't!"

Brigadier General Malcolm C. Grow recalls with amusement the time that host-Stapp invited guests to dinner; then scientist-Stapp became so engrossed in discussions he forgot to serve the meal. But one thing is sure —no one ever leaves Stapp's home with a hungry mind; he provides rare stimulation through his own complete absorption with everything that is new or good or worth-while. And there is usually fine musical background for this conversation. With the instinct of a connoisseur, he acquired the finest hi-fidelity equipment long before the current craze; on it he plays African tribal music, Bach, and all the in-between stages to far-out modern. His musical role is not just a passive one, since he lacks only one year of winning a degree in music. The Stapp talents are expressed equally on piano, organ, and bassoon.

But these pleasures were, and are always, in snatched moments. At Holloman Air Force Base, he had work to do, his "Curbstone Clinic" patients to call on, and a zoo to look after. He affectionately regarded the anthropoids as his worthy "assistants" in research and would teach visitors how to shake hands with them—the technique being to use the back of the hand flat against the cage.

But just as any society has its practical jokers, there was among the group a chimpanzee named Anita who always disrupted the peace and calm of the compound. Her greatest moment of glee came on the day a general officer stood unsuspectingly before her cage—and she rendered her candid opinion of high ranking brass by jumping on a ripe tomato. It is not too surprising a fact that most generals do not like to have their uniforms splattered with tomatoes, so strategist Stapp decided the moment had come to pit his wits against the playfulness of Anita. He brought the grasping chimp a big avocado and stood back. She responded in expected fashion, making one big jump on to the avocado. A howl of pain testified that this would be the last time she'd ever jump, however, for the big seed of the avocado taught her the lesson Stapp had intended.

Other lessons were being learned at Holloman on the 3500 feet of track. A run at 504 miles per hour had proved Stapp right in a major change— instead of making the test with his head unprotected and bowed against the onslaught he donned a safety helmet created for him by Protection, Inc. As the designer of the helmet Dr. Lombard explained it: "If the head is permitted to go forward when the deceleration is strong, the column of blood is quite long and puts very high pressures into the head and into the eyes. By holding the head upright, this shortens the column of blood that would be forced into the brain and eyes."

As Stapp proudly said of his new gear, "Now I have a helmet that will stay on my head, whether or not my head stays on my body!" Such joking —grim though it may sound—helped ease the strains that multiplied as the project progressed. Superata had a corny, stand-by gag that he always pulled after Stapp was secured in the sled, awaiting blast-off: "Don't go away!" These were the human compensations of men grimly occupied in a potentially deadly task. The margin was indeed narrow, for the goal now was to travel nine tenths the speed of sound!

Stapp was invaluable as a test subject for one special reason that Nichols pointed out: "We get complete information from him about the sled, as well as the subject. Paul has the kind of mind that retains every reaction that he feels; not only second by second but, unbelievable as it sounds, he retains the memory of what happens in split seconds."

On the evening before the big ride, Stapp remembered many of those split seconds from previous rides. Yet he calmly occupied himself with writing a scientific paper and was the one to reassure Nichols—who re-figured his calculations time and again—with the remark, "You know why we are doing this, George." Nichols knew. Stapp being the person that he was, there was no alternative.

On the eventful morning of December 10, 1954, Lombard and Bloom were awakened by Stapp's shout, "Hey, fellows, come look at this sunrise!" Perhaps it was coincidental, or perhaps it was subconscious reaction, but all three men were reminded once again that Stapp's greatest concern was for his eyes. "With that force, they'll be ripped out of their sockets," some people alarmingly predicted. No one knew for sure.

Clouds unfortunately caused an overcast before they reached the test area, and the ride was ordered delayed; it was all important to have sufficient light for the motion-picture camera strapped to the sled so that every instant of the critical run might be preserved. The weather man's prediction was doubtful; he was unsure about a time for a breakthrough of the sun. Stapp made his own calculations, estimating for the long countdown, and guessed it so accurately that his ride was taken during the only ten minutes of the entire day when the sun was out!

After a physical checkup, including an electrocardiogram, Stapp walked to the Sonic Wind, an entourage of mechanics and workers by his side. Even the jokes were a little forced as they lowered the helmet over his head and zipped up the cloth neck shirt and fastened his blue flying suit. The harness was fastened so tightly that breathing was restricted to his diaphragm. Another strap pinned his elbows to his sides, and there were straps as well for his wrists, legs, and ankles. The camera trigger was placed in his left hand, and there was an overly casual moment of conversation just before the rubber bite block was placed between his teeth. The plastic visor was tightly screwed into place over his face, and nylon webbing giving five thousand pounds of restraint secured his head in an upright position.

All the while George Nichols was running through a comprehensive check list by intercom and was keeping all operations under visual observation with binoculars from the control bridge in the tower. When completed, the firing sequence was started.

The crew left the sled, waving a cheery "See you at the other end, Colonel." Stapp stared down the 3500 feet of track that stretched before him. Thoughts raced in orderly sequence through his mind, crowding out the memory of rockets that misfired and exploded or the dread possibility that the water brakes devised for this hazardous run might not stop him before the narrowly calculated fifteen feet from the end.

This man, so brimming with originality, had the most conventional kinds of thoughts in the moments remaining. "If this is it, Paul, it's been a good life. Isn't there an easier way to make a living?" The last platitude was said, even to himself, with as much of a smile as he could muster with the rubber block in his teeth. In a later detailed report he wrote with absolute detachment, "Subject had considerable apprehension and uneasiness with cold sweat of axillae (armpits) and palms."[5] No detail escaped the methodical doctor.

The engineer closed a ten-second time-relay switch, activating the circuit to the igniters. The speaker system blared the countdown, a procedure which producer Bill Bloom terms "one of the great dramas of the 20th century."

Ample time for setting off the rockets was assured by fifteen feet of length in the cables to the igniter quick-disconnect plugs which separate when the motion of the sled begins.

Ten, nine, eight, seven, six, five, four, three, two, one, fire!

Forty thousand pounds of fiery thrust assaulted John Paul Stapp to make him the fastest man on earth! Speeding faster than a .45 caliber bullet, he raced to an incredible 632 miles per hour within five seconds! After three seconds he suffered complete visual blackout which lasted until the burnout of the rockets at five seconds. As the sled hit the water brakes and gigantic forces of deceleration gripped him, there was quick change in his vision. "It went from black to yellow; I saw the water splash when I hit the brake, and then came the red-out. After that I didn't see a cockeyed thing."[6] The excruciating pain in his eyes blocked out all other sensations. "It felt as though my eyeballs were being pulled out of my head," he related. The ghastly jolt of stopping had given Stapp the same impact as an automobile driver hitting a brick wall at fifty miles per hour.

Superata was the first to reach Stapp. "I can't see," he breathed. Frantically Superata loosened the straps and harness, and Stapp reached up to force his eyelids open. He still couldn't see. As he tried to get to his feet, eager hands lifted him off on to the stretcher. Effort was made to put an oxygen mask on him, but he pushed it away. Part of the test was to see what normal recovery would be under such circumstances.

Within two minutes the miracle occurred! The fervent prayer of every soul in that tense cluster of men was answered. The salmon blur which had clouded Stapp's vision gradually gave way to blue. As focus returned, he realized he was looking at the blue sky overhead. With remarkable understatement he said, "That was one of the pleasantest moments I've ever gone through."

An hour later in the hospital Stapp welcomed the crew into his room. He sported two of the blackest eyes a man could ever display; his body was laced with bruises where the harness had dug into his flesh. The conversation was scarcely more than babble, but it really didn't matter. Mission was accomplished. Stapp was all right. The ride had gone exactly as planned. These were the only important considerations. At such a moment, words were poor conveyors of thoughts.

Fully recovered from the ordeal within five days, Stapp wondered, "Why are we always underrating man? Take, for example, the four-minute mile. For years we thought that was a physical limit, just a bit beyond human reach. Well, it was psychological limit, and once there was a breakthrough the barrier seemed never to have existed."[2]

The progress of aviation was spurred by the valuable findings from these rocket-sled rides—findings that proved man could take the stresses that engineers yearned to heap upon him to provide a faster approach to the enticing infinity of space.

In the flush of his achievement orders came through that greatly perturbed Stapp—he was "grounded"! On June 25, 1956, *Aviation Week* magazine reported the incident in these words: "Brigadier General Marvin C. Demler, Deputy Commissioner for Research and Development, ARDC, said Stapp will be allowed to make only routine track runs. General Demler said Stapp 'didn't like it one bit,' but his superiors felt Colonel Stapp's 'tremendous experience and know-how' make him too valuable to risk on any more high-speed rides. Stapp has really crowded the limit of human tolerance and has established several significant points on the curve of human tolerance. We don't believe he or anyone else should stretch his luck any farther."

This was a grievous disappointment, for Stapp had determined on a sled ride to equal the speed of sound—on his last ride he had gone nine tenths that velocity. During the twenty-nine rides from 1947 to 1954 he had taken as high as 46 g's and had established that the human body can withstand forces in the amount of 10,000 pounds for durations of a quarter of a second. Actually, the sonic ride he planned could have added no new dimension to his work. In basic integrity, it stands unblemished—monumentally complete.

Tributes and honors showered upon the doctor: the Legion of Merit with Oak Leaf Clusters; the Air Force's Cheney Award for valor and self-sacrifice; the Institute of the Aeronautical Sciences' John Jeffries' Award for outstanding contributions to safety in aviation; the Commander's Order, Legion of Merit; the National Air Council Award; the Air Force Association's Air Power Award for Science; the Guggenheim Flight Safety Foundation's Flight Safety Award; the Civil Air Patrol's Airman of the Year; the Aeromedical Association's Liljencrantz Award; the Association of Military Surgeon's Gorgas Award; from the University of Minnesota, the Distinguished Graduate's Service Award; and from Baylor University, an honorary Doctor of Science degree.

Another honor accrued to the doctor in the most amusing manner. Some rival Navy officers were holding an informal scientific meeting in Los Angeles and were discussing the third rate of the motion, the rate of onset, which they called the "jerk." With dry humor, one officer suggested they rename this for Stapp, because he was such a jerk. A correspondent for *Time* magazine came in during the middle of the discussion, took them seriously, and made a story out of it, which appeared April 11, 1955, loftily proclaiming "Stapp has joined the select company of men, e.g. Volta, Ampere, whose names have been given to a physical unit of measurement." Because of this, the word Stapp as a unit of measurement is now listed in some dictionaries. This is one joke that really backfired on the Navy and brought added honor to the Air Force doctor!

On a quiet evening spent in his brother's and sister-in-law's home in El Paso, this man of unyielding will and granite strength capitulated. Though he had withstood the pounding of 46 g, he melted when strikingly beautiful prima ballerina Lilli Lanese smiled at him. Formerly with the Ballet Theatre of New York she had come to El Paso as a guest teacher.

In her vivacious, straight-forward manner she related, "Paul never proposed—we just started talking about when to get married." (December 23, 1957, was the date agreed upon.) With Stapp's deep respect for creativeness and his own rich talents for music and writing, the life they have shared has been abundant in interest and activities. As for the technical aspects of his work, even that is shared: "Every husband worries out loud around his wife, not necessarily expecting her to understand. He's just able to talk out his problems."

Though now "grounded," Stapp was determined to complete the research project, started with his own sled riding, on the subject of human tolerance to mechanical force. During the eleven years which he had spent on this study, there were moments so trying that he phrased this motto for inspiration: "Don't be misled by kakorrhaphiophobia into osphresiolagnia." Translated it said, "Don't be misled by exaggerated fear of failure into believing everything stinks."

As a continuation of the research on human tolerance, Stapp, Colonel David G. Simons (then Major), and Otto C. Winzen planned the Manhigh balloon project that for the first time put man in a space-equivalent environment.

This "floating scientific laboratory," which conducted twenty-five distinct scientific experiments, ascended on August 19, 1957; the most important "instrument" aboard was Simons. Stapp, in the role of planner and flight surgeon, was minutely cautious in every detail. The responsibility for another's life was more devastating than when he had been his own subject in a project.

As the three million cubic foot balloon ascended to 102,000 feet, Stapp, the ever present advisor-comforter, quipped via the radio, "Dave, you are now reaching the high point in your career." The experimental flight was an unqualified success. Far-reaching were the effects of some of Simons observations. "And, of course, the ultimate outgrowth of the manned balloon capsule could be only one thing: a manned satellite," wrote the Historical Division of Holloman AFB in their report.[7]

Another of Stapp's important undertakings was Project High Dive—the program to investigate human tolerance to actual conditions of escape from 60,000 feet on up and up—as high as aircraft fly. Stapp well recognized the dangers in the parachute jumps proposed in the project, for in tests dummies which were parachuted by remote control from 88,000 feet went into destructive flat spins which gained momentum to as high as 400 revolutions a minute.

Stapp retreated to the laboratory to see what this would do to a man. He rode the eight-foot turntable to investigate. A man will lose consciousness in ten seconds at 165 revolutions per minute. At 220 revolutions no life would survive more than two minutes.

After exhaustive tests the young volunteer, Captain Joseph W. Kittinger, bailed out of the open gondola of a balloon at 76,400 feet, convinced he had countered all difficulties. But he had not allowed for what Stapp terms Murphy's Law: "If anything can go wrong, it will." The fifty-pound pack of scientific instruments on Kittinger's back caught on the aperture, and it took six and one-half seconds to get loose. The timing of the highly complex jump was thrown off. The drogue chute did not deploy properly. In the free fall he started rotating around his own axis like a whirling dervish. Radar tracking on the ground verified that his chute had not opened at 18,000 feet. The rotation continued to increase, reached 88 revolutions per minute, and caused Kittinger to gray-out. He dropped at 740 feet per second. At 17,000, no chute—nor did it open at 15,000 or 13,000!

In horror the group who had helped plan and execute this jump stared fixedly at the speck hurtling downward in the sky. At 12,000, there were gasps as they saw the reserve chute deploy, to stop the rotating and waft Kittinger to the ground. Too weak to get the pack of instruments loose to drop on its own chute, Kittinger landed heavily, with a total weight of 310 pounds—but two hours afterward he was completely composed and conducted a briefing on the near fateful jump (and, incidentally, was already planning for a repeat of the hazardous experiment).

Such is the fiber from which basic research men are cut. Stapp helped set the mold; he knew how to select successors for the risky assignments he planned. Evaluating the importance of this fundamental research toward future space flight, Stapp observed, "Whether man will be an on-board component in space operations will depend on proof that he is still worth his weight in black boxes under conditions of space flight."[8]

His findings on man's tolerance in space flight will apply during further stages of technological development, for he reminds us, "The human body comes in only two shapes and three colors. I don't expect there will be any changes, so what we learn about it now will serve us for a long time to come."[2]

Now deeply involved in new research projects that are of a classified nature, he labels them "fairly bold pushes of the imagination that have brought some instantaneous negative reactions—but that doesn't stop us!" Nothing stops a man like Stapp, who has had influence on a great portion of the lives he has touched and has inspired those who know him only as a legend.

With thought-provoking phrases he projects that "our generation is on the launching pad for the greatest era of scientific exploration that man can hope to undertake."[9] Stapp continues, "The age of technology, applied science, engineering, started with Bacon. Each fifty years that passes represents as much progress as five times the previous span. We've gone through reciprocating engine aviation in fifty years, through jet engine aviation in ten years. Nearly everything today in missile development has been in the last five or six years. You can look into the future and see that the pace of technology will increase. The humorists cry that we should slow down and catch up. My reply is that they should stop crying, stop daydreaming, and catch up. The world is not geared to daydreaming but to the realization of dreams."

This man who is the living symbol of his words said to the June, 1958, graduating class of the University of Dayton, "These are not easy times in which you live and hope to find your proper place. Yet, there is no call to yield integrity because the heads of states can brandish thunderbolts that go around the earth. The stone-age club could strike you no less dead, and death is made no worse by all the threat of megatons. After having seen the world, what an inconsistency it would be to never look again beyond your nose. You are now a part of the world, and all the world is your concern. That it runs well is partly your responsibility."

In an age when "thinking" is almost unfashionable, when every outside interference and diversion conspire to muddle and distract each person, a few rare souls go apart and ponder the direction of our rocket-propelled race with destiny. When, from this basket weave of confusion, a thread of truth can be extracted, there is evidence of uncommon mortal strength. In 1956 Stapp wrote these paragraphs, of which he comments, "They express my philosophy a little better than anything I have written since:

"There is an utter security and abiding joy in being dedicated to and identified with something impersonal and serenely everlasting—the overlife we call civilization; it is a community of life arising from an accumulation of living; it has the sustained continuity of an orchestra whose music goes on unchanged as players quietly slip out and are as silently replaced.

"In a few centuries of lifetimes, great cathedrals were continuously created from inanimate materials, bought by the offerings of generations of peasants, formed by successions of artisans and builders into a living symbol of their community culture; in the universal sense, all the cathedrals, the great thoughts conceiving them, and their intangible counterparts in the constellations of human endeavor are symbolic creations in the over-life of civilization, continuously augmented by individual endeavors.

"Civilization is the intangible wealth of mankind in creative genius, scientific method, communication through the arts, words, and mathematics, and all other attributes evolved by man as a sublime attainment beyond mere biological existence. The collective best of every man thus added to the common fund of human greatness persists long after his demise, untarnished by his personal frailties. To have a little of one's self thus transfigured through the effort and discipline to live beyond selfish pursuits is to attain immortality among those who share civilization: this is the ineffable greatness of man."

An old hymn contains the phrase, "He whose deeds and aims were one." The aims and deeds of John Paul Stapp could well be symbolized by the rails of the rocket-sled tracks running out into the desert. Not only have they run parallel, but when viewed from a distance, they appear to grow closer and closer together. Most promising of all, there is a great distance yet to be traveled in this remarkable life!

REFERENCES

1. *This Is Your Life,* television program, October 26, 1955.
2. *Time,* 66:80, September 12, 1955.
3. *Activities Report,* vol. 6, no. 3, October 1954. (Published by the Research and Development Associates, Food and Containers Institute, Inc.)
4. *Saturday Review,* 41:49–50, December 13, 1958.
5. *Collier's,* 133:25, June 25, 1954.
6. *Aviation Week,* 62:15, January 3, 1955.
7. Bushnell, David: AFMDC, *History of Research in Space Biology and Biodynamics, 1946–1958,* Holloman Air Force Base, New Mexico, 1959.
8. Gantz, Kenneth F.: *Man in Space,* p. 63. New York, Duell, Sloan and Pearce, 1959.
9. Stapp, John Paul: *Man's Mission in Space,* address before the American Rocket Society, June 8, 1959.

Early Russian theorist on the
principles of space flight

KONSTANTIN EDOUARDOVICH TSIOLKOVSKY

Moscow was wrapped in a covering of snow, yet young Konstantin was not conscious of the cold that penetrated his *poloushubok*. The city was deserted at the midnight hour. In the Square, he paused—not to look at the Cathedral, but to peer skyward for the thousandth time. Riding on the pitch of his own excitement, he was being swept toward a vision of achieving space flight!

Along the still streets of the Russian capital he wandered, intoxicated with the newly formed idea that through centrifugal force man could spiral his way toward the heavens. Each star in the darkened sky beckoned to the sixteen-year-old like a tempting Lorelei. The engulfing consequences that his invention would occasion flooded over the youth. Though he knew nothing of the world beyond his home village, Ijevsk in Ryazan Province, and the hundred miles of road that had led him to Moscow, he tried to conjecture the world's reaction to his discovery in that year of 1873.

Suddenly dredged from his memory the moment when he first became captivated with the thought of ascending into space. "Bird," his mother had called to him across the courtyard. (Why this nickname had attached itself to him he had never known, but what an interesting coincidence that it was synonymous with flight.) As he ran toward her, she presented him with a tiny balloon made of collodion. "Don't let go of the string," she cautioned him as he grasped the fascinating object, whose hydrogen contents caused it to rise.

Since that day, his thoughts had soared upward and upward. Now and then he was spurred by some new bit of knowledge he managed to ferret out during the endless hours of self-teaching. Suddenly from this reverie he was jostled as a horse and angry rider brushed by him. Konstantin realized he had been standing where two streets crossed. What had the man shouted to him he wondered? What would it be like to hear the faint sounds of morning as the city began to stir? "Bird," that nickname of his boyhood, had been gradually abandoned as deafness had made him morose. How did a bird's call sound he tried to remember.

Those questions jarred the floodgates. A wave of other doubts poured through. What was it exactly that he had learned about centrifugal force? In what manner had his vivid hope pictured that it would send man into the cosmos? Suddenly his vision shattered, its bright fragments sinking into the mire of reality. When he was an old and honored man, he wrote of this experience, "My disillusionment was as strong as my excitement had been. That night left an imprint on me for the rest of my life. Ten years later, I still dreamt occasionally that I was rising on my machine toward the stars, and I felt the same elation as on that memorable night. . . ."[1]

The possibility of space flight has always been present; it only awaited the workings of keen minds to perceive and reveal the scientific truths that would enable man to fulfill his dream. Tsiolkovsky laid the theoretical groundwork for this Space Age. The first Tsiolkovsky Gold Medal Award was given in 1957 for outstanding work in the field of space flight. The USSR Academy of Sciences, in establishing the award, resolved that the competition be open to both Soviet and foreign scientists who have done original work of major significance in astronautics. Another recognition of Tsiolkovsky is in the town of Kaluga, where an obelisk marks the place that he was laid to rest in 1935. Carved upon it are his prophetic words, "Mankind will not remain bound to the earth."

This aspiration dates back perhaps 4000 years. Wanderings of souls through space were envisioned in early Sanskrit writings. The Egyptians are said to have believed all planets could sustain life; writings of flight into space are found in tenth-century Persian literature; so persistent was curiosity about surrounding space that a disturbed Christian church dogmatically tried to end it early in the twelfth century by labeling it "heresy"; but even this could not stem the speculation. A bishop wrote a serious treatise on a moon journey in 1638—serious in its desire, but little more practical than one of his predecessors' thoughts of training a flock of geese to make the journey.

Soon after, a man who has become legend because of his physiognomy—Cyrano de Bergerac—inadvertently sowed the seed of truth in a fanciful novel about a moon flight when he described it as being achieved by a box with firecrackers attached. It is highly doubtful that Tsiolkovsky ever heard of the de Bergerac novel, but he devised in theory a "box with firecrackers," in the form of a liquid-propelled rocket. The truly amazing proportions of his achievement can only be fully grasped when there is drawn a clear picture of his life, times, and surroundings.

In 1928 a close associate asked Tsiolkovsky for a résumé of his life. This was the reply: "I would have liked to write my autobiography for you, and I started on it rather well, but I could not bear it and I gave it up. It is repugnant to rummage in the past, not because the past was bad, but because I long to move ahead to new endeavors and achievements."[1]

What kind of a spirit was this, which—at the age of seventy-one and ailing—still was determined to look ahead? And what was the story of his past life that obviously so disturbed him?

Perhaps a wandering gypsy fortuneteller would have decried that Konstantin was branded with the scars of flame upon his soul, for his Mother, Maria Ivanova, had Tartar blood in her. [It was the Tartars who had suffered cremation from the Chinese war rockets in the midthirteenth century and had then brought the evil weapons back to Europe.] The fanciful spinning of a tale might have continued, by chanting that the mark of ill fortune and struggle would be upon this home of thirteen children!

The strong will of a freethinker dominated the simple home, for Father, Edouard Ignatievich Tsiolkovsky, was a stubborn and independent man. He had migrated from Volyn' in Poland to the Province of Ryazan in Russia, but it held disappointment for him. After only a year of teaching natural sciences and philosophy, he was discharged—his nonconformist attitude perhaps being a source of irritation to the head of the school.

Konstantin and his brothers were enthralled with their father's many ingenious inventions—among which was a threshing machine. But as Edmund Burke said, "Invention is unfruitful." Father Tsiolkovsky became a worker for the Department of Forestry in the rural area, bringing home but a pittance of wage with which to feed his huge family. He could offer Konstantin little but encouragement, the encouragement to study and develop his bright intellect. Father had difficulty in getting along in life, largely due to his basic honesty that, all too often, evidenced itself as tactless candor.

Mother Tsiolkovsky was from a family of artisans and had a rare knack of making their drab, small dwelling abound in warmth. Though all else was skimpy, there was lavishness of love—of which Konstantin gathered a full measure. The family laughed merrily at his amusing antics and would urge "Bird" on to futher jests.

In 1867, France was caught up in the carousel of a thrilling cycle of fictional writings! Several authors, including Jules Verne, Alexandre Dumas, Camille Flammarion, and Henri de Parville, contributed works that spun tales, as alluring and seemingly as never ending as the Arabian Nights fables, of journeys from the earth to the moon or Mars.

But in that same year in remote Ryazan, a ten-year-old boy lay gravely ill with scarlet fever. Father had not worked in a long while; the family had trudged through another move as he searched for better opportunity; now, all other difficulties paled beside the fear that Konstantin would not live. Mother devotedly nursed him, trying to fan away the discomfort and keeping restless hands from irritating the rash. She yearned to put more nourishment into the thin broth, and the other boys and girl would quietly peer at their beloved brother.

Konstantin's thoughts finally cleared as the crisis passed, and he cried out in childish fright at the realization that he could hear nothing! He saw his Mother's soft lips move and watched his Father's heavy boots upon the wooden floor. The only sounds he was to hear from that time on were faint, muffled, indistinguishable.

Months passed. As the sun came out on brighter days, he sat remotely in a corner of the kitchen, seeming to see little more than he heard. Only once had he ventured out into the neighborhood, pale and unsure. With the cruelty that children can inflict, he had become the target for jeering from his prancing erstwhile playmates as they made crude gestures to their ears. School, which he had always enjoyed, became an impossibility.

One evening he watched Mother and Father in earnest conversation, stealing an occasional glance toward him. The next morning Mother left her duties and usual routine and sat down beside him, her lap full of books. Suddenly, the boredom of silence lessened. Within the brown and black covers of each volume, he began finding answers to questions that had been waiting, half-formed, in his mind. But it was an insatiable process—the more he read, the more he sought.

Sounds began running through his head, sounds from within a mind that yearned to ease wounded pride. They were words—verses. Eagerly he scribbled them on bits of paper and would timidly offer them to Father each evening just after he lit his pipe. They were absurd little rhymes, but it gave Konstantin a satisfaction to see his Father nod approval and smile.

When the curtain of deafness cut him off from the world he had known, the capacities within him expanded. An independence developed, and a strong will—which he delighted in comparing with his Father's. So great had this strength grown that he cried but little when his Mother died, leaving another baby sister, Mariya, to the sorrowing brood.

This was an important time in the formulating of Konstantin's capabilities. He wrote, "At fourteen, I acquired some theoretical knowledge of balloons from Gano's book on physics. I tried to inflate a bag made of tissue paper with hydrogen, but the experiment was not a success."[1]

How similar this experiment was to one conducted many years later by the American "father of rocketry," Dr. Robert H. Goddard. It is recalled that when the boy, Goddard, constructed a balloon and could not get it to perform, he made the entry in his notebook, "Failior crowns enterprise." Similarities do not end there; both possessed a dedication to the realization of space flight, both suffered severe illness, and both became teachers.

Konstantin Tsiolkovsky early showed strong signs of his rightly inherited inventiveness. "I was greatly interested at that time in mechanical flying with the aid of wings. I also built inferior lathes, which nevertheless could be used for turning; I constructed different machines and, among them, a carriage which was supposed to move in every direction with the aid of the wind. The model turned out wonderfully well and moved along the roof, along a board, against the wind. At the same time, another model ran on the floor; a carriage propelled by a steam engine of the turbine system."[1]

Then another fascinating subject overcame the young explorer into science: Balloons!

Ninety years before, the Montgolfier brothers had wondered if a bag filled with smoke might rise. It did, and ascended toward the clouds that had first inspired the experiment. News spread fast from Annonay to Paris, where a subscription was taken up to repeat the experiment—on a grander scale. The physicist, J. A. C. Charles, embellished the idea by having the bag made of thin silk varnished with an elastic gum substance and by substituting hydrogen gas for the smoke. The flight was a huge success, but the landing of the balloon terrified the peasantry, who, never having heard of a balloon, promptly chopped the sack into bits as if it were an invading dragon.

Next balloons carried passengers aloft. The first man to ascend was Jean François Pilâtre de Rozier of Metz. The fever reached such heights that a 200,000 cubic foot gas-filled bag was constructed, which carried aloft a model of a cottage in wickerwork—complete with a small printing office, a photographic department, a refreshment room, and other assorted features! Among its thirteen passengers was a lady, the Princess de la Tour D'Auvergne.

None of this carnival spirit reached Tsiolkovsky. He knew of balloons from factual accounts. His interest was that of a budding scientist, whose dreams were always skyward. He thought often of the tiny balloon his

Mother had once given him, and determined to live up to the faith she had shown in her long hours of tutoring him.

Now he had learned to be alone but not lonely; nature's supreme law of compensation had been brought into play. But it was an unbalanced development at best. As an elderly man, he described the situation in this way: "You understand that the deafness which I suffered from early childhood deprived me of contact with other people, thus leaving me with an immature knowledge of the practical life—which remains with me up to this time. Willynilly, I kept away from the practical life, and found pleasure only in books and in my thoughts. My entire life consisted of work; the rest was beyond my reach."[1]

A friend, interpreting the meaning of "the rest," pointed out that Tsiolkovsky never knew what it was to play games or otherwise become a part of the normal social structure. But lest great pity be aroused, this remarkable appraisal from Tsiolkovsky, himself, must be considered: "I clearly realized that it was to my deafness that I owed the originality of my work."[1]

Another factor conducive to originality was the unavailability of material. To our society that is today so accustomed to generously stocked public libraries in practically every community, there must be compared the conditions that prevailed in Ryazan. Konstantin could only read and reread "a limited number of books of dubious quality"[1]—these were his only teachers. He adds, "I became so used to independent work that, reading through textbooks, I considered it easier to prove a theorem without the book than to find the proof in it."[1]

A need was clearly increasing, for he says, "I began to develop (intellectually) at fourteen or fifteen years of age."[1] As his growth continued, his Father faced the problem: Konstantin had drained the small district of its miserly store of scientific information. There must be found a means of allowing the young man to expand this remarkable bent that he displayed toward mathematics and physics. The older man pondered this and slept upon it, for there had been a day when his own hopes had reached out, only to be crushed beneath the burden of circumstance. This must not be repeated.

As dawn invaded the blackness of his room, an idea took form. Father Tsiolkovsky's thoughts materialized as quickly as the morning sunrise progressed. In the close way of communicating that a family develops under such circumstances, he conveyed his plan to the barely awakened Konstantin. The boy would go to Moscow to study!

It was a bold step all agreed but, as the family made plans for it around the evening meal, Konstantin showed a lightness of spirit that had been absent for many years. "Bird!" they were shouting at him; he saw his brothers' lips form the name, and he smiled. This would be an evening to remember.

It was something of a game to prepare Konstantin—one brother gave his shoes; another his favorite belt. Father carefully wound Konstantin's throat in the heavy scarf that he himself had always worn and glanced anxiously at Konstantin's gloveless hands—there were pockets in the great-coat that would have to suffice. Father knew he could spare little to help sustain the boy in faraway Moscow, but somehow it would work out. With firm handclasps, the first period of Tsiolkovsky's life ended, and the next began.

The city was forbidding and cold in a way that did not relate to tem-perature. There were magnificent buildings, and throngs of people hurry-ing about the business of living. Fear, embarrassment, confusion—all con-sumed Tsiolkovsky in his first encounter with Moscow. Only one emotion was stronger than all of these combined—the obsession of traveling into space!

Quietly he searched out means of preparing himself for the incalculably huge task ahead. He devoured the books he found upon shelves in the li-brary, ravenous for learning to satisfy the hunger within his soul. Father sent just enough rubles for him to eke by on, but this did not allow for the purchase of materials with which to experiment. So, he pared his food consumption to small amounts of black bread which he purchased every few days; then with the few rubles he could salvage he proceeded with experiments on aerostats—dirigibles. Although his stomach cried out from emptiness, his head was "full of dreams"!

While the balloon had defied one of nature's laws by rising from the earth, it still left man victim to nature's winds and currents. Crude attempts to control this by means of oars failed, of course; only when a steam engine and a propeller were added to the assembly by Henri Giffard in 1852 did the controllable lighter-than-air craft come into being. Konstantin had been through elementary mathematics and was prepared to put his knowl-edge to use. "Above all I was fascinated by aerostats, and I already had assembled enough data to solve the problem: of what dimension an aero-stat, with a metal skin of a specified thickness, should be in order to rise in the air with people aboard. It was clear to me that the thickness of the casing could increase indefinitely with the increase of the dimensions. From that time on, the thought of an aerostat with an all-metal skin stuck in my mind. Sometimes it tired me out, and then I occupied myself for months with something else, but in the end returned to it again."[1]

Persistence, so the definition says, is fixed adherence to a resolve. Is it a grim joke of Fate that this quality is bestowed upon some who are faced with seemingly insuperable conditions? Of all the attributes shared by the men who have contributed importantly to the creation of this Space Age, none seems more significant than that of persistence—in the face of poverty, illness, scorn, and defeat. Like the slender shoot of a weed that will be seen to work its way up through an infinitesimal opening in cement of the heavy paving of a roadway this quality in a man may be crushed and buried, but soon a fresh green shoot eagerly, hopefully appears.

During those years that Konstantin Tsiolkovsky studied in Moscow, the world saw change. The great panic of 1873 gripped the United States, and this country went on the gold standard. Stanley achieved the dramatic singular victory of finding Livingston! Edison was active. The rotary printing press made its debut. The seagoing British succeeded in evolving a prototype of a battleship that was to endure for twenty-five years. Verdi composed his *Requiem Mass* and Jules Verne penned *Around the World in Eighty Days*. The Universal Postal Union was formed, making possible worldwide mail service. But these events, and tens of thousands of others, in no manner touched the Russian student. His thoughts were only of study; he was as insulated as if he were already in the cosmos which he fancied.

Aside from the cursory nod he gave to the old couple from whom he'd secured a small room, and his perfunctory greeting to the custodian at the library, he knew little human contact. Books were his companions and his solace; they were also his abettors in his battle against ignorance—the common inheritance of all newborn. Tsiolkovsky fought with unorthodox strategy, making singular jabs into the ranks of knowledge. Penetrations were deep in the areas he attacked, but left wide gaps in his battleline. After an assault on mathematics and physics, he waged a surprise attack on astronomy.

"Astronomy interested me because I considered then and consider now that not only the earth, but to a certain degree the universe too is a property of future generations of mankind,"[1] he said. This was a natural step for a man whose true love was the dream of space flight.

The Hsi and Ho of China were punished for not foretelling an eclipse of the sun in 2136 B.C., so the story relates; they were the legendary forerunners of very real persecution. Throughout the chronicle of civilization to the superstitious mind anything dealing with the skies above had particularly involved connotations. Mostly, it was decreed that such things were not to be contemplated—under pain of the rack.

But the unfolding of truths can never be obliterated, only delayed, by the perversity of humans. The ancient Egyptians gifted civilization with the 365-day calendar. The Babylonians understood the behavior of the seven planets and divided the heavens into zones. The daring but imperfect heliocentric theory of Copernicus started a movement to more scientific appraisal. Kepler's efforts to prove the theory led to his three laws of planetary motion. Galileo contributed to the mosaic of astronomical history with the important discoveries he made with the telescope.

The Royal Astronomical Society of Britain was already over fifty years old when Konstantin started his study in a solitary manner. As he poured over the rotations period of Saturn, the profusion of double stars and the general structure of the stellar system, it was difficult indeed to concentrate on facts. His thoughts kept straying off to a new concept, which placed man among the planets as master of the universe.

One thing became clear. He needed more mathematics. "At seventeen I taught myself from the books the course of differential and integral calculus and solved problems in analytical mechanics, without having the slightest idea about it—solving them, as it turned out later, correctly."[1] He was one step nearer his destination, but what is one step when the journey is to the moon?

The vision was as ancient as hope itself, and the schemes as impractical as utilizing a bottle of dew or being propelled out of a cannon. As the dedicated young man carried his thought about with him night and day, treating it gently lest the spark of development be crushed, he paused and sat in the park. He wrapped the scarf close about his ears, for the snow had turned to ice. A cart stopped on the road near-by, and gay spirited youngsters—undoubtedly returning from a skating party—started jumping from the rear of the cart. As each youngster bounded off with enthusiasm, the cart was pushed a bit in the opposite direction. Tsiolkovsky rose excitedly! He wanted to thank them, hug them, share with them the idea that had just crystallized in his mind. But what could he say? Only an idiot would have suggested "I can send you to the moon or Mars with the same force that pushed the cart as you jumped off"! Newton's Law of Action and Reaction became a living symbol in that instant, heralding the possibility of travel beyond the earth.

Beyond the atmosphere, beyond the oxygen supply which it offers to steam engines or gasoline motors, only one kind of engine would operate: reaction type. This does not require air in which to function; indeed, he reasoned, it would operate better in the vacuum of space. (This remained theory, however, until four decades later when Dr. Robert Goddard conducted practical tests to prove it.)

Rockets were still in use by the Russian military during these years, but Tsiolkovsky lacked both the means and the energy to embark on experimentation. His notebook would be his laboratory, his own clear logic the proving-ground. But it was becoming more and more difficult to concentrate, and a cough had developed and persisted for weeks. When an old friend from Ryazan obliged the elder Tsiolkovsky by searching out his son, he hurried along the message that the boy was sickly and emaciated. Reluctantly, his Father determined he must return home. Young Tsiolkovsky walked slowly around the library on the final day of his Moscow stay, tormented to leave the countless volumes unopened upon the shelves. Though he had fed for three years on the wisdom they contained, he had only just sipped the still full cup. Resignedly, he turned and headed for the road to Ryazan, nodding a final good-by to the custodian of the library.

"I am an entirely self-taught man,"[1] he said.

Though he had not attended school beyond the age of ten, though there had been no means to give him special teachers, though his deafness had kept him from even the free lectures that might have been available, Tsiolkovsky passed the examination and was granted the license to teach in 1879. He gave thanks for this opportunity for a wage, and the chance still to devote his spare hours to study and a small amount of experimentation, as his means could afford.

To the country school of Borovsk in Kaluga Province he took his abilities. What a monumental effort was required for this shy, retiring young man, who lacked the assurance of a degree, who had spent his years in solitude, who had himself been ostracized from any usual childhood, who now was to start teaching though lacking one of his faculties, to enter the classroom on that bleak Monday morning that marked his first day! How does a teacher explain to a class that he is deaf? What if the young ones laughed, as children had laughed at him earlier in his life? (But no matter —now he understood the combination of embarrassment and confusion that brought this forth.) But, how does a teacher teach? The questions spun within Tsiolkovsky's brain.

He would not be just a teacher—he would be a good teacher. This would not be a means of buying food and continuing his study—it would be a dedication. Firmly he resolved these things and fell into a brief sleep before dawn tinged the sky.

His approach to the work was restricted. "Because of my deafness, I did not like to ask the students questions and therefore I confined myself to the lecture method, even though I incurred disapproval by doing it. Occasionally I would call on a student seventeen or eighteen years of age, have him or her stand near me at my left ear, and I would listen that way to their answers. The class would laugh good-naturedly." There were other unusual features in Tsiolkovsky's method of teaching: "I did not stint on interesting experiments, so that we had real 'performances'; a part of my salary went for these experiments." As self-confidence replaced the doubts, he added, "The students liked me very much for my fairness, good grades, and tirelessness in explanations."[1]

Tsiolkovsky's small quarters became a gathering place for the community. There were small experiments, such as flying his remarkable model made in the shape of a hawk. Also, he devised a few inventions that were inspired by memories of his Father's efforts. Though still occupied mostly with his thoughts and calculations, he learned the comfort of a neighborly visit and the pleasure of having a place that was his home—however meager it might be.

In the year 1880 the members of the Society for Physics and Chemistry in St. Petersburg (now Leningrad) learned of the existence of K. E. Tsiolkovsky. Scientific papers which he submitted to the committee for reviewing caused that group to go through a progression of reactions. First, one of indignation arose, that anyone would precipitate such a fraud as to submit a paper on *The Theory of Gases,* presenting conclusions that had been known for over twenty years! "Why, anyone could copy down accepted principles."

"But wait," another member adjured. "The conclusions in this paper of K. E. Tsiolkovsky's are the same as those that are known, but notice, if you please, his detailed method of working them out! This is not copied from any textbook. This is original work!" So they pondered. "Was it a joke?" That possibility was quickly discarded—no one with this much devotion wastes time on jokes. They were forced to one opinion—incredibly, the young man had simply not known that his great findings were a repetition of accepted scientific fact. A letter was sent to Tsiolkovsky in Borovsk informing him of this fact.

Time, precious time, for which Tsiolkovsky constantly fought, had been uselessly squandered! The hours which he had stolen from his great need for sleep and rest were spent to no avail! But, as reflex gave way to reflectiveness, the young scientist reconsidered. Was this actually the case? Though he "discovered" things that were already known, was it not important for his own sake to have done this tedious work and to have reached correct conclusions? From such accomplishment should not assurance spring? Besides, as he read and reread the letter which had been sent to him, he felt increasing gratification in the signature at the end: Dimitri Ivanovich Mendeleyev.

This was one of the world's most respected scientists, who had worked on periodic law and classified the elements into a periodic table. Mendeleyev's letter obviously was no form reply; rather it was a special consideration that had been shown. Two other papers had accompanied the one he sent on the kinetic theory of gases—*Duration of Stars' Radiation* and *Mechanics of Animal Organism.* The latter received a commendation from Professor I. M. Sechenov, the eminent physiologist.

Then there was the closing paragraph of the letter, which Tsiolkovsky had almost overlooked in his first feeling of disappointment; he had been unanimously elected to membership in the Society! It was a great honor— and yet, it was with no small degree of apprehension that he considered this privilege.

The great blunder of his work on gases had occurred because of gaps in his learning. As he said, "I studied very little systematically, especially in the later years; I read only what could be of help to me in solving questions which interested me, which I considered important. One could say that I studied by way of creating—although often unsuccessfully and too late."[1]

What would it then be like to belong to an organization made up of highly educated, well-trained, and brilliant scientists? He glanced down at his simple, almost threadbare clothing. How could he ever attend a meeting of the group? What a figure he would make—the country schoolteacher who had ideas about flight into the cosmos! As his fear mounted, the picture in his mind included even such details as derisive amusement in the eyes of the sophisticated and learned members. Tsiolkovsky was a proud and sensitive man. His infirmity and his poverty had caused him sufficient hurt in his life; he could not risk more. Further, there was a membership fee. For too many nights, his dinner plate would have been altogether empty if he were to have met this obligation.

"At the age of twenty-five to twenty-eight, I became enthusiastic about the development of steam engines. I had a metal steam-driven engine and a wooden one (with a wooden cylinder), both poor, but operating. At the same time I constructed good blowing machines and various pumps, which I did not market anywhere, but built only for curiosity's sake and as an experiment, and also for soldering and forging. A few years later I dropped all that, since I saw clearly that I was weak in technical work and in respect of carrying out my ideas."[1]

Objectivity. What a blessing it can prove to be! A square peg forced into a round hole may eventually wear at the corners—but it is still a square peg. Events may lead a man into a certain path, or perhaps his own desires can guide the choice—yet, if he were scrupulously objective, he would sometimes find that this was not his destiny. But too often by that time the devil named Habit has him well-trained. His life has settled down to a pattern, and it would require too much effort to climb out of the rut. So it goes on—not really fitted, not actually doing the job well.

Tsiolkovsky never lacked the courage to change abruptly the course of his efforts. He also brought change into his personal life during this period by gaining a wife who was understanding and uncomplaining. She would sit quietly sewing as he bent over his table writing, figuring, theorizing. Occasionally their eyes would meet, and she would shyly glance away, reluctant to invade the world of his dreams.

There must be an intermediate step into space Tsiolkovsky realized. Therefore, in 1885, he made the firm resolve to devote himself to aviation. He hoped for an interplay of certain phases of the effort by also undertaking the theoretical working out of a mechanical, piloted balloon. Indeed, the very atmosphere throughout the world was charged with the consuming desire for flight. (The desire did literally "consume" too many misguided souls, who conducted such unscientific experiments as stepping off from high places with wings attached to their arms.)

Leonardo da Vinci propounded that "the movement of the air against a fixed thing is as great as the movement of the movable thing against the air which is immovable." This genius in many diverse fields grasped what Newton was to set forth some two hundred years later. But the isolated instances of sound advancement were like scattered mirages on a desert wasteland. Though 1866 saw the founding of the Aeronautical Society of Great Britain, among the first papers was one by Francis H. Wenham, dwelling on the technical problems of flight—not the solutions.

"I worked almost without interruption for two years," said Tsiolkovsky. During none of his productive life did this remarkable man ever have a facility resembling a laboratory. There were the usual demands upon him as husband and father, and the constant pressure of his teaching. "I was always an ardent instructor, and I would return home from school very tired, since I was leaving the greatest part of my strength there. It was only toward the evening that I could tackle my calculations and experiments. I had little time as well as strength, which I spent on my students. So I decided to get up at daybreak and, after having worked on my own writings, I would leave for school.

"After two years of such nervous strain my head felt heavy for a whole year. Nevertheless, in the spring of 1887 I gave my first public lecture on an all-metal piloted balloon at the Polytechnical Museum attached to the Society of People Interested in Natural Sciences in Moskva."[1]

As he entered the capital what deep emotion welled within his soul! At sixteen he had trod the streets in a great state of fear; now, at thirty, the fear had subsided, but apprehension took its place. He was still the country boy, unused to the customs of the city, shy at the amenities, yet so deeply proud that he silently pleaded to do well at his lecture.

He paused once more in the Square, reliving the night he had exuberantly been deluded into the idea that he had solved the problem of space flight. The same surge of hope stimulated his thoughts, impelling him to let this interest in aviation and dirigibles be but the way station to his ultimate goal.

Slowly he strolled to the Museum, thankful not only for the privilege of delivering his paper on dirigibles, *The Theory of the Aerostat,* but also grateful for the very personal comfort of now having a cloak warm enough to turn the chill and of a stomach full enough not to cry out in pain as he passed taverns and food stores.

In the moments before he began his lecture, a chill gripped him. The memory of the foolish, tragic mistake which he made in his paper *The*

Theory of Gases created a sudden alarm. What if his lecture now on the all-metal piloted balloon were similarly open to ridicule? Perhaps he should not risk it, but turn and leave. Then the soothing balm of confidence returned. He smiled to himself. He had spent the days of the last ten years lecturing at school. He would merely think of this group as his children. He glanced at his audience for a moment, considered they were a bit old really for schoolboys, then calmly proceeded with his lecture.

Modestly he admits, "I was received very well. Professor Stoletov turned the manuscript over to Professor Nikolai Egorovich Zhukovsky for consideration."[1] This was tribute, to be sure, for Zhukovsky stood high in the ranks of science. Moreover, Mendeleyev was continuing the display of interest he had first revealed in his letter to Tsiolkovsky many years before. Tsiolkovsky was aware of the benefits to be gained from living in Moscow and asked if he might be transferred to a teaching position in the capital. The transfer was promised.

Then, as this hope filled him and the pleasure of his fine treatment at the Museum encouraged him to renewed effort, he fell very ill.

He lost his voice.

Now he could neither speak nor hear. Misery closed tight upon him, parading before his eyes the sorrowful specter of his wife, burdened so heavily with endless work, the care of their children, and now not even the means to buy food. He did not believe the black of his grief could be painted darker, but then fire struck! His precious library was destroyed, his models consumed in flames. What terrible sacrifice had gone into the accumulation of these things, now but fodder for a scavenger that left only ashes! Grief-stricken, his wife could but shake her bowed head and reach out a hand to touch him.

With the unbelievable fortitude that he could summon from his soul, he found one circumstance for which to be grateful—the manuscript of his Moscow lecture was safe in the hands of Professor Zhukovsky. Paced as a dirge, the days of a year passed before Tsiolkovsky regained his voice and recovered from his illness.

The Moscow assignment never came through, but in 1892 he was invited to a teaching post in Kaluga, which would offer him increased opportunity, for this was a bustling industrial city. The railroad passed through, providing much greater communication with the rest of the nation; there were over thirty churches, a cultural center, a park, hospitals, and many schools. Tsiolkovsky taught in the high school and in a diocesan school for daughters of the clergy.

He acquired a bicycle to shorten the time of the trip to and from the school and plunged into work with a vigor in some ways surpassing any demonstration of his youth. The friendly townspeople were attracted to the gracious teacher and forgave him when he didn't return their waves—often his concentration on a problem blinded him to their greetings.

He pressed every available moment into service to help materialize his idea for an airplane with a metal frame. It would be a monoplane—an advanced design for airplanes that appeared nearly twenty years later. He envisioned wings that were thick in profile, with the leading edge rounded. The fuselage, of course, would have a streamlined shape. His article *The Airplane or a Bird-like (Aviation) Flying Machine* appeared in 1894; it was widely commented on in many circles, but did not appear to receive the recognition that would have been expected from the official Russian science group.

Eleven years before he had expressed the idea of applying jet propulsion principle to flying. But there were obstacles to the working out of such design that appeared insurmountable, without the benefit of actual experience. How could one learn the manner in which this design would behave in flight, without its actually being air-borne? By simulating the conditions of flight upon the ground, if the air is moved and the airplane held captive the same characteristics will develop as if the air were still and the airplane were moving. At his two-story home in Kaluga, Tsiolkovsky built the first wind tunnel in Russia (though others may have existed in Europe). It was the shape of a shoe box, built of wood; in the metal lining were slits through which air was blown. With the ingenuity of an inventor's son, he forced the currents through with an arrangement of bellows.

At last the theories of aerodynamics could be put to test and guide his further theory on the airplane. No longer was air resistance a matter of guesswork. Though small and incredibly crude by today's standards, Tsiolkovsky was able to discover the errors in existing beliefs and arrive at a more accurate appraisal of the conditions of flight. By fitting this knowledge into his previous theories, he was given the answer to a problem he faced fifteen years before: in designing his metal dirigible he had arrived at a power-to-weight ratio—except for the unknown element of wind resistance. The wind tunnel figured importantly in one of Tsiolkovsky's major contributions—the working out of the aerodynamic principles of flight.

How vivid was this illustration of the importance of experiments! Yet constant adversity had precluded much of this kind of research throughout his career. He had been restricted to the purely theoretical work in so many instances. Therefore he was as grateful as he was astounded by the gift of 470 rubles from the St. Petersburg Academy of Sciences for the purpose of research! In addition, there had accumulated fifty-five rubles—donations from private citizens throughout the country who had heard of the noble work being performed by the self-sacrificing professor through the newspapers for which he had written articles. Excitedly his thoughts tumbled over one another, planning further tests with his wind tunnel. He continued these vital experiments, determining drag coefficients of a sphere, a cylinder, a flat plate, a cone, and other basic shapes.

To this man of vision, all elements of the skies and the universe fitted together to form one over-all picture. Though in linguistics, a separate name is applied to each element, the overlapping of interests and of purposes precludes any clear distinction. Therefore it was not a deviation of his activities at this period for Tsiolkovsky to author articles on astronomy. Among them was *Will the Earth Ever Be Able to Inform the Living Beings on Other Planets of the Existence on It of Intelligent Beings?*

The unusually long title of the article must not obscure its significance. Herein was depicted a facet of the man Tsiolkovsky not to be overlooked. It was, perhaps, the quality in him that guided his life. Why did his creativeness not apply itself toward a new implement for farming, or an improvement on the horseless carriage? With all of his sound and logical thinking, why did he choose to bridge from his time into an entrancing, nebulous future? What was the call that he answered—the lure that he saw?

Speculation on the possibility of life in other parts of the universe has continued to today. The Queen of the Land of Oz has inspired the naming of our own Project Ozma, the highly scientific activity that is now being conducted in a remote valley of the West Virginia Hills. There, at the National Radio Astronomy Observatory, the electronic ears of a huge dish-shaped antenna are cocked toward the two stars nearest to the earth. Yet even these nearest ones would have had to have sent out signals eleven years ago, with the signals traveling at the speed of light since 1949, for them to be reaching us now!

Will the usual calm of Dr. Frank Drake be transformed to overwhelming excitement one of these days when he detects amid the crackles and natural noises of the cosmos some systematic signal that his listening device has picked up? If that time comes, we will be faced with the very question that Tsiolkovsky posed in his paper sixty-five years ago—how do we let those beings know of our existence? (Or, as the pessimistic ones choose to phrase it, *dare* we let them know?)

Tsiolkovsky's hypothesis, set forth in *Monism of the Universe* and *The Unknown Intelligent Forces,* envisioned other worlds populated by beings of a highly developed order. His thoughts grew increasingly fanciful as he related that these beings existed to bring about "humane colonization versus painful evolution."[2] Their method was to travel to other planets for the purpose of colonizing them; the beings which they encountered of lesser intellectual levels, the product of evolution, they would painlessly eradicate.

The ephemeral borderline between fact and illusion is markedly influenced by the individual's frame of reference. The nature of the man Tsiolkovsky gave him views different from other men; his deafness closed out much of reality. Perhaps one key to understanding him rests in his statement, "Life brought me many sorrows and it was only the happy world of ideas that helped me to endure them."[1] Had he not employed metempirical thoughts, could the vital contribution that has made him notable ever have emerged?

"The thought of contact with outer space never left me."[1]

Through this obsession he set forth the first scientific theory of space flight. He did it without the benefit of great contact with the scientific progress of the time, in surroundings less advanced than were many areas of the world, and in spite of incessant mundane difficulties. Perhaps the only discernible influence was the helpful criticism and guidance of Mendeleyev at an important moment; without this Tsiolkovsky's work might have been far more fanciful than it was. Indeed, but for the kindliness and perception of Mendeleyev, this Russian theorist might never have been heard of!

In 1895 in an article appearing in *Nature and Men,* Tsiolkovsky summoned the courage to mention in print the term "space flight." Three years later the principle emerged from the patient work, which his notebooks indicate dated back twenty years, and appeared in the form of a handwritten paper, fifty pages long, entitled *Exploration of Outer Spaces by Rocket Devices.* Through his friend, V. A. Assonov, it was submitted to the editor of the magazine *Scientific Review.* For reasons which Tsiolkovsky never understood the article was held until 1903 before it appeared on the magazine's pages.

Expectantly, he waited for comment, reaction. It never came. Nor was there the opportunity for further discussion of the fascinating topic, for the sudden death of the editor brought about the discontinuation of the periodical.

It is somewhat remarkable that so momentous a treatise could pass unnoticed at the time, despite the fact that it was written in the Russian language. (Here there is marked dissimilarity to the furor caused by Dr. Robert H. Goddard's first published report which touched on the possibility of lunar travel, *A Method of Reaching Extreme Altitudes.*)

Tsiolkovsky's logical study (which was published in the same year that the Wright Brothers achieved powered flight) correctly deduced: that only a reaction type of engine, a rocket, would operate in space; that it would have to have a greater exhaust velocity to escape gravity than that produced by the then-known powder rocket, therefore, would have to burn a liquid propellant; that the longer a rocket continues to accelerate due to rocket-engine thrust the faster it goes, reaching and exceeding the speed of its own exhaust; and that as the weight is reduced by the burning of the fuel the acceleration, and hence the velocity, is increased. His rocket contained a long metal combustion chamber, fuel tanks, a fuel pump, and a sealed cabin with oxygen supply for the crew.

In this work, and in subsequent additions to the problems and propositions of space flight, Tsiolkovsky put forth these solutions and suggestions: To stabilize the rocket he realized external fins would be effective only so long as it was in the atmosphere; beyond, stabilization would have to be achieved with control vanes in the exhaust stream. One of the greatest problems that present-day scientists faced has been that of the excessive heating on re-entry. Tsiolkovsky foresaw that when he wrote, "So that a rocket should not burn out like a meteorite when returning from space it should be placed in a special gliding trajectory in order to extinguish the speed more slowly."[3] He spoke of cooling the walls of the chamber with a liquid oxidizer and of using liquid hydrogen and hydrocarbon fuels.

Though a multistage rocket was not new even in 1903 (since it can be traced back to K. Siemienowicz in the seventeenth century), Tsiolkovsky was probably the first to apply it to space travel. He had two versions: (1) "rocket trains," a series wherein the bottom rocket would drop off after burning until only the lead rocket remained; (2) "rocket squadron," wherein all rockets fire until one-half the propellant has been used up, and then the outermost empty their remaining contents into the remaining rockets and drop off, the process being repeated until only the lead rocket remains.

Tsiolkovsky also described the special condition which the astronaut will encounter in this poetic manner: "We shall not have weight, only mass. We can hold any mass in our hands without experiencing the slightest weight. . . . Man does not press himself against anything and nothing presses on him; every spot is as soft as any down bed can be. . . . There is no top or bottom."[4] He suggested periodic rotation of a spaceship to produce artificial gravity and proposed that we might populate outer space with entire "cities" having artificial gravity.

This imaginative scientist also described an earth satellite in *Dreams of the Earth and Sky,* written in 1895; he saw that this satellite could serve as a technical station for interplanetary rockets. He envisioned this satellite of the earth or the sun as an "ethereal dwelling," projecting the thought that it could be assembled from sections transported by rockets.

In his work, *Goals in Astronavigation,* he brought out the fact that the sun radiates two billion times more energy than is received from it here on earth. He wrote, "That is the kind of energy that man can possess if he is able to establish himself in celestial space. One can hardly compare the achievement of this goal with the discovery of two thousand million new planets such as the earth!"[4]

Though it sounds like a fairy tale, Tsiolkovsky felt enormous streams of "sunbeams" could be captured in huge hothouses in space, and utilized to grow plants for a double purpose—to regenerate the air and to provide food for celestial inhabitants. He put forth an intriguing speculation—that plants and organisms, regardless of their complexity, will develop faster where they do not encounter the pull of gravity!

Tsiolkovsky's prognosis was remarkable. The fundamentals of space were generally contained within his writings, though of course they do not all date from the original 1903 publication; in his works to 1933 space is the recurring theme throughout.

Dr. Robert Goddard possessed the dual ability to dream, then turn his vision into hardware. A problem which might be dismissed in a paragraph by the theorist might require one, five, ten years of work to solve in the laboratory. Tsiolkovsky, fortunately or unfortunately, extended but few of his theories into experiments. So it may be a just comment that he was inclined toward oversimplification—though truth is often characterized by simplicity. Once stated, how often a principle brings forth the reaction, "Of course!" But, to be the first to arrive at that truth requires the imagination and skill to evolve it and the wisdom to recognize that it is truth. (Often correct solutions have been reached, only to be ignored by one not gifted enough to know that the answers were right!)

The Russian was a prolific writer, especially in view of his full-time duty as instructor, leaving only "spare time" for his endeavors. Without indicating tergiversation toward his primary theme of science, it is interesting to note how the spectrum of his interests broadens as the years progress. In writings from 1891 to 1913, titles of published works indicate a complete preoccupation with his work. The philosophic nature of the man begins to come into the scene in 1914 with the work, *Nirvana*. It expands with the publication the following year of *A Common Alphabet and Language,* and *Knowledge and Its Dissemination*. There is a strong resurgence of the trend in 1928 with *Self-Love or True Egoism,* and *Intellect and Emotions*.

There can be only speculation as to the extent of the influence upon Tsiolkovsky of Dr. Yakov I. Perel'man, who popularized a series of articles which the former wrote from 1911 to 1913 for the magazine *Aviation Reports*. Many who would have overlooked the purely scientific report were intrigued by the flair of fiction added by Perel'man. Now the scientist's name was brought up in conversation among professional groups and artists, as well as men of his own field.

Perel'man authored the booklet, *Tsiolkovsky, His Life, Inventions, and Scientific Work* in 1932 to honor Tsiolkovsky's seventy-fifth birthday. Though Perel'man proved himself a devoted admirer of the scientist, and an associate over a long period of time, he was successful in getting only the most limited amount of biographical material from Tsiolkovsky. In

1914, he could elicit but a brief paragraph, prefaced with "Regarding my life, I can (for certain reasons) give you only the following information," and closing with the apology, "Forgive me for this brevity. My biography has not yet appeared anywhere."[1]

What were the reasons? Why did the man of science have such reluctance about revealing even the fact that he was married? (This was such a guarded secret to the general world that it was not commonly known until a photograph of him with his grandchildren appeared.) Why did he choose to wrap so tightly the cloak of mystery about a life that appeared dedicated and undeviating. Or, were there depths that gave him reason for seclusion?

Tsiolkovsky spent forty years in the classroom, during which time he says "approximately 500 boys and 1500 girls, secondary school students passed through my hands. I gave not less than 40,000 lectures. . . . I taught either mathematics or physics (seldom both). Occasionally I gave lessons in cosmography and chemistry. After the revolution, I lectured at the People's University, and later I was 'shkrab' (schoolworker) in the vocational high school. These were difficult times; we sat in overcoats, in darkness. I received a monthly pay which was not enough to buy five pounds of black bread. I was granted academic rations (from 1 October 1921), but for a long time I did not receive them. We starved quite a lot. Later, I did not suffer any need, thanks to the aid given me by various Soviet organizations; I suspect it was the influence or intercession of the Society of People Interested in Cosmology, initiated by Yakov I. Perel'-man."[1]

It is difficult to understand how or why Tsiolkovsky received no recognition for so many years. The fact that his writings were in Russian does not in itself seem sufficient reason; the Wright Brothers prior to their flights of 1903 were well aware of the work of the Kuchino Laboratory outside Moscow and of the Polish propeller-theory pioneer, Stefan Drzewiecki.

There was an especially bleak period in Tsiolkovsky's life soon after he moved to Kaluga. "It is hard," he wrote later, "to work completely in the dark for four years without seeing a glimmer of light or receiving any worth-while support."[5] Pathetically this condition prevailed until after World War I, when two incidents brought about a change: In early 1920, there was a furor as the newspapers of the world sensationalized the reference to a "moon shot" contained in Dr. Robert H. Goddard's scientific paper *A Method of Reaching Extreme Altitudes*. In 1923, Dr. Hermann Oberth published his pamphlet, *The Rocket into Interplanetary Space,* which received wide comment throughout Europe; a year later he reprinted a German translation of some of Tsiolkovsky's works.

This growing world-wide awareness of rocketry caused the Russian people to realize that recognition was indeed due to one of their own. They reprinted his 1903 paper with a title page both in Russian and German and a preface in the latter language. Though it is now difficult to determine just when the long-overdue respect for Tsiolkovsky took form within the Soviet government, they have, in later years, proudly acclaimed him the "Father of Space Travel."

An enthused group in Moscow founded a society for space travel; in 1929, Perel'man and I. P. Fortikov founded a serious scientific organization known as GIRD—the initials standing for the Russian words for "Group for the Study of Reactive Motion." By 1932 the ailing, retired schoolteacher in Kaluga was a national hero! His seventy-fifth birthday was occasion for a great celebration. And now a crater on the moon bears his name.

The elderly scientist underestimated the verve with which the world would at last embrace the idea of space flight, for he had said, "Probably a hundred years will pass before the opinions expressed by me find application, and people use them to disperse not only the face of the Earth but over the face of the whole universe."[6] Tsiolkovsky died in 1935. But his dream found fulfillment in far less than a hundred years: October 4, 1957, marked the beginning of the Space Age with the launching of Sputnik I!

Each day brings closer the moment of man's realization of the experience that Konstantin Tsiolkovsky would have considered the most magnificent that he could undergo: "To set foot on the soil of the asteroids, to lift by hand a rock from the moon, to observe Mars from a distance of several tens of kilometers, to land on its satellite or even on its own surface, what can be more fantastic? From the moment of using rocket devices a new great era will begin. . . ."[4]

REFERENCES

1. Perel'man, Yakov I.: *Tsiolkovsky, His Life, Inventions and Scientific Work,* Moskova, 1932.
2. *Science,* 131:3403:872 f., March 18, 1960.
3. *Science Digest,* 46:84–89, September, 1959.
4. Krieger, F. J.: *Behind the Sputniks, A Survey of Soviet Space Science,* Washington, D. C., Public Affairs Press, 1958.
5. Gartmann, Heinz: *The Men Behind the Space Rockets,* New York, McKay, 1956.
6. *Space Age,* 1:10–14+, August, 1959.

*Physicist whose discovery of the
Van Allen Radiation Belts is a
milestone in space achievements*

JAMES A. VAN ALLEN

Vivid greens and yellows splashed across the northern skies with the brilliance of lightning, the impressionism of a Van Gogh. Nature unleashed a magnificent display spreading like a mammoth curtain in a graceful, fluted arc above the horizon. Instantly the pattern changed, the colors intensified, reaching an extravagant degree of beauty. This gigantic kaleidoscopic outburst, the aurora borealis crashed like a Wagnerian overture to herald the opening of the International Geophysical Year, July 1, 1957.

Such a dramatic show of lights transpiring in past centuries was oft viewed with superstition. But in the "enlightened" era of today, it merely stimulated observers of the sixty-six participating countries of the IGY to renewed attacks on the riddles of the aurora.

"We dance around in a ring and suppose. But the secret sits in the middle and knows." Dr. James Van Allen uses this couplet of Robert Frost to state poetically the view of science on the baffling phenomenon. But before the International Geophysical Year ended, Van Allen was to contribute an important step toward solving the puzzle of the aurora which was as old as the word "why?" and as enigmatic as a hall of mirrors.

The Hawkeye state—noted for such varied things as its corn, its football teams, its abounding friendliness, and prairie plains—can now add to its credit of scientists this man of inordinate stature. Iowa has always been James Van Allen's home; he was educated there and returned to teach at the State University. Yet he is also a citizen of another select aggregation.

The Straits of Magellan were named in a day when man could by courage, perseverance, and employment of one of his simple basic senses, become immortal. Then the world became so complex that merely to see what others could see, or hear what any ears could detect, was not enough. The elite of the group must now engage in thorough investigation by trained and intuitive minds and couple these qualities with data compiled from highly intricate equipment to reveal an existing—though previously undetected—phenomenon. The Zener Diode, the Lorentz Contraction, the Pfotzer Maximum—these have been so detected and named for their discoverers. And now are added the Van Allen Radiation Belts.

These bands are deemed the greatest discovery of the IGY and have influenced the entire concept of exploration. Like two giant moats they guard the universe, challenging man to cross through their deadly radiation. At the same time the circle of their configuration provides two inviting openings—the areas at the poles—which serve as drawbridges into space.

After a lengthy scientific question-and-answer period recently held in Los Angeles, Van Allen was bombarded with queries about the threats and dangers inherent in these belts. At last one interested participant pleaded, "Can't you tell us anything good that has come from the discovery of the radiation belts?"

"Yes," Van Allen retorted; "I've made a pretty good living off them!" It would seem that the professor is neither too impressed nor too preoccupied to smile at himself, though he is responsible for a discovery that is fundamental to the exploration of space.

It is difficult to trace precisely the threads of Van Allen's accomplishments to their real sources. Perhaps they are so interwoven with the fabric of his busy life that they have become a part of every experience—fused with both his desire and opportunity.

While many influences played upon the forming of his career, they were but searchlights helping to mark the path to science. The real illumination was self-contained; the first glimmer was developed by the family habit of study, and deep-seated inquisitiveness caused it to brighten into a perpetual seeking of books, classes, experiments.

Father opened *The Book of Knowledge* to the place carefully marked from the previous night's session. James sat with the quiet respect that was expected of a ten-year-old in the Van Allen household. Though interested in the Civil War history that his father was reading aloud, he secretly wished for more discussions of electricity and the laws of physics, such as they had had the week before.

Dinner had provided an abundance of Mother's hot bread and fried chicken, but Jim never acquiesced to the inclinations of a full stomach. He sat stiffly on the edge of a straight-backed chair, his eyes on his father's face—a face that had the strength of Dutch ancestors etched deeply into its expression. Jim glanced at big brother George and younger brother Maurice; they were as dutifully rapt in the reading as was he. Only baby brother Bill was occasionally swinging from the arm of the big couch—a transgression permitted a three-year-old.

The room was stuffy, but father feared a draft might cause colds which would keep his boys out of school—this must not be. Momentarily Jim's thoughts were of the even warmer evenings ahead. He had often heard his father say, "The only trouble with Iowa is that there are nine months of summer and nine months of winter." Jim couldn't figure that out. Maybe when he got to algebra he'd understand. He wanted to get to it now. The battle of Vicksburg was taking so much time to read—besides, he knew which side would win. Maybe Father would turn to that section on astronomy tomorrow night. He could peer out of his bedroom window and see all sorts of things in the heavens, but there wouldn't be much peering tonight; his eyes were getting awfully heavy. He was glad the battle of Vicksburg was almost over.

The memories of boyhood were like mementos tossed in an old trunk—each treasured and meaningful, but not necessarily related.

It was when Jim was about twelve years old that he and Maury worked together building a high-voltage machine. In the semidarkness of the basement, it was exciting to see the "lightning" they could produce. Jim considered the contraption a thing of great majesty, with its coils and metal ball on top. On weekends, after they had raked the yard, he and Maury planned to devise other inventions.

But dinner time always seemed to interrupt—and they dared not be late. What would they discuss during the meal tonight Jim wondered? Father always guided the conversation into some channel of learning, for he realized that the interest he cultivated could become flowers instead of weeds, providing he used care in selecting the seeds that were sown. Well tended, thoughts and growth could produce a harvest of real meaning, while neglect would allow fertile ground to become overgrown with trifles.

On Saturdays Jim often visited his father's office. It was impressive to see the gold letters on the door: Alfred M. Van Allen, Attorney at Law. It was the same office grandfather had occupied, and there was already the plan for George to study law and continue the practice. A kind of mutual ownership had grown up between the Van Allens and this county seat,

Mount Pleasant—they seemed to own each other. Father served on the school board, the city council, and even did a turn as mayor of this town which was as agreeable in atmosphere as its name would promise.

As shopping center for the surrounding area of southeastern Iowa farmland, its tree-lined streets stretched between "our two institutions." As the local people said, "We have the state mental hospital in one end of town, the college in the other." It was not a very funny joke, but visitors always laughed perfunctorily.

In the center of the town was the characteristic "twenty steps up off the street" Carnegie-endowed library. This was a favorite spot of Mother's. Other interests of hers centered around community activities; in determining which to serve, she tried to select the ones to which she felt she would be of most help. But her social consciousness did not assume an imbalance— she was dedicated to her family and saw to it that she was always home in time to get her wood stove fired up and cook for her ever hungry men. (Incidentally, such a favorite of hers was this wood-burning stove that she kept it until a few years ago, often using it instead of the later-installed gas range.)

The focal points for the Van Allen boys' activities were in schools—the debates, lectures, musicals. Father always discouraged their participation in sports, considering it a pure waste of time; but this edict really didn't bother Jim—his classmates all outweighed him, so he wouldn't have been any asset to the teams.

C. A. Cottrell, the high school physics teacher, once remarked to a colleague, "You know, that boy's father was a member of the school board when I applied for this position. And I still recall he quizzed me at great length; he wanted to be sure I knew my science before he'd give his approval to me. Now I see that he had a special reason for inquiry." It seems evident that the professor taught the Van Allen boy well!

Regularly it was necessary for Cottrell to "sweep Jimmy Van Allen out the door" so he could lock up the laboratory as the day ended. Where physics was concerned, Jim could be precise about every element—except the element of time (his own time!).

There are carefully constructed tests for intelligence, a series of examinations that will indicate aptitude and dexterity, but what is the real evaluation of the student's possibilities? Strongest among the variables seems to be the degree of drive from within. It will emerge to offset a dozen weaknesses, and so strengthen capabilities that little else counts. This drive flows as a hidden river; it may rise to the surface like a spring, or wells may have to be dug to seek it out. But when the drive is strong, it can no more be stemmed by discouragement than can water be dammed up by admonition. From the day Jimmy Van Allen started school at the age of four, it was clear that within him was this force that would not be stopped.

The habit of worth-while reading, the utilization of time to its fullest, the strong emphasis which his father placed on education—these motivated the Van Allen boys. Socially, their lives were meaningful and complete within their home. They did not need to search for diversion, seek for companionship. Friends had their place, but the family was paramount. Father treasured their gatherings, and Christmas was a holiday of special importance because of these ties. For as long as he lived, Father had his four sons and his beloved wife with him each December 25th.

The 1959 *Croaker* was dedicated to James Van Allen.

This may not be any earth-shaking news to the country at large, but to an alumnus of the class of 1935 of Iowa Wesleyan College it was a tribute, indeed, to have the yearbook single him out for such honor. By way of explanation for the unusual title for this book, the editors who selected it in 1906 pointed out that "there are croakers and there are croakers"— the individual's reaction to a frog's sounds will depend on the association in his mind. Perhaps it will remind him of an early morning bike ride when he was a youngster, or instead it may recall a moonlit evening when he strolled beside a pond with his best girl.

What James Van Allen associates with the croak of a frog may remain his secret; but his association when he thinks of Wesleyan College is very apt to be of the three-story, vine-covered brick physics building—for that is where he spent all possible moments. There he studied under Professor Thomas Poulter.

Poulter, now at Stanford Research Institute, is Director of the Laboratories bearing his name. He has this recollection of the association: "It was not Van Allen's ability as a scientist that first attracted me to him as a college freshman at Iowa Wesleyan College, but rather his rare personality. Jim is very quiet, unassuming, serious, but with a good sense of humor. It may seem a bit surprising to refer to him as a scientist when he was only a college freshman. Colleges and professors all too frequently like to take credit for developing their students into scientists or other outstanding personalities. I have no such illusion about Jim. Even as a student I preferred to think of him as a professional associate rather than a student, for he was a better scientist as an undergraduate student than many college professors."

Continues Professor Poulter, "As an undergraduate student in 1931 and 1932 he rendered invaluable assistance in the development and checking of instrumentation for use in the scientific program of the Second Byrd Antarctic Expedition of 1933–35, [Poulter was Chief Scientist on this expedition] and he took every opportunity to familiarize himself with the scientific equipment which was being assembled and tested in the Physics Department for use on the expedition.

"With this equipment Jim made a magnetic survey in the surrounding area, reoccupying magnetic stations previously established by the Coast and Geodetic Survey. In checking the equipment we had developed for meteor observations he made many observations during several meteor showers as well as cosmic ray measurements at ground level." Though Van Allen was not aware of any great influence at that time, this, perhaps, was when the first seed of his later interest in cosmic rays was sowed.

The cosmic rays have been space travelers since long before there were men to dream of such things. They shoot about at speeds nearly equaling that of light, usually above the earth's atmosphere. But a few rebel rays penetrate the reaches of instruments. However, most which enter the atmosphere soon become hybrids as they collide with atoms in the air and become secondary cosmic rays.

But what good are cosmic rays? When the English scientist, Michael Faraday, was asked what was the good of his pioneering work in the field of physics of electricity, he aptly replied to a member of Parliament, "I can't tell you what it will be good for. But I can tell you this: one of these days you'll be taxing it."[1] (Faraday was right—his discoveries led to machines which convert mechanical energy into electrical energy and, as such, are indirectly taxed!)

Though cosmic rays have yet to be taxed by Congress, they have generously supplied man with a good deal of scientific information. They have made possible the discovery of some of the basic building blocks of matter and have illustrated the interchange of energy between matter and radiation. On one hand, their tiny wave lengths make them useful as a "microscope," by studying their interaction with nuclei. Their scope also extends to the vastness of the universe, for they are messengers who receive their energies from the fields of force in the stars or deep spaces between.

Through the applications made by W. F. Libby, the usefulness of cosmic rays has spilled over into the areas of geology and archaeology also; they provide a timetable dating back 15,000 years for organic matter. Radioactive carbon, in the atmosphere through cosmic rays, is absorbed by every living organism. It has been determined that the decay rate of radioactive carbons decreases by a factor of 2 every 5570 years. So, therefore, an analysis of bones, wood, or any other remnant of living organism, can determine the amount of radioactive carbon yet remaining and establish a date when the organism ceased living.

Scientists often seem to play the role of the detectives of natural history, gathering fragments of evidence, piecing together scraps of seemingly unrelated stories, guessing and gambling on their own intuition, until another mystery gives way before their probing. Perhaps the playing of this highly developed game of seek-and-solve is related to Dr. James Van Allen's liking for the mysteries of that master of suspense, Alfred Hitchcock.

Though cosmic rays were identified around the turn of the century, it was not known whether they originated on the earth or came to the earth from the outside. Tests to analyze the elusive rays were so inconclusive and confusing that the first part of the answer did not come until 1911 and 1912. At this time V. F. Hess made courageous balloon ascents to 5000 meters, discovering that above 700 meters the ionization steadily increased with altitude; therefore, he concluded from his experiments that the rays were of cosmic origin. He also deduced that since the tests were the same during night or day, the rays did not come directly from the sun. Experiments conducted by the distinguished Dr. R. A. Millikan from 1922 to 1926 confirmed that the atmosphere absorbs but does not produce the primary cosmic radiation. Such girders of basic fact were erected. But they nakedly stood awaiting the fabrication of further research.

James Van Allen entered the State University of Iowa, seeking his Master's degree in physics. The title of his thesis would never find its way on to any theater marquee: "A Sensitive Apparatus for Determining Young's Modulus at Small Tensional Strains." Nor was this prospect heightened by the name attached to his doctoral dissertation: "Absolute Cross-Section for the Nuclear Disintegration $H^2 + H^2 \to H^1 + H^3$ and Its Dependence on Bombarding Energy."

These years from 1935 to 1939 spent at the University at Iowa City formed an association that was destined to bear fruit at a later period when he was summoned back to head the physics department. But upon completion of his graduate studies, Van Allen became a research fellow of the Department of Terrestrial Magnetism, Carnegie Institution in Washington, D. C.

With World War II the picture changed. With others of the Carnegie Institution—which was not set up to engage in large-scale war research —Van Allen was transferred to the research center which soon became the Applied Physics Laboratory of The Johns Hopkins University in Silver Spring, Maryland. Because of the pressing necessity, the complexion of activity changed. Here it became a matter of applying what was known— not discovering new things. The assignment at the Laboratory was to build a radio-proximity fuze. In lay terms, this meant in part that the delicate instrumentation of a radio transmitter and receiver had to be so designed as to withstand the shock of being fired out of large caliber guns.

In the almost jaded attitude the world has adopted today about scientific "miracles," this seems, perhaps, routine. But in 1942 the specifications for the proximity fuze were startling. Resourcefulness was demanded of the young physicist, and the lessons he learned in this project fell into place as another important element of his future activities; he learned how to get a tremendous amount of scientific instrumentation into a tiny space and to make it so rugged it would withstand unbelievable shock.

Here in this Laboratory where Van Allen matured as a scientist, there predominated an example of teamwork that is unique. As A. V. Gangnes, one of his fellow workers, recently recalled, "The project came first. If the best thing that a scientist could do at one given moment was to sweep the floor and allow the technicians to work, he swept the floor. A story is related about the time that one of our girl workers was wiring up a proximity fuze, and the Director of the Laboratory was peering over her shoulder. She finally said, 'You make me nervous. If you're going to stay around, at least go get me a Coke.' He got her the Coke. That seems a small incident, but it typified a whole attitude that prevailed."

Here, working days were long. Van Allen finally decided it was hardly worth the effort to drive to his lodgings and found a couch in one of the lounge rooms. A few snatched hours provided the only rest for many nights. This, also, is the simple explanation to a comment passed by a friend, "Van's clothes sometimes looked a little slept in."

In 1942 he was commissioned as Lieutenant, Junior Grade, and went out to take the fuze to the fleet. His roving assignment took him into the Pacific area twice, where he taught gunnery officers how to use the fuze that the research teams had developed. The device, which was used in antiaircraft and shore bombardment, was considered by many to be the Navy's most important World War II achievement. As a Lieutenant Commander in the reserve, he went on inactive status at the end of hostilities and returned to the Laboratory.

Working there had brought him an unexpected and rich reward in meeting one of the mathematicians at the Laboratory, Abigail Fithian Halsey II. She had "bumped into him"—quite literally—when her car accidentally had backed into his. They awaited only his return from service to be married; the wedding took place in the fall of 1945 in Southampton, New York.

Abbie had grown up in the stimulating surrounding of a home where "men of thought" were frequent visitors. Her father, the Reverend Jesse Halsey, was the minister of the Seventh Presbyterian Church of Cincinnati; Abbie recalls with pleasure that among the guests in their home were novelist Thomas Mann and the Labrador missionary-doctor-explorer, Sir Wilfred Grenfell—who once remained with them for two weeks.

With this rich background, she became a remarkable counterpart for Van. They share some of the same values—high respect for intellectual achievement, a straightforward attitude toward life, and a dislike for any sham or showmanship. Despite a heavy schedule, they are rarely too busy to be thoughtful of others. When members of Van's staff were away on assignments, Van and Abbie were attentive to the lonely wives. Mrs. James Jenkins recalls how they took her with them to hear a folk-music concert of Burl Ives one evening when her husband was away, and how Abbie would volunteer to go shopping for the women who did not have automobiles.

Abbie is very much a "doer." Mrs. A. V. Gangnes relates that one day Abbie called Van at the office to ask where he kept his saw. He returned home that evening to find that she had transformed a large davenport into a two-piece sectional! She then proceeded to make slip covers for it.

Major General (then Colonel) Holger N. Toftoy had been the U.S. Army officer who instigated and directed the transfer of 127 of Germany's top rocket experts to the United States following V-E Day. He also ordered the capture and shipment of 100 V-2 rockets to White Sands Proving Ground.

Then as Chief of the Rocket Branch of the Army Research and Development Division, he started making plans for effective utilization of the captured missiles. Intricate details were worked out for testing—such as painting the rockets in a black-and-white pattern so that it could be determined if spin occurred during the first twenty seconds of flight. This General, ever the man of vision, established the policy of reserving space in the rockets for scientific instrumentation; he wished thereby to expand the scope of the tests beyond military purposes.

Toftoy asked the director of the Applied Physics Laboratory, Dr. Merle A. Truve, to assign some outstanding young scientist to the program. This proposed project of high-altitude research in which other groups were also participating had pitfalls. There were no precedents to go by, for no one had ever before used rockets for such a purpose—balloons had been the vehicles to float instruments 80,000 feet into the upper atmosphere to measure cosmic rays. The questions compounded as deliberation continued —what would the full extent of the difficulty be when instruments were shot 100 miles high in the nose of a V-2? Van Allen was assigned the job of finding out. He started the new year of 1946 with the conviction that important results could be accomplished from the proposed work at White Sands Proving Ground in New Mexico—though it meant periods of separation from Abbie, so soon after his return from World War II.

Scientists fall into many general divisions. There are men who can follow the instructions laid down by others; there are those who write the instructions from findings. Another group produces the findings through accepted methods of research. Yet, when traced back to its root, there is that basic species of scientist still, who can view the gigantic pile of stone called ignorance and plot an attack upon it. He says to himself, "I'm searching for one pebble within that pile. I don't know what it represents, I won't necessarily recognize it when I hold it in my hand. Yet, categorically, I know it exists. Therefore, with all of the skill I have acquired in the classroom, with all of the intuition developed in research laboratories, I will begin the immense task, hopeful of results, yet not discouraged if—after sorting through all of the 10,000 stones—I have not found the right pebble."

It is apparent that such an undertaking involves more than basic education and specialized knowledge. An underlying philosophy must motivate the scientific pioneer; he performs the work for its own sake—not for the reward of acclaim. (How often, when acclaim comes, it has proved a source of distraction and embarrassment to the personality so geared.)

James Van Allen is such a scientist. Quiet, yet not introverted, studious without being pedantic, modest regarding his own talents, yet confident of the results of serious application, he is always driving toward a definite objective, while being outwardly easygoing. And, as all of these qualities might indicate, he has a simple appearing personality that proves upon inspection to be enormously complex.

Says Dr. James Jenkins, who long worked with Van Allen at the Applied Physics Laboratory, "Van's real contribution was one of seeing what experiments should be done to expand knowledge of a given subject, next carrying out the experiments, then coming up with an explanation about what the phenomena represent." This was the triple-barreled assignment that the thirty-one-year-old Iowa physicist accepted when he embarked on the experiments with the V-2s.

Van Allen was not alone in this endeavor—there were others invited to participate. It was big news that V-2 rockets were being launched, and that in the nose-cone of each there was space for instruments! The scientific community seems to have a way of passing along news at a speed so rapid that there would seem danger of a disassociation of particles! The flood of scientific interest started, equivalent to the forty-niner gold rush in the quest for domain.

Toftoy had thought the war was over, but suddenly he was besieged with a force so mighty an immediate counteroffensive was required. He reacted with military acumen by summoning Van Allen, outlining the problem, laying it in his lap to organize a screening process—then taking the sting out of the assignment by flashing one of his encouraging "you can do it" smiles at the befuddled scientist.

The V-2 Rocket Panel was formed. (It has since been known as the Upper Atmosphere Rocket Research Panel, then made another name change to its present designation, the Rocket and Satellite Research Panel.) Van Allen served as chairman from 1947 to 1958; he is currently a member of the executive committee.

This placed the scientist in the position of utilizing to its full extent one of his unique qualities, which is characterized by a phrase often heard from him in conferences: "Don't you think that . . . ?" It further manifests itself, say colleagues, by his tossing out an idea, allowing it to develop under someone else's thinking—then giving full credit to the man who evolved it.

Those who worked under his direction at the Applied Physics Laboratory testify to this generous quality. Says Gangnes, "The cosmic ray experiments there were principally his own ideas, drawing upon the experience of his previous work. The part I played was in designing the instruments, testing, reducing data; all I'd do was put down the facts. Then Van rewrote three papers, put them into polished form for the American Physical Society, and gave me credit as coauthor." Such an approach enlisted complete support from his "team."

The very great value of Toftoy's suggestion to utilize rockets for upper-atmosphere research intrigued Dr. Truve and Dr. Henry H. Porter of the Laboratory so that they started planning a follow-up program almost before the V-2 testing had begun. They requested that Van Allen undertake a survey to determine where they could secure additional rockets for use after the V-2s had all been launched; he set out to find which company in the United States could deliver a rocket capable of high performance yet modestly priced. The Jet Propulsion Laboratory of the California Institute of Technology had already developed such a vehicle in the WAC Corporal; however, in the firings of 1945, its pay load capability had been ten pounds and this was far short of the specifications decided upon by the Applied Physics Laboratory for its new project.

After months of considering various possibilities, a contract was concluded for the delivery of twenty 2600-pound-thrust rockets, capable of carrying 150 pounds of instrument pay load to an altitude of 300,000 feet. Taking the first syllable from the name of the manufacturer, Aerojet Engineering Corporation, and the second syllable from the Bumblebee family of missiles developed at the Applied Physics Laboratory, Van Allen coined the name for the new rocket—Aerobee!

Technical direction was delegated to Van Allen. He encountered only one serious hitch—Lieutenant Colonel H. R. Turner, USA, commander of the White Sands Proving Ground, stopped construction of the launching tower for the Aerobee because of concern over the safety factor in launching unguided missiles. Van Allen solved the problem by designing a tiltable tower that could compensate for the winds and by installing a radio command in the rocket which could cut off its fuel supply should the rocket deviate from its plotted trajectory. The program then proceeded to the first launch on November 23, 1947, and continued through 171 rocket firings over a ten-year period. Projects undertaken included investigating and measuring solar radiation, sky brightness, atmospheric composition, and many other factors including airglow—those mysterious patches of light that move across the heavens at night but are invisible without the use of new instruments. In gathering research data, Aerobees were launched not only from White Sands Proving Ground but also from a Navy ship which roamed the waters from the magnetic equator near Peru up to the Gulf of Alaska.

Mrs. Van Allen recalls visits of many distinguished individuals who have come into their home, and says, "When they are in an atmosphere which brings out the free play of intellectuality, it is thrilling to listen to the ideas that are developed." On April 5, 1950, one such evening led to far-reaching consequences.

Dr. Sydney Chapman (the former Oxford University professor now at the High Altitude Observatory, Boulder, Colorado), who is regarded as the world's foremost geophysicist, was in Washington, D. C. at the time. He mentioned to his friend, Van Allen, that he would enjoy visiting with other men of his field. A small dinner was arranged, and out of what Van Allen terms a "postprandial discussion" the idea for the International Geophysical Year emerged!

Among those present were Dr. S. F. Singer, an imaginative young physicist, then at the Applied Physics Laboratory, and Mr. Lloyd Berkner, associated with the State Department in the organization and direction of the first military assistance program of the North Atlantic Pact. He had authored the report *Science and Foreign Relations*.

As the several viewpoints to the progress and problems of their field were projected, one thing became most clear—one of the greatest voids of the entire effort was that of co-operation and communication between scientists. Great new instruments had evolved out of World War II to aid in research—radar, rockets, improved types of spectroscopes, computers— but their potential was being diluted by the isolated manner in which scientists of various countries worked, too often repeating or duplicating experiments. Moreover, there needed to be direction and purpose to the over-all approach.

Mr. Berkner had been on the first Antarctic Expedition with Admiral Byrd and was well aware of the value derived from the International Polar Years in 1882 and 1932; also, his work with the State Department emphasized in his mind the international aspect of science. He, therefore, put forth the suggestion for a Third Polar Year.

As they say in show business, the suggestion was an overnight hit! Furthermore, everybody wanted to "get in on the act." The farther the thought spread, the more momentum it gained. The benefits to be reaped scientifically from such an endeavor were obvious. Perhaps, also, in the mind of most of the advocates was the thought that the greatest lack in the world today, which contributes to dividing peoples, is that of understanding and co-operation. If such an example as the Third Polar Year could be established, would it not demonstrate that a unity of interests could surmount selfish divisions? From the outset, the factors that could have destroyed the IGY concept—political considerations—were assiduously avoided.

Mr. Berkner presented the plan three months later in Brussels at the Mixed Commission on the Ionosphere, and a date was decided upon for the beginning of the eighteen month "year." July 1, 1957 was chosen because this would place it in a period of peak sunspot activity and also include a time during which there would be several eclipses. In addition, the date would mark the twenty-fifth anniversary of the Second Polar Year, though soon it was pointed out that the emphasis should not be placed on research in the polar regions; therefore, Dr. Chapman—who was elected president of the Special Committee to organize the effort—proposed that the broader name, International Geophysical Year, be adopted. Thus expanded, a later conference in Rome pointed out that improved technology had now brought two primary regions within our reach—the Antarctic and outer space—and proposed that they be widely explored.

There was great discussion about plans to launch an earth satellite—an idea long advanced by some farsighted United States scientists. Van Allen had actively campaigned for a satellite as early as 1948 when his paper, relating some of the benefits that could accrue from such a project, was read before the meeting of the International Union of Geodesy and Geophysics in Oslo.

Yet, as the extensive IGY planning got underway in 1954, no satellite was scheduled. But much consideration was being given to upper-atmosphere research—a natural follow-up, considering the locale of the IGY's inception. A schedule was worked out for World Days—three days per month during which all participating nations would be occupied with concentrated observation in the several scientific fields. Other vital co-operative ventures were worked out before the beginning of the IGY, such as the establishing of World Data Centers—three areas which would each house a total set of all IGY data, one center being located in the United States, one in Russia, and the third being divided among western Europe, Australia, and Japan.

Unbounding effort and consummate skill were employed by thousands of dedicated scientists to bring the IGY to fulfillment; Dr. Chapman terms it "the greatest example of world-wide scientific co-operation in the history of our race."[2] During this period of the IGY's maturing, there were some marked advancements in the field of upper-atmosphere research at the hands of Van Allen.

In 1951 the State University of Iowa had a post to be filled—that of head of the physics department. An invitation was extended to one of their most distinguished graduates, Van Allen. This position offered dual opportunities for which he was grateful—the chance to return to his home state, where his mother and two of his brothers live, and the chance to combine teaching with further research efforts. He accepted.

A confusing picture must have existed in the minds of those students who enrolled in his classes as they awaited the chance to become acquainted with the new professor. They pictured him as a remote figure, importantly involved in the nation's capital with vital research and mingling with the outstanding scientists of the world. Yet, the older folks around Iowa who had known studious Jimmy Van Allen since boyhood, wagered that he'd still go around home barefoot on warm summer evenings. In a sense, each conjecture proved true, for Van Allen is a casual, simple-appearing man who is actually a very complex individual, as stated before.

A most important consideration affecting his decision to move back to Iowa was the fact that he prefers to work with a small, independent group rather than with large-scale operations where too much time is consumed writing reports and "going through channels"—even though the latter has the decided advantage of more substantial financial support. However, relative to this point, Van Allen has made an outstanding name for himself for "getting the most for the least." Thus, he has gained a very favorable reputation among appropriation committees and other administrative officials, who have learned to expect that moneys invested in his experiments will return an unusually high proportion of results.

Van Allen displayed this ability when, at a cost of about five per cent of the investment in the Aerobee, he evolved the Rockoon, which combined both the names and benefits of the rocket and the balloon. The late Navy balloonist, Lieutenant Commander M. Lee Lewis, had been the inspiration for this idea when, as he watched Aerobees being shot, had asked in effect, "Why not carry a rocket aloft through the friction-producing layers of the lower atmosphere on a balloon—give it a headstart on its climb?" His theory proved sound, for though the rockets Van Allen used were relatively small ones, by being launched from an altitude of about fifteen miles, they would climb an additional fifty to seventy miles on their fact-finding journeys into the fringes of space.

But to have launched Rockoons from the University campus would have been something like practicing on a trombone in a hospital ward— it just wasn't the place. The Coast Guard came to the rescue by providing transportation to the waters off Greenland and Newfoundland. Thus cosmic rays could be studied in the high altitudes and latitudes before they were deflected or absorbed by the atmosphere.

Van Allen and groups from the University laboratory spent the summers of 1952 and 1953 aboard the naval vessels, endeavoring to develop a profile of cosmic-ray intensities. The readings from their Geiger counters and ionization chambers were just as they had anticipated, until the data interpretation from two rockets lofted in 1953 posed a puzzle: Dr. Melvin Gottleib, assistant professor of physics, and graduate student Leslie Meredith, encountered particles thirty miles above the waters off Newfoundland that had far greater intensity than they had expected. A quick check of instruments indicated that this was no error—they had unquestionably come upon some new condition.

Rockets fired either north or south of the area had reported back the expected count. But, here in this auroral zone, greater activity seemed to be centered. This was not coincidence the investigators of the upper atmosphere deduced; it was perhaps circumstantial evidence that this high count and the aurora were linked. Van Allen's mother had often smiled as she saw her son gazing into the heavens and asked, "Are you so curious about what nature is hiding up there, Jimmy?" He was. Now, as a respected professor of physics, he still evinced much of the little-boy spirit of wonderment. He must rip through the hazy veil and learn what was happening high above in space! But the designation of a feminine gender to nature has not been without logic—she is perverse, perplexing, preternatural, and chooses to relinquish her secrets in the piecemeal fashion of a fickle woman. The scientific group was not yet to learn the significance of their findings.

Research.

What a misleadingly simple, dry word it is. To the men approving budgets, it is a little area to nip at when cuts must be made. To the citizen whose money is being spent, it is a pretty nebulous field. Anyone engaged in research can testify that it is a hard commodity to "sell." Yet, to curtail it is like shutting off the flow of fresh water into a pool; stagnation is inevitable. In his urging for more funding of research programs, Van Allen has made the bold estimate that ten times the investment might increase results a hundredfold. But, remembering such experiences as Faraday had, he recognizes that the question of immediate, practical application will always recur. One of the wisest replies was voiced by Benjamin Franklin as he watched an early balloon ascent and a skeptic asked, "What is the use of this new invention?" The sage countered with: "What is the use of a new-born child?"[3]

In 1955 the weight of proof and the urging of scientists finally gained governmental approval of an earth-satellite program under the IGY. This was encouraging news indeed! As chairman, Van Allen called a symposium of the Rocket and Satellite Research Panel in January, 1956. The problem was complex: how best to make the satellite "pay off," considering the restrictions they faced. (For instance, a nearly polar orbit which they desired for the investigation of auroral radiation was not technically feasible at that time.)

The advantages of a satellite for research purposes were numerous and exciting. As opposed to a rocket, a satellite would be a kind of "long-playing record"; the extended time duration above the atmosphere would obviously provide more extensive and more accurate data. Further, there could be widespread geographical coverage with the circling of a satellite.

As chairman of the Working Group on Internal Instrumentation of the Technical Panel on Earth Satellite Program of the IGY, Van Allen had the responsibility of directing the review and evaluation of the many proposals submitted. It became a zealously sought privilege to get instruments aboard the United States first earth satellite, and the competition was keen among the various scientific bodies.

When the first IGY conference on satellites was called in Barcelona in August, 1956, a vital matter of co-operation was on the agenda. Van Allen met with Dr. I. P. Bardin and other members of the Soviet delegation to work out items of mutual advantage, such as broadcasting the radio signals from satellites on standard frequencies which could be picked up by tracking stations throughout the world.

The IGY members did a remarkable job of keeping "politics" out of their discussions and considerations. Except for the incident of irreconcilable conflict between the Chinese Nationalists and the Chinese People's Republic, there was an objective approach to the IGY that did much to fulfil the concept of those who initiated it. It therefore becomes somewhat ironic that, in Van Allen's estimation, the United States' effort was greatly impeded by what he termed "armed service rivalries."

Ernst Stuhlinger, of the Army Ballistic Missile Research Center of Huntsville, Alabama, one of the most brilliant members of Dr. Wernher von Braun's team, visited the University in Iowa in November, 1956, enlisting Van Allen's support for the Jupiter-C rocket. The governmental green light had been given to the long-range development of the Navy's Vanguard, while the Huntsville team already had a vehicle which they said could orbit a satellite. To verify this contention, the Army pointed to the first test flight of the Jupiter-C on September 20, 1956, during which it traveled a record 3100 miles, reaching an altitude of 682 miles.

Van Allen, deeply concerned, made a thorough study of the situation and concluded that the IGY satellite should be placed on the Jupiter-C rocket; he sent telegrams to members of the Technical Panel on Earth Satellite Program, IGY, requesting that they also urge the shift. But the Vanguard remained, at that time, the rocket designated to loft the satellite. Van

Allen proceeded, using the precaution of making his package of such dimensions that it would fit into the Jupiter-C nose-cone—just in case.

The fabrication of America's first satellite instrumentation package was undertaken by Van Allen and his group of graduate students in a basement area of the University. Here, on wooden benches lining a hallway and with comparatively simple facilities, the creation of miniaturized instruments was begun by George Ludwig, under Van Allen's direction. The components had to meet unbelievable standards of reliability; anyone who has ever worked with Van Allen can testify that he is a "stickler for testing." The package had to undergo the violent, shattering shock of the rocket launching, then function from distances never before required under conditions for which there was no parallel. The assignment was extremely difficult and was compounded by the knowledge that United States scientific prestige would hinge on the performance of those instruments. This was not just equipment they were putting together—they were molding an object destined to make history. For a year, Ludwig labored on the preliminary design and testing. He slaved to trim slivers of size and grams of weight off the intricate instrumentation, to meet the six-inch dimension and twenty-pound limit. From 1954 to 1958, a fivefold reduction in the once suggested size of instrumentation was achieved. As Van Allen said, "Two recent developments have made the earth satellite possible of achievements: one is improvement in jet-propelled engines; the other, development in the electronic art. Electronic equipment is necessary to take scientific advantage of a satellite in orbit. Transistors, high-energy-content chemical batteries, and other components have arrived, technologically speaking, just in time." At last they completed the package; it awaited the completion of the rocket which would endeavor to launch it into orbit.

As part of Van Allen's participation in the IGY, he boarded the *U.S.S. Plymouth Rock* for study of cosmic rays, aurora, and the geomagnetic field in the northern polar regions. There a remarkable incident occurred, so against chance-odds that it would require a super-computer to even figure the variables, Van Allen and his graduate student assistant Laurence Cahill, launched a Rockoon near Greenland. They noted the results and regarded it as a routine experiment until somewhat later when they received an excited message from Dr. Kinsey Anderson, a member of the University faculty, telling the rest of the story. First, the balloon had remained intact after the rocket's firing—this in itself was an unusual happening. Second, the balloon had drifted 2000 miles. Third, it had landed at Fort Churchill, an IGY base on Hudson Bay, within 200 feet of Anderson and his party as they returned to their camp in the early dawn hours after a balloon launch of their own!

The group which Van Allen soon built up after taking over the physics department of the University gained world-wide stature in its research and experimentation. Dr. Ernest C. Ray, an assistant professor, helped to co-ordinate theory and experiment. Dr. Frank McDonald, another assistant professor, utilized giant Skyhook balloons to carry heavy apparatus into the higher altitudes, launching them from Iowa, Texas, Minnesota, and the island of Guam; his findings from this research verified the theory that protons, or hydrogen nuclei, are the principal component of primary cosmic rays. A young graduate student who performed unusual work during his studies at Iowa was Carl McIlwain; when he was only twenty-six he had acquired more data about the auroral particles than any other person, according to Van Allen. Ludwig, Cahill, and McIlwain were each working toward their doctoral degrees in doing this research.

On October 4, 1957, Van Allen and Cahill were aboard the *U.S.S. Glacier* in the South Pacific on their way to the Antarctic when the momentous news of Sputnik I was blared over the ship's radio. Great excitement prevailed, and Van Allen persuaded the ship's radio operator to monitor the satellite's transmitter. As he listened to the "beep-beep" of the Soviet accomplishment orbiting in the skies above, it seemed a great pity that the United States, which he thought could have performed the feat first, had failed to do so.

As the *Glacier* continued its voyage south, top government officials were spurred into a flurry of activity by the satellite. Von Braun repeated his oft-voiced promise that the Jupiter-C could put a United States satellite into orbit—and this time it fell on receptive ears. Dr. William Pickering, director of the California Institute of Technology's Jet Propulsion Laboratory in Pasadena, had been in a state of semireadiness for some months to complete his portion of the responsibility—which was to furnish the upper stages for the Jupiter-C rocket. When the shift came, Pickering needed Van Allen's immediate approval to transfer his pay load of instruments from the Vanguard Project to the Jupiter-C. He contacted the Navy and the Coast Guard to try to locate the Iowa professor. After some attempts, they reported back that they were unable to make contact with the party. In desperation, on October 29th, Pickering dictated the following message to Western Union: "Dr. James A. Van Allen, *USS Glacier,* South Pacific. Would you approve a transfer of your experiment to us with two copies in spring. Please advise immediately. W. H. Pickering." It was only a vague hope that the cable would be delivered, for he could tell them only that the *U.S.S. Glacier* had left New Zealand ten days before, heading south. But two days later, the staff in Pasadena was jubilant when a return cable was received from Van Allen. (Western Union must surely have enlisted the aid of a few alert penguins to track him down!) Pickering's request had been so cryptic, due to the great secrecy surrounding this high level change, that Van Allen replied, "Unable interpret your work transfer due ignorance recent developments." But he had complete faith in his colleague from Pasadena, so he gave Pickering full—though blind—authorization.

George Ludwig, who had his bag packed within thirty minutes after hearing the news, went to Pasadena to prepare his precious unit for its new housing. The Jupiter-C would carry a slightly different pay load, so the process of repackaging the equipment was started. One eight-ounce sacrifice that really hurt him was having to remove the two-and-a-half-inch tape recorder. Ludwig and the physics department's skilled instrument makers had spent almost a year masterfully creating this tiny machine. It had the fabulous capability of storing as much as two hours of space data, then "reading out" the information during a five-second period on command from an observing station. But the device could not be carried aboard this time; the information which the satellite was gathering would have to be broadcast continuously, not stored up.

On January 31, 1958, Explorer I was launched! With that event, America had three new national heroes—von Braun, Pickering, and Van Allen. Their unusual skill and teamwork had enabled the United States to orbit its first satellite.

To most people, that told the story. To Van Allen, it was merely the preface. Next came the real purpose for all of his effort—a close view of space! The little satellite was hungrily gathering information as it streaked through the heavens and faithfully sending it down to the eager crew at the University. The Geiger tube was reporting a count of about thirty cosmic rays per second when the satellite was near the earth. But in its elliptical orbit as it swung into altitudes above 600 miles, the count sharply increased to about 140 counts per second. Then a mystery occurred—as the satellite continued its climb no count was reported!

The information was too fragmentary—they would have to await further data before any analysis could be made. Explorer II failed to orbit. Then Explorer III deluged them with equally confusing information. Said Van Allen, "One day, as we were puzzling over the first tapes from Explorer III, McIlwain suggested the first plausible explanation for their peculiar readings. He had just been calibrating his rocket instruments and called our attention to something that we all knew but had temporarily forgotten: A sufficiently high level of radiation can jam the counter and send the apparent counting rate to zero. We had discovered an enormously high level of radiation, not a lack of it. As Ernest Ray, a member of our group, inaccurately but graphically exclaimed, 'Space is radioactive!' "[4] This was the first message from space, and it was a deadly one! No man could survive long exposure to such high-intensity radiation without enormous shielding.

But there was urgent need for more elaborate reporting on the exact nature of the condition. With deftness born of experience in the ways of Washington, D. C., Van Allen managed to secure support for additional research, as an adjunct to the IGY. A period of furious work at the University laboratory produced an instrument package which included a small tube hooked into a circuit which would scale down the count by a large factor, a Geiger tube shielded with a millimeter of lead, a plastic scintillator and photomultiplier tube, and a basic Geiger tube for "simple-minded" detection, as Van Allen said. Explorer IV carried these instruments nearly 1000 information-reporting orbits around the earth. This time it was not the counters that were swamped—it was the Van Allen crew! Like the "Sorcerer's Apprentice," they could not stop the volume of data with which they were being flooded—relayed from ground stations ringing the earth: Quito, Woomera, Singapore, Heidelberg, and others.

The radiation belt was confirmed, but Explorer IV had penetrated only the lower portion of it. What was above?

Extrapolated from the ocean of data, the formation of the trapped particles began to take shape: The contour follows the shape of the earth around the equator but, approaching the northern and southern latitudes, the belt swings upward, downward, then sharply upward again, forming a claw that reaches toward the earth near the auroral zones. This was bearing out a theory first projected fifty years before by the distinguished Norwegian physicist, Carl Störmer, that the earth's magnetic field might trap charged particles.

Only hypothetical thinking could extend it beyond the altitudes reached by the Explorer satellites. In seminars and at lunch-time discussions, Van Allen and his crew projected two diagrams: a doughnut-shaped belt with ridges around the edges (at the poles); or two distinct belts, with the outer one curving down at the poles to almost encase the lower belt. The single belt was the simpler explanation and was the one the majority of the group chose, though they saw logic in the stalwart belief of McIlwain that there were two belts. The answer could come only with another, more extensive, experiment. This came aboard the moon shot, Pioneer III. There are two belts! The inner one reaches its peak of radiation at about 2000 miles from the earth, the outer one at around 10,000 miles.

What puts the radiation there? Explains Van Allen regarding the outer zone: "Most of us believe that this great reservoir of particles originates largely in the sun. The particles are somehow injected into the earth's magnetic field, where they are deflected into corkscrew trajectories around lines of force and trapped. In this theoretical scheme the radiation belts resemble a sort of leaky bucket, constantly refilled from the sun and draining away into the atmosphere. A particularly large influx of solar particles causes the bucket to 'slop over,' mainly in the auroral zone, generating visible auroras, magnetic storms, and related disturbances."[4]

A theory of the origin of the inner zone is proposed by Nicolas Christofilos of the University of California Radiation Laboratory and by S. N. Vernov, the Soviet physicist: They contend that the neutrons which are released in large number in the earth's upper atmosphere by cosmic rays travel through the magnetic field without deflection; some decay into electrons and protons which are trapped.

Which of the theories will prove to be correct? Or, since neither one explains why there are two belts, will yet another emerge before the mystery is solved? Part of the enormous fascination of science is that it resembles a never ending "cliff hanger"—each solution poses another question!

A stream of long-distance telephone calls and the volume of his daily mail bespeak of the present pressure which has built up around Van Allen. There is constant demand for his expert consultation to solve problems which have been encountered by the military planners in the Pentagon or those of the civilian space agency, the National Aeronautics and Space Administration.

Cape Canaveral, the Jet Propulsion Laboratory in Pasadena, or any other vital installation may summon him for a conference—biting big chunks out of his tightly scheduled time. This causes him to operate on such a split-second schedule that recently when his brother, William, appeared at the Iowa City Airport, the girl at the airline ticket counter exclaimed, "Oh, no—not another Van Allen! I can't stand the nervous strain!"

When James Van Allen attended a White House dinner in February, 1958, which brought together the military and scientific leaders who figured importantly in the launching of Explorer I, Abbie went with him; but such occasions are the exception. Usually, she and the children—who now number five—understandingly stay at home, accepting the demands made upon him, the inevitable obligations of eminence.

During the IGY, space science advanced more than in the centuries since Galileo and Copernicus. Of all the contributions that were made to the great world-wide effort, the identification of the two radiation belts has been deemed the major scientific discovery of the IGY. In September, 1958, at an international meeting in Geneva, the professor from Iowa heard the name of Van Allen Radiation Belts applied to his discovery. Though he appreciated the honor, he would have preferred to share credit with all who contributed to the effort. To have the radiation belts so named does serve as a rightful symbol of his leadership!

He stands with other leaders who are making scientific reaches into the realm of imagination. As the world watches, asking in a spirit of wonderment, "What next?" the scientists are quietly occupied with transforming fantasy into reality. They are working in

> "This narrow isthmus 'twixt two boundless seas,
> The past, the future,—two eternities!"[5]

REFERENCES

1. Van Allen, James: *Why Probe "Invisible Rains" in Space?*, United Press Features, April, 1958.
2. Sullivan, Walter: The International Geophysical Year, *International Conciliation,* no. 521, January, 1959.
3. Bartlett, John: *Familiar Quotations,* pp. 868 (Parton, James: *The Life and Times of Benjamin Franklin,* vol. 2, pp. 514–515, 1864), Boston, Little, Brown, 1938.
4. *Scientific American,* 200:39–47, March, 1959.
5. Bartlett, John: *Familiar Quotations,* pp. 337 (Moore, Thomas: "Lalla Rookh. The Veiled Prophet of Khorassan," Part 1), Boston, Little, Brown, 1938.

Dynamic long-time advocate of space
flight and designer of the rocket
which placed America's first
satellite into orbit

WERNHER VON BRAUN

The story of Wernher von Braun is a true story. It has to be. It is too improbable to be accepted as fiction. Witness the following events:

On March 15, 1944, he was arrested by the Gestapo and charged with treason—this was while he was directing the V-2 project, Germany's last frantic hope of reversing the tide of battle at the end of World War II. . . .

In August, 1949, England, the country which was devastated by 1100 of the V-2s, extended to von Braun one of the highest tributes to be given a man in his field—he was invited to become an Honorary Fellow of the British Interplanetary Society. . . .

In the last part of September, 1945, this German scientist arrived in the United States and crossed the country, "escorted" by a U.S. Army major; he traveled incognito during this train trip, for the brief time since V-E Day had not allowed emotions to cool from their war-time fever. . . .

Yet, on January 31, 1958, Americans everywhere erupted in a demonstration of wild exuberance, and von Braun was their hero—he had been largely responsible for the successful orbiting of the United States' first satellite, Explorer I.

These are a few of the startling contrasts experienced by this German of noble birth, whose father's position as Minister of Agriculture imposed no earth-bound fetters on him. His life has been consumed with a dedication to space travel, which he expressed in these words: "Everything in space obeys the laws of physics. If you know these laws, and obey them, space will treat you kindly. And don't tell me man doesn't belong out there. Man belongs wherever he wants to go—and he'll do plenty well when he gets there."[1]

Governments have changed. Attitudes have changed. The world has undergone a drastic upheaval in countless respects. But Wernher von Braun has not changed. With the forcefulness born of absolute conviction, this vital man has crusaded for advancements in space since he was a youth. When Americans first came to know his name, they regarded him as an unrealistic dreamer who belonged in the realm of science fiction. Gradually they listened to his ever present talk of space stations, of shipyards in space, of round-trip journeys to Mars which would last two years and 239 days, and little by little it all sounded less fanciful. At last the day came when this was accepted fact and von Braun was the missionary who had led their conversion. Through it all, he had never wavered; it was the public consciousness that had readjusted.

It is unique that any man can possess the qualities of a super space-salesman and also gain the highest respect from his scientific colleagues. He can discuss space at a church supper or at an astronautical congress with equal facility—and he is sure to be occupied with this topic whichever the gathering.

In the matter of the direction of his efforts, here again he has been constant in his views, and conditions around him have evolved. In Germany, circumstances led him into work on military rockets; under Army auspices, his work in this country has followed the same pattern—until 1960 when he and his team were removed from the military and placed under the civilian space agency. At last, von Braun's dream, to concentrate on the use of space for exploration and advancement, has materialized. It was never of his choosing that his talents be directed toward weapons of war. Yet he asks, "Do you think scientists should be blamed for wars? Einstein? He looked for fundamental truths, and his formula was used for an atomic bomb. Alexander Graham Bell? Military orders that kill thousands are transmitted over his telephone. . . . Any real scientist ends up a religious man. The more he learns about natural science the more he sees that the words that sound deep are really poorly contrived disguises for ignorance. Energy? Matter? We use them, but we don't really know what they are. Or take the mystery of heredity. It will never be solved. . . . None of us have anything to do with the most fateful event of our lives—picking our parents."[2]

The parents of Wernher von Braun were snatched out of the Russian-dominated area by cloak and dagger methods after the end of World War II. Deeply moved by this remarkable feat, Wernher and his brother wrote these words to the U.S. Army Colonel, James P. Hamill, who instigated the event:

"Having received the message that our parents entered Landshut, we want to express thanks for the help you gave us in this matter. A bitter grief has been taken from us by this news.

"We consider your aid in this really arduous task of getting our parents out of Poland a new proof of your sympathy also for our private needs.

"Considering the very difficult situation that most members of our group have to face, this humane interest of yours in our private worries is certainly an essential factor in our joint efforts towards the common goal. Yours faithfully, (signed) Wernher von Braun and Magnus von Braun."

The Baron and Baroness Magnus Freiherr von Braun reared three sons on the ancestral family estate in Silesia. This dignified atmosphere of tradition inspired the second son, Wernher, to an appreciation of music and to the serious study of languages. Yet he failed to respond to some of the school's curricula and disturbed his father with poor marks in mathematics. Only a more challenging approach was needed. In another school he emerged such an outstanding math student that he aided the instructor by teaching an advanced class.

The Baroness, a truly exceptional lady, was an amateur astronomer, and her encouragement aided her son's bent toward the heavens. "For my confirmation," says Wernher von Braun, "I didn't get a watch and my first pair of long pants, like most Lutheran boys. I got a telescope. My mother thought it would make the best gift."[1]

Through this hobby, he happened upon an article in an astronomy magazine that crystallized the pattern his life should take. He relates, "I don't remember the name of the magazine or the author, but the article described an imaginary trip to the moon." "It filled me with a romantic urge. Interplanetary travel! Here was a task worth dedicating one's life to! Not just to stare through a telescope at the moon and the planets but to soar through the heavens and actually explore the mysterious universe! I knew how Columbus had felt."[2]

The stimulus reached him through every sense! While still in high school he heard the names of Max Valier, Fritz von Opel and Friedrich W. Sander, and of their daring exploits with rocket cars! He beheld lengthy newspaper reports about a man named Dr. Robert H. Goddard in faraway America who talked of building a rocket for high altitude research. The very atmosphere of Germany of that era was charged with the interchange of data and speculation. Through this hub filtered reports from Russia, England, and the West.

But for all his verve, von Braun approached the matter of his education sanely. At eighteen he had completed high school with top honors. He determined to build his career on a thorough, down-to-earth foundation. He continued his schooling with lecture classes at the Charlottenburg Technical High School while working at an apprenticeship at a Berlin locomotive shop. Yet he couldn't be rail-bound; he had to grasp at stray tendrils reaching into the sky. So he went calling at the home of a man whose writings were causing quite a stir in scientific circles, Willy Ley.

Reminisces this famed historian of the rocket era, "One day in the fall of 1929 I came through my front door to hear Beethoven's 'Moonlight Sonata' being played on the piano. The musician was a visitor whom my aunt had admitted, a very polite young man who introduced himself as Wernher von Braun. He told me that he had just graduated from high school, intended to become an engineer, had heard of our experimenting in the VfR (*Verein für Raumschiffahrt,* which translates as the Society for Space Travel) of which I was one of the seven founding members. This young man concluded by saying he had read my book and wanted some advice. The first thing von Braun actually did was to assist on what I think was the first exhibit ever held on space travel in a department store in Berlin."

Through Ley's efforts, von Braun met Oberth. Here was a name to instill wonder in the hearts of any aspiring rocketeer! Hermann Oberth, author of *Wege zur Raumschiffahrt,* the textbook on space flight, crusader for travel into the universe! Wernher's spare time was spent working with this leader of German rocketry. Their dreams of the future removed from their activities any stigma of the commonplace, even though the contraption upon which they first concentrated consisted of a grocer's scale, a combustion chamber immersed in a pail of water, a gasoline tank, a small Dewar vessel for liquid oxygen, a bottle of compressed nitrogen, and some copper piping. They were convinced that these elemental experiments constituted the stepping stones into space.

Another assistant to Oberth was flamboyant World War I fighter pilot Rudolf Nebel, who possessed a gift for promoting. After Oberth had returned to his home town in Roumania, in the fall of 1930, Nebel went out in search of a base for the VfR's experiments and delighted the members with his results—he secured a 300 acre, overgrown ammunition dump on the outskirts of Berlin for a rental fee of four dollars a year! Proudly, the enthusiasts named the area *"Raketenflugplatz Berlin"* (Rocket Field Berlin).

What did it matter that weeds had almost claimed the area and that the bunkers were badly in need of repair? Here was a central point from which to launch ideas, where visionary plans could orbit in a sympathetic surrounding. The VfR members who were temporarily distressed found handy cots for lodging, and there was a supply of hearty food to keep stomachs as full as minds.

Away back in mid-1927, when the organization was less than a year old, it had acquired almost five hundred members. Among them were almost all the important scientists who had begun the probing of space, including such men as Professor Nickolai A. Rynin of Russia and Robert Esnault Pelterie of France. By the end of 1929, membership was nearing 1000. Now, in 1931, with the impetus of new quarters, expectations soared.

As solicitations from industry brought in donations of equipment and supplies, the spirited group earnestly set about conducting tests. Though somewhat less orderly than today's blockhouse routine, the VfR had its version of the "countdown," which consisted of "fire, gasoline, oxygen!" The experiments progressed with irregular success until that cold winter of 1931 when an egomaniac was making his appearance felt on the political scene of Germany.

Von Braun clearly recalls his father's warning that if Hitler would ever attain power in Germany the country was headed for disaster. But when youth is obsessed with a dream such as space flight, reality seems vague and far-off.

Nor did the group sense ominous overtones when, in the spring of 1932, three members of the German Army ordnance visited *Raketenflugplatz*— Colonel Karl Becker, Major von Horstig, and Captain Walter Dornberger, who later became commanding officer of Peenemünde Rocket Research Center. As von Braun recalls, "It is, perhaps, apropos to mention that at that time none of us thought of the havoc which rockets would eventually wreak as weapons of war. . . . To us Hitler was still only a pompous fool with a Charlie Chaplin mustache. We were very much in the position of aviation pioneers when the airplane could only be developed because of its military value. With considerable reluctance, we agreed that we could not ignore Colonel Becker's offer."[3]

The proposition to the young enthusiast was that if he were to study for a degree at the University of Berlin under physics professor, Erich Schumann, who also was in charge of the research section of the Ordnance Department, he would be allowed the use of the Army facilities at Kummersdorf for the experimental work necessary for his thesis. Von Braun accepted. On November 1, 1932, he became a civilian employee of the Army. (In 1934, he received his doctorate in physics from the University of Berlin.)

On the 30th of January, 1933, Hitler came to power. It is ironic that the VfR, the group which was banded together with such adhesiveness through their mutual vision of the future and operated so successfully on their base with promoted equipment and token rental fee, should finally have been vanquished by a ridiculous happenstance. During the years of occupancy by the *Raketenflugplatz,* faucets had been dripping in some of the unused buildings. Thus the organization which was founded with its eyes to the sky suffered defeat with a mundane water bill that was astronomical only in its size.

Another oversight influenced history. The drafters of the Treaty of Versailles omitted any reference to rockets when they carefully spelled out their restrictions on Germany to prevent rearming. Who among the dignified statesmen would have thought of consulting with the mad predictions of Jules Verne before preparing this momentous document? Yet this omission gave Germany the loophole through which it might fit the V-2.

The V-2 from the outset was planned as a very heavy and powerful rocket, for it was first conceived as an outgrowth of the destructive Paris gun of World War I. The specifications for the rocket were tremendous —seemingly impossible—in their demands. The range of the V-2 was to at least double that of the Paris gun, specifications calling for a 160-mile minimum. (Actually, subsequent production models averaged 190 miles!) Other detailed provisions stated it should carry a one-ton warhead, have a total weight of about twelve tons, and be capable of attaining a velocity of 3350 miles per hour. Compared with the tiny Mirak rocket with which the VfR members had experimented, this was indeed a tremendous project. But the indefatigable energy with which von Braun attacked the problem was not merely the momentum of enthusiasm nor simply the confidence that comes with not knowing "it can't be done." From the day the V-2 first took shape as a dream of 1936 until September of 1944 when the silent terror first exploded on British soil, a "miracle" had to occur. Though it was a team effort all the way, under the remarkable command of Dornberger, von Braun must be singled out for primary credit. (After that first shoot, he sadly commented, "It landed on the wrong planet.")

The first ingredient of this accomplishment was the utilization of the sum total of knowledge of rocketry to that date—knowledge which included the theories of Konstantin Tsiolkovsky which mushroomed into the tremendous achievements of Dr. Robert H. Goddard, who combined theory and application. Nor did von Braun have during these critical first years at Peenemünde the presence of the other gifted early rocket experimenter, Oberth; this Rumanian professor did not hold German citizenship, so had become entangled in the machinations of Nazi suspicions and military service rivalry. Therefore he was kept "on ice" (as he termed it), occupied with unimportant work for the *Luftwaffe.* Oberth was not transferred to Peenemünde until the fall of 1942, at which time the V-2 (then called the A-4) was already completed, tested, and ready for production.

Von Braun proved master of the task before him. He possessed the aptness literally to absorb knowledge; Colonel Hamill later made the observation that the mind of this rocketeer "operates like a blotter, literally soaking up technical information from any domain of the physical sciences, then comprehending and translating it into useful data."

Yet no rocket was ever constructed through the capacities of an IBM machine alone. A creative talent—one which has often been termed "genius" in the case of von Braun—was the catalyst to transform knowledge and dreams into hardware.

Another element which was granted to him cannot be overlooked: Support. This is indeed a vital factor in fostering development in a new field.

Bitterly America has realized its folly in not strongly supporting the efforts of Goddard. Though the grants of the Guggenheim Foundation, the Smithsonian Institution, and the Carnegie Institution enabled him to experiment on a limited scale, the potential of his work was slashed to a fraction by the financial restrictions under which he toiled.

When, in October, 1942, the mighty V-2 rose majestically in its first successful test firing, Dornberger was moved to comment, "Today the spaceship was born! But I warn you that our headaches are by no means over—they are just beginning!"[3]

How prophetic were his words!—for this was no spaceship to the desperate Nazi dictator. He placed the V-2, then still known as the A-4, on top priority and heaped impossible production demands on the crew at Peenemünde.

Plans for the bunkers from which the V-2s were to have been launched specified concrete roofs twenty-three feet thick! The British bombers did not bomb the areas when the digging was started—they waited until the concrete had been poured, then placed some "eggs" strategically so that the wet concrete filled up the underground area. Peenemünde was the target for 600 of the Royal Air Force bombers just before mass production was to have begun on the V-2. While the German war effort hung in the balance, production on the weapon was almost halted.

Political intrigue within the country also hampered developments. Gestapo chief, Heinrich Himmler, wanted his blood-stained fingers in the nation's top program, so approached von Braun, saying that he could eliminate the bureaucracy and red tape which was hampering him in the Army regime. Von Braun insisted he had had finest co-operation from Dornberger and declined the offer. But Himmler was not a man to be lightly refused, as von Braun relates in this episode.

"Three weeks later members of his Gestapo came to my quarters at 3 A.M., awoke and arrested me. After two weeks in prison at Stettin, I was hauled up for a faked trial. It was then I began to learn firsthand about the realities of any totalitarian regime. The men in power—and they often hold power because of machines developed by us engineers and scientists —never know when a friend may become an enemy. So their police spies build up a file on *everyone,* ready to be used whenever it appears expedient.

They had a very complete one on me, which included some political remarks I had made years before."[4]

The charges against von Braun were enumerated: He had been more interested in rocket development for spaceflight than for use by the Third Reich as weapons—a charge which von Braun could not honestly deny but one he considered not too serious, since most of the team at Peenemünde shared the viewpoint. The second charge of treason was one that would be almost impossible to disprove: he was accused of planning to escape to England, using the small government-owned airplane in which he piloted himself in trips around Germany.

Dornberger furiously went into action, pursuing every avenue to secure von Braun's release, for he had been informed that von Braun and two others arrested with him would likely lose their lives. It was only when Hitler's headquarters were informed that there would be no V-2 production without von Braun that the order for his release was forthcoming.

In a recent address, the noted scientist made the interesting observation that people can endure and adjust—that even with the threat of secret police it is possible to learn to live with a situation. He makes this simile: "We don't deny ourselves weekend auto trips in spite of the National Safety Council's warnings about multiple deaths. Just so the man living under dictatorship adjusts himself to business-as-usual, whether he likes it or not, because he must, in order to survive. Something like 700 million people are living today under communist rule and, in all probability, they have learned to live in the face of such possible 'road accidents.' "[5]

Sometimes the road that a man travels throughout life has a sudden fork. The choice rests with him which direction it shall be. Such a choice fell to Wernher von Braun in January, 1945, when the gunfire of the rapidly approaching Red Army could be heard in Peenemünde. Before him were conflicting sets of orders—the Army corps commander defending the area and the local party leaders demanded his group to help against the advancing Russian troops, and the High Command and the Ministry of Armament instructed it to move west. This provided von Braun with the latitude to choose the side to which he would surrender.

He explains, "The reason I chose America in particular is that Americans had a reputation for having an especially intense devotion to individual freedom and human rights.

"Furthermore, their traditional disinterest in conquest and their careful system of checks and balances in government offered the highest guarantee that any knowledge we entrusted to them would not be used wantonly."[4]

Calling the members of his team together, he asked for their individual decisions. All but one of the key men chose to try to make it to the Allied forces. Then another game started—the game of staying alive and reaching a point from which to surrender.

PORTFOLIO OF ILLUSTRATIONS

KRAFFT A. EHRICKE
ROBERT H. GODDARD
BERNARD A. SCHRIEVER
JOHN PAUL STAPP
KONSTANTIN EDOUARDOVICH TSIOLKOVSKY
JAMES A. VAN ALLEN
WERNHER VON BRAUN
THEODORE VON KÁRMÁN
JOHN VON NEUMANN
CHARLES YEAGER

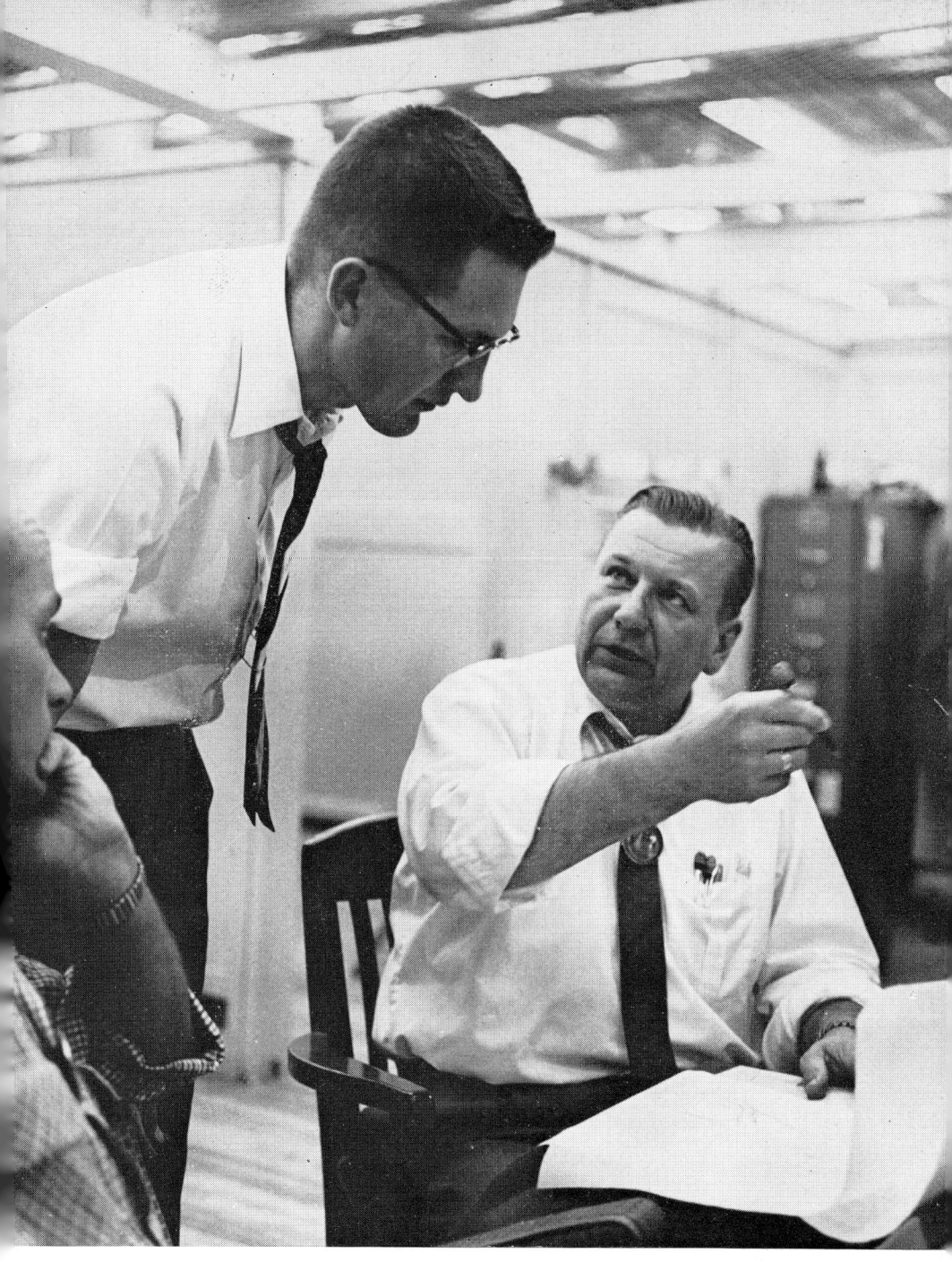

Krafft A. Ehricke, dynamic, forward-looking scientist, is one of the nation's outstanding authorities on astronautics. Here he is discussing plans for a space vehicle with Mark R. Tyson and Freeman D'Vincent of Convair's preliminary design group.
(*Convair, a Division of General Dynamics Corporation*)

Dr. Robert H. Goddard, the father of modern rocketry, combined theory and technology. At his lathe in Roswell, New Mexico, he turned dreams into hardware.

Lt. Gen. Bernard A. Schriever in the data reduction center, giving a briefing on the progress of Pioneer I. He undertook what was termed "the biggest job in the country" in the managing of the Air Force program which developed the Atlas, Thor, and Titan ballistic missiles. (*U.S. Air Force Photo*)

Col. John Paul Stapp, intrepid Air Force doctor, in his rocket sled ready for blast-off. In his experiments to determine the limits of human tolerance, he subjected himself to 46 g's and traveled 632 miles per hour, becoming the "fastest man on earth." (*U.S. Air Force Photo*)

Konstantin Edouardovich Tsiolkovsky, the remarkable theorist, worked out many important principles of astronautical developments in the early part of this century.

Dr. James A. Van Allen, discoverer of the Van Allen Radiation Belts, is poised to photograph the ascent of a giant Skyhook balloon. During the International Geophysical Year, over one hundred space vehicles carried research instruments from the State University of Iowa, where Dr. Van Allen heads the physics department.

Dr. Wernher von Braun headed the team responsible for the Jupiter-C missile which put the first United States satellite, Explorer I, into orbit. Excitement and great tension are mirrored on the faces of those in the blockhouse during the countdown for Explorer III launching. Left to right: The Honorable Wilber M. Brucker, Secretary of the Army; Maj. Gen. John B. Medaris, CG, Army Ballistic Missile Agency; Dr. Wernher von Braun, ABMA; Lt. Gen. Arthur G. Trudeau, Chief, Research and Development, Department of the Army; and Dr. Kurt Debus (behind Trudeau), ABMA. (*U.S. Army Photo*)

Dr. Theodore von Kármán, esteemed aeronautical/astronautical scientist whose talents include the ability to be a catalyst between men of various scientific disciplines and diverse parts of the world. (*U.S. Air Force Photo*)

Dr. John von Neumann, the mathematical genius whose committee vitally aided the development of our ICBM, is welcomed on his visit to Redstone Arsenal by Maj. Gen. H. N. Toftoy. The General is known as "Mister Missile" because of his long-time crusade for their development.

Lt. Col. Charles Yeager was the first man to fly supersonic, October 14, 1947, in the Bell X-1 rocket ship. By smashing the "sound barrier," he opened the path for further climbs into space. (*U.S. Air Force Photo*)

Wrote Willy Ley of this period for the scientists, "Not only did it look as if their lifework had been destroyed—they had to fear for their own lives. There were rumors that the SS or the SD—in short, one of the organizations which was part of the secret political police—had been ordered to liquidate them rather than let them fall into Allied hands."[6]

Kammler, reputedly one of the most ruthless of the SS generals, ordered 450 of the key personnel to a prisonlike camp in Bavaria; it is von Braun's opinion that the scientists would have been used as hostages by the SS commander in dealing with the enemy—whether it had been the Russians or Allies who reached there first. Officially, they were told that they were to have been assembled here to continue their high priority research work.

With forceful persuasiveness, using the danger of air raids as a reason, von Braun persuaded the SS to allow his team to disperse into twenty-five villages, instead of grouping the 450 in the camp. Then came the painful period of waiting in the plush and pleasant atmosphere of a Bavarian ski lodge.

This keen scientist had moments to reflect on the fast moving events that had propelled his life during the years since he had become an employee of the German Army. As he rested in the mountain retreat near Reutte, Austria, he was physically uncomfortable from a bulky cast that encased his arm—an arm broken when in the exhausting escape from Peenemünde his driver fell asleep and the car crashed. That journey had been charged with all of the suspense of a Hollywood thriller, for they were bluffing their way through roadblocks with fancy "official" stickers von Braun had printed.

He wondered about the fate of the technical equipment he had tried to ship out of Peenemünde—12,000 tons of it earmarked for Bleicherode, south of the Harz Mountains, but later captured by advancing Russians on the docks of Lübeck.

Suddenly on that mountain top, reality ebbed away. The waiters were well trained, the food was amazingly palatable, and the scenery was superb —a constant and unruffled element against the earth-shaking events that were being reported on the radio in a constant flow of newscasts. "Der Führer is dead! The Allies are victorious!"

The weeks had passed from April into May. It was necessary to make contact with the Allies. But how?

Wernher's brother Magnus spoke good English. He would not be recognized too easily. He could get some inconspicuous clothes and a bicycle. The downhill road promised an early encounter with some patrolling American soldiers.

The story about a little green man approaching someone and saying, "Take me to your leader!" is a pretty bad joke. But it had its counterpart when Magnus walked up to Private First Class Fred P. Schneiker of Sheboygan, Wisconsin, and announced, "We are a group of rocket specialists up in the mountains. We want to see your commander and surrender to the Americans."[7] The private took a dreadful chance, whatever he did, but such are the risks of war! On the outside possibility that this was legitimate, he took the amiable-looking young man to Counter Intelligence Corps Headquarters. But in the existing confusion of rapid Allied advances, the officer there had not been briefed on a vital program recently activated by the United States called Operation Paperclip—so designated because the cards of the key scientists were marked by paperclips. So when Magnus reported that the men who developed the V-2 were nearby, he was merely told to return next morning with his colleagues.

Wernher von Braun recalls the first action that was taken after his formal surrender—two eggs were fried for him!

It was understandable that skepticism was the initial reaction of the American officers, for who would have expected the top scientist of the vital rocket program to possess the charm, poise, and appearance of a film star? Furthermore, he was smiling and jolly—a great upset from the usual motion picture stereotype of a stoic-looking German scientist, with piercing eyes and sidelong glances.

At an office activated to question German scientists, three of the men who first interrogated von Braun were ones with whom he now has regular contact in performance of his work—Dr. Clark Millikan and Dr. Fritz Zwicky of the California Institute of Technology, and Dr. Richard Porter of General Electric.

The Chief of Army Technical Intelligence in Europe, Major General H. N. Toftoy (then Colonel), was in Paris writing a report when he learned of the windfall of scientific brainpower that had come into U.S. possession. (One of Toftoy's men, Major Staver, had performed a "Paul Revere" to spread the word, flying piggyback in a single-seat fighter from Germany!) Toftoy recalls the unfolding of the project in these words: "After my field intelligence teams started to interrogate the German scientists, I soon felt the information on missiles was so great and so important that it should not be handled by routine field reports. I then cabled Washington recommending that 300 of the top V-2 scientists be brought to the U.S. for detailed interrogation by U.S. missile people and for possible employment.

"No action was taken on this request until I returned to Washington and personally pleaded the case. The recommendation was finally approved (by the War Department, the Department of State, and the Department of Commerce), but the number was sharply curtailed to 100. I then returned to Germany to negotiate the trip and handpick those to come."

Toftoy's plan marked an epoch in the history of warfare. Never before had any nation taken reparations in scientific brainpower. The drama of the event was heightened by austere surroundings, for Toftoy and von Braun met in an abandoned schoolhouse in the small town of Witzenhausen, to start the difficult task of selecting the 100 men to carry forth the art of rocketry. The German scientist and the farsighted American had been plucked from backgrounds utterly diverse to inherit this vital task, but they shared the mighty conviction that the achievements which produced the V-2 must be transplanted to America, to flower in the warm climate of freedom. With scrupulous integrity, they searched the list, evaluated the capabilities of each, and handpicked 127 of Germany's finest scientific men to invite to the United States. (No objection was raised in official quarters that Toftoy had thus exceeded his quota!)

Next came a brief trip to England, where, von Braun commented, he was accorded most respectful treatment by the man responsible for developing Britain's rockets, Sir Alwyn Crowe. He proudly described to von Braun the accurate estimates they had made of the V-2 from assembling the pieces of a test rocket that had misfired and landed in Sweden.

One chapter of his life thus ended, von Braun was imbued with hope as he sailed for America.

"My first impression of von Braun was that here was a very forthright man. He was perfectly willing to talk on any subject, and I saw a look of wonderment on his face at times as he perceived what the new world held. Though he was ill when we met at Fort Banks, on an island in Boston harbor, he still reflected great strength, both physically and mentally." This summation came from Colonel (then Major) James P. Hamill—the U.S. Army officer who was to remain with the German scientist on a twenty-four-hour-a-day basis for the period of his trip across the country, then continue as his commanding officer for many years.

Hamill, in his midtwenties at the time, shouldered a heavy responsibility. His charge was vitally important to this country—a one-man storehouse of knowledge and experience about the advanced art of missilry. Yet, V-E Day was just past, and this man was an enemy alien in military custody. Even the legal status of his entry was cloudy. (It eventually took a trip to Juarez, Mexico, and re-entry across into the United States, to satisfy the State Department that the scientists of Operation Paperclip were officially cleared and able to apply for citizenship!)

Hamill has vivid memories of the trip via train from Washington, D. C., to El Paso. "It was uneventful until we changed trains at St. Louis. Then the conductor cheerily informed me that he had put us in Car B with some buddies. I was stunned to learn that this was a car filled with wounded men of the 101st and 82nd Airborne Divisions." It seems obvious that these men would have accorded the scientist who was responsible for the V-2 a welcome somewhat less than cordial. Hamill scrambled to get the seats changed and consequently had to sit at the opposite end of a car from von Braun.

As the train approached Texarkana, Hamill was disturbed to see the seat companion bidding von Braun a hearty farewell. Von Braun explained the encounter to Hamill in this way: The man had asked what nationality he was—a logical query in view of his pronounced accent. Von Braun replied that he was Swiss; the man inquired as to the nature of business, and von Braun replied, "Steel." Unfortunately the man was familiar with the steel business and had spent quite some time in Switzerland. The train arrived at the man's getting-off point just in time—for von Braun was running out of information about Switzerland and steel! The warm parting was accompanied by the man's earnest commendation, "If it hadn't been for the fine work of you Swiss, the Allies might have had great difficulty in winning the war."

Unlimited enthusiasm. This characterized von Braun's efforts and attitude in the establishing of the colony of Paperclip scientists at Ft. Bliss, in El Paso, Texas. His co-operation was ready and vital to the success of the undertaking.

Hamill, in the administering, had to "write the book" as he went along; no Army manuals covered the thousand daily problems that faced him. Should the Germans be given post exchange privileges? Were there to be fences around their quarters? When would they be allowed to go into El Paso without an escort? What about mail back to Germany? Could they send food and necessities to their families at home?

Rules, regulations, policy, and protocol were voluminous from the beginning. But later that mountain was to shrink to an ant hill when compared with the problems created with the arrival of the wives and children of the scientists. Toftoy's efforts brought about the reuniting of the families in 1947.

As association between German and American wives progressed, German accents gained a superimposed Texas twang and El Paso markets sold sauerkraut as never before!

In March of 1947, von Braun was permitted to return to Bavaria to marry Maria Louise von Quistorp, his eighteen-year-old second cousin —to whom he proposed by mail. Because an attempted kidnapping of this valuable scientist was not beyond the realm of possibility, our officers kept watch on him for his protection. The happy couple had the somewhat unusual situation of being accompanied by intelligence officers on their honeymoon. When they arrived at Ft. Bliss, Hamill recalls his first impression of the bride—"a sensitive person who looked like a Dresden doll."

If the probelms in establishing the Rocket Research and Development Center at Ft. Bliss were tremendous, so, also, was the progress; "the team," as it was always called, performed.

Though at all times their outward behavior was one of model conduct, understandably there were differences within the organization. Like a group in any land and in any work, there were varying opinions, jealousies, rivalries, and infractions. But these existed to a far lesser degree because of the remarkable leadership of von Braun. He possessed strength, knowledge, and the courage to act. His very bearing was one of a man accustomed to respect. Here was an indispensable man; this was not his opinion—it was fact.

Though deeply proud of it, he does not have an exalted evaluation of his team and their accomplishments. He is the first to credit the achievements of other groups, but merely points out that the German group has been at the business of rocketry so much longer that they had gone through the same cycles of development, made the same mistakes, and had some of the same troubles perhaps two or ten years before most Americans seriously approached the new art. Even the production models of the V-2s were so filled with Gordian knots that von Braun jokingly commented that those in the launch area were as gravely endangered as those in the target area.

The von Braun team has remained surprisingly intact. Prior to its arrival in America, the only key member lost in the massive British air bombardment of Peenemünde was Dr. Walter Thiel, who had been in charge of the rocket motor development and the test stands. Since the term of their employment by the United States Army, only a few have left to go into industry. This fact in itself is a significant indication of loyalty and spirit, for the salaries of industry could be a tempting factor compared with the earnings of civil service employees.

Von Braun has commented on the ready acceptance of the German group by Americans, even from the earliest days of their arrival. He volunteers, "In America you don't seem to carry grudges, as do many Europeans who have been enemies."[4] The rocket scientist and his team sought and gained American citizenship as soon as it was legally possible for them to do so. Philosophically, there was no readjustment, for the United States became the world's strongest standardbearer of Western culture.

Opera and symphony were instituted in El Paso—and later in Huntsville —through the group's efforts. Von Braun admits he's a "frustrated pianist." He makes the interesting analogy, "Science is as much a universal language as music."[2]

The story of von Braun is not that of one man. It is his relationship to the team which he headed, a recounting of their collective efforts, and a reporting of the span of the history of rocketry through which they passed. The American phase of the story begins when the team was settled at Ft. **Bliss.**

Their first assignment was to instruct Army crews in the intricate assembly and launching of the V-2—a project which required eight months. A store of these German weapons had been located just after V-E Day at Nordhausen—an underground site built after the destructive raid on Peenemünde. Under Toftoy's directive, Hamill had gathered together from this storage area the components of 100 rockets. This proved a masterful feat in itself, since he had no plans or blueprints to guide him.

Sixteen Liberty Ships were required to transport the parts across the Atlantic, the components ultimately coming to rest on the American desert at White Sands Proving Ground, New Mexico. Interestingly, it was at nearby Roswell that Goddard had long before demonstrated the possibilities of the rocket.

This aptly named test range stretches 120 miles into the barren desert and is accessible to Ft. Bliss and El Paso. From 1946 until the fall of 1952 the launchings of the V-2s from White Sands continued; no longer equipped with deadly war heads, they carried instead nose cones of delicate, scientific instruments.

Suddenly, man beheld the earth as he'd never before seen it—photographed from sixty miles high, clearly showing the gentle curve of a 1400 mile stretch of horizon! The giant birds rose to 130 miles, searching out information vital to mankind's progress, then increased their range to an amazing 250-mile altitude when carrying aloft a WAC Corporal missile as a second stage. Monkeys and mice were shot high, then wafted back to earth for observation and study.

Scientists throughout the United States became so intrigued with the possibilities of high-altitude research that the group was flooded with requests for various instrumentation packages to be taken aloft. This clamor finally had to be co-ordinated through Dr. James A. Van Allen and the Upper Atmospheric Rocket Research Panel.

Toftoy commented that advice was freely given by the scientists; their warnings of certain problems and pitfalls, alone, saved American industry millions of dollars and great time that would otherwise have been spent in research. An amazing plan which the team revealed was one for the launching of a V-2 from 100 miles off our East coast; the bird encased in a submergeable barge, would have been towed into position behind a submarine. When Toftoy directed that this proposal be revealed to the U.S. Navy, great interest was evidenced in further investigation. In 1947 the team proved to the Navy that a large missile could be launched from an aircraft carrier by staging a shoot from the deck of the *Midway*.

Though these military applications of the rockets were thoroughly explored, it did not overshadow the activities in pure scientific research. So it was that while the debris had not yet been cleared from cities that had felt the destructive impact of V-2s, the vehicles were being intelligently, constructively utilized.

As von Braun has said, "The main question is how we use our technical advances. They can either kill us or elevate us. In ancient Greece, slaves did the dishwashing while Sophocles wrote his tragedies. Literally, we don't have slavery today, but the bulk of humanity is in bondage to physical chores. Technology offers millions a chance to investigate the higher aspects of life."[2]

But if scientists and science-fiction enthusiasts had eyes and souls aloft, they were still hopelessly outnumbered by butchers, bakers, and policy-makers. World War II was over. Toasters and waffle irons were again available. Orders were being filled for new cars. "Space" was a word for dreamers.

Wernher von Braun applied his scientific logic to the matter. Potential plus X equaled space advancement. X represented a progression of elements, but they all started with public consciousness. This, in time, would lead to support—via the blessed free ballot of this nation—of vitally needed funds when allocated by the elected representatives. So he reasoned the problem.

No Fuller Brush salesman ever attacked a route with more vigor than this German-American scientist employed in his campaign to "sell" space. He was endowed with the personality, the faith, and the great technical knowledge to gain results. Fortunately, he was persistent—for the job took far longer than he likely had anticipated in 1948.

In that year he attended his first scientific convention since his arrival in the United States and delivered a paper on satellites. Gradually momentum gathered in his crusade. He gained attention to be sure. Family magazines published articles on space flight—but they seemed either to treat it as a fanciful dream or to delude the public into believing that such wonders were but a step away. *Collier's* carried a series of articles by von Braun which brought a flood of comment—even staid scientists were intrigued, though highly skeptical, of what they read.

Why was this advocate so successful that he gained the identity of Mister Space? Willy Ley suggests, "If a salesman believes in a product and has something to back him up, he can be successful. What Wernher has been selling, essentially, is his own belief in the inevitability of space travel." And has his great imagination figured in this? Continues Ley, "Of course. When you want to plan a project that has not yet been done, you must imagine it and plan details in order to talk about it. But what strikes me about Wernher is that his imagination is so completely practical! He doesn't just tell you that a certain mission needs 36,000 pounds of thrust for 322 seconds—he describes the bank of eight rocket engines that will use this exact amount of fuel which will in turn produce that specified thrust. There's never anything nebulous about his proposals."

The Korean conflict jarred Americans from their delusions that the world would remain a peaceful place. Military allocations jumped. Facilities expanded. Von Braun and his team were moved to Huntsville, Alabama —the little town from which the order was issued in 1861 to fire on Ft. Sumter. The Army's Redstone Arsenal had been drowsing in idleness since 1946. It awakened without even a yawn and met the instant and brisk demands of the invading "spacemen." Huntsville henceforth would forego its past proud title as the "Watercress Capital of the World"—now it was destined to become "Rocket City, U.S.A."

The team had become eclectic. From El Paso, they had acquired a taste for enchiladas and ten-gallon hats. From the antebellum atmosphere of Huntsville they would gather the habit of slower speaking and cultivate a taste for corn bread. But, basically, they were still men with a mission —and their leader had the course fixed on the moon and Mars. *Mars Project,* a novel of three years' effort, reached completion at Huntsville. In this, Wernher von Braun describes a remarkable plateau of mutual cooperation which is achieved between the people of this earth and the fictional inhabitants of Mars. The journey to the planet is carefully plotted, allowing two years and 239 days for the round-trip voyage, and accomplished via a fleet of ten spaceships. Though this story, and particularly the experiences of the expedition members on Mars, is a fictional dream from the mind of the creative scientist, his thinking returns to reality when the technical details of the voyage are discussed.

In a Congressional committee report in 1959, von Braun estimates that man will fly around the moon within ten years and will land on its surface a few years thereafter. In the same report he also projects careful specifications for three satellites orbiting at an altitude of 23,000 miles, spaced 120 degrees apart in the same equatorial orbit, to act as relay points for communications—radio, television, telephone, telegraph.

He further states, "Rocket vehicles, of course, will be the key to accomplishment in the Space Age. If we are to expand our capability in space exploration, we must initiate a national integrated missile-and-space-vehicle program which utilizes all existing development teams and facilities."[8]

As von Braun looks forward into the next decade, he has the credits of the last decade on which to build. At the Redstone Arsenal, as Director of Development Operations, he, his deputy, Dr. Eberhard F. M. Rees, and the ten men who head the laboratory groups, are all veterans of Peenemünde.* Oberth joined them in July, 1955, but has since returned to

* The ten scientists are: Kurt H. Debus, missile firing; Ernest D. Geissler, aeroballistics; Walter Haeusserman, guidance and control; Karl L. Heimburg, test field;

Germany because he had reached retirement age. To answer requirements for guided missiles capable of carrying nuclear pay loads over maximum ranges, yet powered by available rocket engines, the Redstone and Jupiter missile systems sprang into existence.

Serious deliberation was given to a technical problem—should the nose cone (or war head) separate from the missile, or should the entire missile come onto the target? A major consideration influenced the decision to separate—aerodynamic heating during the re-entry dive through the atmosphere.

Some significant technical advances that came during this development were: inertial guidance—the first reliable system; re-entry heating problem—the first demonstrated solution; electric rudder activators—instantaneously reversible to actuate control surfaces. The Jupiter followed the Redstone in development, and the latter will eventually be replaced by the solid-propellant Pershing.

The office of von Braun appears always flooded with sunlight, an illusion from the yellow walls which have encased some of the nation's most vital meetings regarding defense matters. These same walls provide a brief haven to the scientist at noontime, when he claims a few moments of privacy to read the daily papers and eat a lunch of fruit, brought from home in his briefcase.

Though he zestfully co-ordinates the enormous operation, he laughingly remarked to a friend, "Each time I'm promoted I become less of an engineer and more of an administrator." The paper work, the pressure, the traveling, the constant appearances before congressional committees that become the routine of such a position of responsibility, fill the working days so tightly that it spills over into evenings and weekends.

Long accustomed to a role as taskmaster where his own life is concerned, the struggle for time to spend with his family grows ever fiercer. Yet, like the quiet reassurance of a Utopian retreat, the redwood and brick one-and-a-half story home nestled in a wooded area in Huntsville, is always there—eager for his sprightly step through its door. And he goes home to the love of three beautiful blondes and a son—Mrs. Maria von Braun; Iris, born in 1948; Margrit, born in 1952; and Peter Constantine, born June 2, 1960. Boating, flying, community activities—are luxuries sometimes slipped into the pressing schedule.

One of the most remarkable demonstrations to emerge from the Space Age has not transpired in the skies or in any laboratory. It has evolved in

---

Helmut Hoelzer, computation; Hans Herbert Hueter, systems support equipment; Hans H. Maus, fabrication and assembly; William A. Mrazek, structures and mechanics; Erich W. Neubert, functional checkout and reliability; Ernst Stuhlinger, research projects.

the minds of men. A thoughtful reflection of the attitude and outlook of the average individual just a few short years ago will demonstrate the phenomenon. From an attitude of utter rejection of space flight, it progressed through instinctive suspicion, then a curious but disbelieving speculation. Then came limited acceptance—riddled with prejudiced restrictions. The final "breakthrough" in the human mind was subtle, imperceptible. The transformation fulfilled nature's plan of change, a necessity for survival. But it is none the less miraculous, and can be appreciated only when today's blasé acceptance of rocket launchings and plans for interplanetary travel can be painfully compared with the atmosphere of negativism that prevailed as late as 1954.

Yet as every age and every element has its believers, its advance guard of prophets, so did a voice sound from the man who was then president of the International Astronautical Federation, Frederick C. Durant, III. He suggested a meeting between his friends, Wernher von Braun and Commander George Hoover; others who shared the aim were invited to attend. On June 25th, in room 1803 of the T-3 building of the Office of Naval Research, several perceptive men gathered to discuss an event of staggering importance—putting up an earth satellite! Among the group were Dr. Fred Whipple, astronomer; Dr. S. Fred Singer, physicist; and David Young, propulsion expert. Remarked Hoover, "By the end of the meeting, they were all quite surprised by von Braun. He had been doing so much writing that they had almost forgotten what a very practical scientist he is. When he discussed the combination of the Loki-Redstone configuration as a possible solution to the first satellite and went into the nuts and bolts of the thing, they were really impressed." Here, again, the German scientist's "practical" imagination evidenced itself.

With existing hardware, the astute gathering concluded that an earth-circling satellite of about five pounds could be put into an orbit of at least 200 miles in altitude. The plans could formulate so quickly because here were men who had spent years compiling the elaborate details for such a mission. Hoover and von Braun were catalysts, blending the many elements into a definite project. They started the battle to gain official approval for this instrument which could shoot American scientific prestige to an impressive high—the world's first satellite!

On this project, hopefully christened Orbiter, Hoover was under Captain W. C. Fortune: certain funds would be made available from the Office of Naval Research. What would the Army's position be about furnishing one of their Redstone missiles? Said von Braun, "I took Fortune and Hoover to see my boss, Major General H. N. Toftoy.

" 'Don't worry about it,' General Toftoy said. 'There's only one method for getting ahead in this game. That's by action. I promise you all the co-operation you need.'

"He did. And he even closed his eyes when we stole time from our Army work to revamp the Redstone for the O.N.R.

"It was interservice co-operation at its best."[9]

When asked for details of these events Toftoy concedes, "I believe I was the first to officially ask the Army for authority to launch a satellite in the fall of 1954 shortly after the agreement was made with the Navy."

But the hopes of the enthused and well-integrated team were "shot down" within six months. The plan for Project Orbiter was aborted.

On July 29, 1955, the Presidential Press Secretary announced that Vanguard would be the project to put up a satellite. But the ghost of Orbiter would not be stilled; it roamed the rings of the Pentagon. Von Braun continued his crusade as this portion of a Congressional report relates: "The Army, confident in its own ability and doubtful that the official project could deliver on time, persisted in pushing its own satellite project. In a presentation to the (Homer J.) Stewart Committee on April 23, 1956, the Army contended that a Jupiter-C vehicle could orbit a small body in January, 1957."[10]

The report lists these facts: "By October 4, 1957, when Sputnik was orbited, two years had been spent on the Vanguard project (from the date of official authorization)."[10] Orbiter had been budgeted at four million Hoover related. "By the beginning of 1959, approximately $111 million had been committed to the ill-starred Vanguard enterprise," the Congressional report states.[10]

It was truly the hand of fate that brought Defense Secretary-designate, Neil McElroy, to Redstone as honorary guest at a dinner on the night the world learned of Sputnik. Von Braun seized the opportunity to repeat the Army's offer. "Sir," he said, "when you get to Washington you'll find that all hell has broken loose. I wish you would keep one thought in mind through all the noise and confusion: we can fire a satellite into orbit sixty days from the moment you give us the green light."[1] General J. B. Medaris, who then commanded the Army Ballistic Missile Agency, was only a shade more conservative when he insisted that von Braun allow himself ninety days.

McElroy had listened. In about ten days after he took office, he pressed the button that lit that green light, and Redstone Arsenal erupted in a frenzy of activity. Like the fireman who keeps his boots handy for that slide down the pole, von Braun had maintained a state of preparedness —even after Project Orbiter was cancelled. He had been further encouraged in his dream when Dr. Homer J. Stewart visited Huntsville and told him of concern over the Vanguard Project and advised him to keep things in readiness as a back-up for the missile.

The assistance of Dr. William Pickering of Jet Propulsion Laboratory was also on stand-by; this gifted scientist had allocated a portion of a research fund to develop a cluster of high-speed upper stages for von Braun's Jupiter-C that would be even superior in performance to the cluster of Lokis. Dr. James Van Allen of the State University of Iowa was enlisted to prepare the pay load of scientific instruments.

On January 31, 1958, at 8:30 P.M., the momentous countdown started. Trouble developed at nine forty-five when a leak of the volatile liquid fuel, Hydyne, was suspected. False alarm—just a spill. At ten thirty-five came another anxious moment when malfunction of the rudders was feared. Four seconds later the countdown resumed. At ten forty-eight sixteen the bird took wings! Its fiery red tail and roaring voice notified the world that the United States was in the skies, headed for space!

To the team, it was a natural, logical culmination—but none the less exhilarating. To the Huntsville townspeople, it was reason for wild celebration. To Americans everywhere, it was an achievement over which to swell with pride. Some of the nation's wounded scientific prestige was healed.

That night a group of men who had adopted this country slept very well indeed, and it was not merely the rest of exhausted bodies—it was the peace that comes with fulfillment. Said von Braun, "It makes us feel that we paid back part of a debt of gratitude we owed this country."[1]

Having necessarily directed the major portion of his lifelong activities to the military use of space, how does the scientist evaluate missiles? "Missiles are really interim weapons. This is because both nations have them. Man will always seek the ultimate weapon. And you know what this is? The ultimate weapon is what the other fellow doesn't have. A Piper Cub would take care of the entire Roman army; one machine gun could have eliminated the hordes of Attila. These are ultimate weapons. And so would the control of space be. Man must establish the principle of the freedom of space as he has done with freedom of the seas. And like everything else, we can only establish this from a position of relative strength."[1]

Realizing the paradox of progress, that the inevitable development of every major stride forward in science multiplies the problems that must be solved, von Braun regards the education of today's young people to be of vital importance. Every breakthrough poses a myriad of new dilemmas to be faced and fathomed. In his earnest effort to encourage and inform the next generation of scientists, the great rocketeer steals time from his bulging schedule of duties to answer letters and lend guidance. Though to accede to every request that is made of him would leave no hours for urgent government conferences and his own killing pace of work, he manages to wedge in a surprising amount of such extracurricular activities.

What are the building blocks to a career in rocketry? Von Braun stresses that the pyramid does not include the kind of amateur backyard experimenting that he did as a youth—he now recognizes all too well that this dangerous business is for professionals. The foundation must be carefully laid with study, with strong emphasis on mathematics and science. The standards are high in this exacting profession; graduate study should be pursued at one of the country's leading universities if at all possible.

Should entire emphasis remain on one special branch of science? Not at all, von Braun feels. A general knowledge can greatly increase a man's value. Furthermore, the scientist stresses that education and interest that is restricted to science alone will incline toward a restriction of character development.

Von Braun reminds us, "We would all have dead souls if we had no esthetic values. Modern educators realize this fact. Witness the stress placed on a humanities-balanced curriculum at Massachusetts Institute of Technology. MIT is one of our finest scientific institutions, and yet they endeavor to balance the physical sciences with liberal arts. I am a technical man, and I would conclude by telling you that I have a Rubens print in my home and that in my youth I played the cello."[11]

In addition to the Doctor's degree which von Braun earned in Germany, these institutions have awarded him honorary Doctor of Science degrees: University of Alabama, St. Louis University, University of Pittsburgh, and Canisius College of Buffalo, Adelphi College of New York, Pennsylvania Military College of Philadelphia. The distinctive honorary Doctor of Laws degree was bestowed by the University of Chattanooga.

Honors for his achievements, his stature as a man, have been extensive; a few of them are: the Notre Dame Patriotism Award, Department of Defense Distinguished Civilian Service Award, Department of the Army Decoration for Exceptional Civilian Service, U.S. Chamber of Commerce Award for Great Living Americans, the Dr. Robert H. Goddard Memorial Trophy, and the Distinguished Federal Civilian Service Award.

While von Braun has employed the mighty thrust of rockets to send his "birds" aloft, he employs the greater force to propel his life—the quality of faith. He explains, "Science has found that nothing can disappear without a trace. Nature does not know extinction. All it knows is transformation! Now if God applies this fundamental principle to the most minute and insignificant parts of His universe, doesn't it make sense to assume that He applies it also to the masterpiece of His creation—the human soul? I think it does. And everything science has taught me—and continues to teach me—strengthens my belief in the continuity of our spiritual existence after death. Nothing disappears without a trace!"[11]

In earlier years von Braun had not felt the need of regular church attendance. But the religious activity of America brought forth such admiration and so impressed the scientist with its willingness to offer help with all of man's pressing needs that he has now availed himself of the benefits of churchgoing. Another quality of this country which he has found stimulating has been our "openness." He saw it existing not only in geographical contour, but in the frankness and candor of personalities, in the free interchange in offices, and in casual, informal living habits. In this climate, his consuming drive has flourished.

To this man of vision, the wheel of progress moves with a slow and rusty creak. He has been plied with the same questions concerning space for thirty years. Though, encouragingly, these questions recur less frequently as the years pass, one still posed is, "Don't we have enough to worry about right here on earth without starting all this foolish talk of space?"

Rightly, the scientist points out that it is part of man's inherited responsibility to fulfill potential—and space is the greatest challenge set before this civilization. Furthermore, if people had felt such reluctance at taking the next step, there would never have been a New World.

Von Braun's faith in his adopted country is limitless. He is convinced that we can "do whatever we set out to do"—provided that we set our minds to it. Such faith is in keeping with his esteem of man. Philosophy and religion are entwined in his thoughts: "We can best make our gift of life count for something if we vigorously champion the Godly life. This means, as I see it, not only loving one another and praying for our enemies, but supporting with missionary zeal the concept of individual worth."[4]

As he stresses the rights of free people, this man who knew the loss of rights also realizes that freedom is everyone's responsibility. Since everyone is involved in its outcome—through the channels of education, economics, politics—all must remain alert to support a vigorous space effort. He told a Congressional committee, "I hope you will not think I am begging the question of *where* we are going by answering with another question: *How much* are we willing to pay?"[8] No price seems too great to this believer, for he contends that the nation which controls space shall control the earth. Therefore, he says, we must keep space free like the ocean.

Von Braun and his team have made tremendous contributions to the military missile power of two nations over a period of almost thirty years, all the while holding as their real aim the exploration of space. At last their period of waiting has ended. On July 1, 1960, the team of some 5000 men was transferred from the Army Ballistic Missile Agency to the jurisdiction of the civilian space agency, the National Aeronautics and Space Administration.

The challenge now before them is immense.

As von Braun points out, "More is unknown than is known. Much of what we have done, much of what is expected of us, strains the state of the art to the breaking point. We must design and fabricate vehicles that can function for months and years under conditions which do not exist on

Earth. We must use materials that will be exposed to extreme vacuum, to high radiation activity, and other extraordinary phenomena encountered only in space. The hypersensitive guidance-and-control systems that steer these fire-breathing monsters must operate over long periods under great stress without any possibility of repair or maintenance. . . . We must develop data-measuring systems and command systems that will convey information from and to space vehicles over distances of hundreds of thousands of miles."[12]

Saturn is the project occupying the majority of the 5500 scientists, engineers, and technicians under von Braun's direction at the Marshall Space Flight Center—the new name given the same offices, laboratories, and test stands at Redstone Arsenal that the team has been occupying for the last ten years.

This gigantic space vehicle, Saturn, will be the transportation system for space exploration. When the basic booster rocket has other rockets mounted upon it for the ultimate three-stage C-2 configuration, it will rise to an overwhelming height of 230 feet, as tall as a twenty-five-story building! Its mighty thrust will hurl 50,000 pounds into a 200-mile orbit! Too huge to be conveyed by truck or train, the Saturn will be transported by barge from Marshall Space Flight Center down the Tennessee, Ohio, and Mississippi Rivers, then towed by ocean-going tugs around the Florida Peninsula to the testing range, Cape Canaveral.

For all von Braun's enthusiasm for the future performance of the Saturn vehicle, he can stand off and interpret current efforts from history's viewpoint. The art of rocketry is still a gangling child, and today's impressive birds are but the Model T Fords of a new field.

This appraisal points up the startling contrasts that exist, not only in the events of the scientist's life, but within the man himself. He is a realistic dreamer. A man of dynamic action, who has yet the quality of philosophical repose. Forceful with his own convictions, he is ready in an instant to abandon them if a better plan is presented. Wernher von Braun has proved an outstanding helmsman as the world has embarked upon what he terms mankind's "last great adventure."

Or is it?

REFERENCES

1. *Time*, 71:21–5, February 17, 1958.
2. *The New Yorker*, 27:75–6, April 21, 1951.
3. Gatland, Kenneth W., ed.: *Project Satellite*, ed. 2, London, Allan Wingate, 1958.
4. *American Magazine*, 154:15, July, 1952.
5. *Vital Speeches*, 24:433–5, May 1, 1958.
6. Ley, Willy: *Rockets, Missiles, and Space Travel: Revised Edition*, New York, Viking, 1957.

7. *Newsweek,* 51:32–3, February 10, 1958.
8. *The Next Ten Years in Space, 1959–1969,* Staff Report of the Select Committee on Astronautics and Space Exploration.
9. *This Week Magazine,* 8–9+, April 13, 1958.
10. *Organization and Management of Missile Programs, Eleventh Report,* by the Committee on Government Operations, 1959.
11. *School Arts,* 59:17, October, 1959.
12. *This Week Magazine,* 2, January 24, 1960. Copyright 1960 by the United Newspapers Magazine Corporation.
13. Von Braun, Wernher: *Conquest of Outer Space,* address before The Cleveland Post, American Ordnance Association, December 8, 1959.

*Eminent Hungarian-American
aerodynamicist who set forth
principles for supersonic flight*

THEODORE VON KÁRMÁN

Antigravity! Release from the forceful grip of our gravitational field which now holds us prisoners to the earth's surface! Freedom, at will, to lift from this planet to which we have always been bound. This may be the next fantastic scientific breakthrough!

Such is the stirring prediction of Theodore von Kármán, the genius who has "seen" with his brain what no eyes could behold—the intricate patterns of the wind. He stands with the giants of science, who, through all time, have relentlessly probed nature for a clearer understanding of her involved workings.

Up to now, man's desperate struggle to free himself from gravity has been a battle of brute force—the massing of enough sheer power to lift him beyond its constant tug. But man's resourcefulness and ingenuity will persist in the search until he finds revealed the means to outwit the relentless master. Man will then circumvent the need for the massive power of huge thrust rockets when he learns nature's most zealously guarded secret, antigravity!

Toward the achieving of antigravity, von Kármán says, "Today we know the particles of negative mass to be very, very rare—perhaps one to several billion particles of positive mass. But, in the future, it may be possible to concentrate these particles of negative mass to produce anti-gravity. This would change our whole outlook on physics. I believe a future generation will combine all the different theories which exist re-garding matter and get one valid theory."

Three times during von Kármán's life physics has taken a decisive leap forward to render obsolete the beliefs of the moment before. Three mo-mentous advancements have cascaded from the wellspring of the world's vast ocean of scientific brainpower to rain benefits upon every living being. And now, with an exhilaration born of confidence and wedded to imagination this scientist foresees another momentous breakthrough.

Perhaps there will yet come from his fertile mind a stepping stone on this path to antigravity? Why not? He's only seventy-nine. At seven years of age he was startling his family with lightning-fast computations. And at seventy he set about to conceive, organize, and administer the most am-bitious world-wide scientific group yet created, the Advisory Group for Aeronautical Research and Development for NATO.

Twenty-five honorary degrees have been heaped on the shoulders of Dr. Theodore von Kármán; yet with the attitude that truly keynotes greatness, he is simple, easy to talk with, unassuming. Even when his body is in re-pose, his lively and perceptive eyes dance about the room, as if in constant watchful curiosity.

In a candid description of himself, he says, "I think I have an honest approach to scientific problems, and I don't fool myself—either I under-stand or I don't understand. I have an interest in young people, and I think I have some art in teaching—in explaining complicated things rather simply. (I believe I got this from my father). And I'm always for the organization of meetings, congresses."

Called the Hungarian name Tódor by his friends, he is most relaxed while wearing a rich black-and-gold Japanese kimono he acquired in the Orient thirty years ago. The furnishings of his rambling home in Pasadena give it the appearance of an antique shop, with mementos of the two dozen countries which he visits regularly. Shelves of his den are lined with the most advanced scientific papers and books—132 of them his own writings! Languages spoken during the constant stream of appointments and visits are as varied as his art treasures; von Kármán is proficient in seven tongues.

"I speak good Hungarian, fair German, bad French, English, and Italian, some Spanish, and," he adds with a twinkle, "a very little Yiddish—enough to tell good Jewish jokes."

Just as the California sun, streaming through the windows, picks up the glint of various pieces of crystal, mirror, or shiny brass as it rises in its arc, so does the conversation of the household glitter with constant bits of

"Kármániana." This term was aptly coined by the American Rocket Society's magazine, *Astronautics,* to describe the gems of humor that the spirited Hungarian sprinkles throughout all discussions.

He has a provision against boredom—a hearing aid that could be turned off with a deft movement. But the problem here would be ever to find a situation in which he is not interested. His personal concerns are as encompassing as his academic knowledge. Often the mind that concentrates on the important values of life is oblivious to the commonplace, but not so with this vital man. His interest is in the totality of life about him. The personal problem of a lonely friend is in his domain as surely as is the scientific puzzle of the disassociation of particles at speeds greater than 185,000 miles per second.

Like the boy who left a trail of bread crumbs to find his way back home, von Kármán forgetfully scatters berets, mufflers, and technical papers across the continents he traverses. Another von Kármán trait is a fondness for Slivovitz, a delicate plum brandy; this is satisfied by gifts from Jacqueline Cochran and other friends. It even figures into the pattern of work, as outlined in this example of Kármániana: "First comes articulation of the problem, then the complexities, then the disagreements, and finally the Slivovitz."[1]

Thinking is von Kármán's forte. His is the theoretical side of the scientific coin. This thinking is punctuated by omnipresent curiosity about all things and the courage to question not only the untried but also the accepted; he dares to probe, to ponder, and reevaluate established theories.

He declares, "I believe in the importance of space exploration—have always believed in it. In 1922, one of the very well-known, very learned German professors gave a talk to the effect that it was impossible to leave the atmosphere and the gravitational field. I stood up and said, 'I am not a fantast. It is just a simple fact that one pound of kersosene has more energy than is necessary to take this one pound out of the gravitational field. It shows it is only a question of technology and progress and time.' The professor was not very happy that I said this. But my father, who was a famous educator, said that the good teacher does not spoil the natural talents and originality of his students."

This incident was an early demonstration of the strongly individual mind of von Kármán—the kind of revolutionary scientific thinking that leads to "breakthroughs." He notes, "The great progress in my lifetime has consisted of the elimination of what I call the scientific prejudices. Einstein's Relativity Theory was the elimination of the absolute time and the absolute motion, which has previously been believed. According to Einstein, nothing is in absolute rest—it is only relative motion. But here is an interesting point. After Einstein had broken down some of these scientific prejudices, then came Dr. Werner Karl Heisenberg and his students with

Heisenberg's Theory of Undetermination—which is the theory that you cannot say where this molecule is nor exactly where the molecule moves; what you observe is the average motion, whereas the individual motion is 'random,' not exactly determined.

"Yet Einstein would not go along with this, though he himself had eliminated old beliefs that were sacrosanct. So I asked, 'Why not, Dr. Einstein? Is it a question of age—that after we get old we don't believe anymore in revolution?' Einstein replied, 'No, I just don't believe the good Lord governs the world by shooting craps.' Einstein was a very religious soul."

His association with the greats of the world came most naturally to von Kármán, for the family of Professor Maurice de Kármán was among the intelligentsia of Budapest in the 1880's and 1890's. Great acclaim came to the Professor for the establishing of the state school system in Hungary; his efforts also created a special plan for the education of the members of the Royal House. Emperor Franz Joseph wished to express his gratitude for this by bestowing upon the Professor the title "Excellence," but de Kármán declined. He wished only for those things which his children could use to advantage; finally he agreed to accept the hereditary title of nobility for his family.

That early remarkable gift of young Theodore's to do mathematics in his head brought about an unexpected reaction from his father. He forbade the boy to be called on to "show off" before family gatherings. The tutor who instructed Theodore, his sister, and two brothers concentrated on history, geography, and literature, the aim being a well-rounded educational foundation. There was wisdom in Professor de Kármán's decision, for his son was thereby saved from the possible fate of becoming a mathematical "freak." Had this one ability been stressed and furthered, his more important powers of logic and deductive thinking might have failed to develop. Like the muscle that atrophies with disuse, von Kármán lost his ability for rapid calculation. Now his mental mathematics are done at moderate pace, and he always computes audibly in Hungarian (to the bewilderment of students or associates).

Professor de Kármán exerted strong influence on his son's development. In retrospect von Kármán says, "I learned from him to play with ideas, to try to have a clear picture of what happens in nature and why it happens. I also learned from my father the separation of the different domains of the human mind and soul. So I never had the problem which confronts many men—that of a conflict between religious belief and scientific thinking. You can look at the natural phenomenon very differently. You can look by organizing your experiences, your measurements, and we call this science. You can make a picture out of these words and work and the influence of the Divinity; we call this religion. To concentrate on science alone would be one-sided, because if it is natural to understand the world, then religion, art, and poetry are other methods.

"One of my father's convictions was that science is just the organization of our experiences—what we see, what we hear. So I have always been attracted by logical system. If there are contradictions, I cannot sleep until I understand why. I am not a gadgeteer, not an inventor in this sense; I am a systematic thinker. The greatest inspiration to me is to create order."

Von KárMán adds, remembering well his paternal teachings, "If my father had lived during this present era with its increased opportunities, he would have had an influence on the times far greater than anything I may have accomplished."

Did von Kármán always have his thoughts skyward? Strangely, no. His doctor's thesis was on the strength of materials. His diversion into aerodynamics might never have happened had he not been prey to the pleadings of a pretty newspaper woman. She had a story to cover at the airport of Issy-les-Moulineaux near Paris on a bleak morning in 1908. "It will be an historic incident!" she insisted. Von Kármán protested that he was not interested in history that takes place at 5 o'clock in the morning— but he went, and it changed his life.

He witnessed the first flight made by any Frenchman. Henri Farman dazzled a doubting crowd by taking to the air for one kilometer of circular flight. Though the Wright Brothers had performed their feat at Kitty Hawk five years earlier, the event had not registered upon the people of Europe.

How do men fly? Rhetorically, the question was centuries old. Yet up to that time the light cast into the shadowy area of aerodynamics was flickering and pale. The general theory had been understood by a few throughout the ages—Leonardo da Vinci's magnificent creativeness set forth principles that could have enabled an Italian first to emulate the birds had correct power been available.

But aeronautical progress was stubborn, reluctant in its forward march from the fifteenth to the twentieth century; also, science had accepted Newton's erroneous law of air resistance.

As von Kármán explains it, "Newton considered the air as consisting of particles. If you apply his law to an airplane wing, the particles strike it and are deflected. So by his law there are only two choices: First you could have the wing at a very small angle, not creating much resistance —but then the wing must be terrifically large in surface. The other choice by his law is to make the wing of greater angle; then great power is necessary to overcome the resistance created.

"But I'm not sure that these errors of Newton's ever really delayed practical flying because the people who were flight enthusiasts didn't read his theory. It only caused the scientists not to believe in the possibility of powered flight. Now there has been an interesting development; with the present-day speeds of aircraft, Newton has suddenly been vindicated! It so happens that when you fly a very high Mach number—several times the speed of sound—his law is correct!"

Bernoulli, D'Alembert, Stokes, Joukowski, Lanchester, and Prandtl each moved a piece of the aerodynamic jigsaw into its proper place. But still those aspects of the wind which delighted poets defied scientists. This was the challenge facing von Kármán.

Already a graduate with highest honors of the Royal Hungarian Technical University, he searched the face of Europe for advanced study in his newly chosen field. At the University of Göttingen, Ludwig Prandtl taught! What a magnificent opportunity for a student of the newly developing science to study with "the father of modern aerodynamics." When today this title is applied to von Kármán, he will correct it quickly, saying, "The honor belongs to Prandtl." Other respected names made Göttingen a mecca for the student: David Hilbert, Felix Klein, L. Hermann Minkowski, Konstantin Carathéodory, and so on.

And what young student worthy of the name would restrict all of his energies to classical pursuit? There was always that favored rendezvous for lively discussion and bountiful food, the Black Bear Inn. In an atmosphere pulsating with the excitement of eager minds, conversations abounded at tables laden with cheeses, goose-liver loaf, and thick slices of black bread. The spirits were livened with songs of adventure and friendship, and laughter buoyed all dreams to a high plateau.

Lively sessions of philosophical ponderings, artistic comparisons, and mathematical speculation continued at El Bokarebo—a house shared by von Kármán and four friends. Word reached them of a Sister from a clinic who wished to make herself independent—to have a house in the forest where she might take care of three or four mentally deranged people. Von Kármán immediately sent word that just such a place awaited her —except that it was not in the forest, but in the city, near the University. She accepted! The students gained a housekeeper-chaperon.

As Göttingen's students neared the time of graduation, the topic for prime discussion turned to promotions—securing teaching positions. The first step was to become a Privatdocent—a teaching fellow paid only by his students' fees—and await an appointment at the University. Von Kármán recalls: "I once said that the Privatdocent is a man who has the *right* to teach and has the *duty* to marry the daughter of his boss—because very often that was the only way he received his promotion to professor. Once there was an international congress in the United States, and all the mathematicians were going to New York on the same ship. Somebody at the Black Bear Inn said, 'Just think—if this ship should go down how many vacancies there would be in Germany!' This was not a very kind point of view, but very practical."

The gifted Hungarian achieved advancement without the aid of such a catastrophe. After receiving his Ph.D., he remained at Göttingen for three years as a Privatdocent. During that time, the instinct of being helpful to everyone brought rich reward. Karl Hiemenz, a doctoral candidate, was trying to achieve symmetric flow of water around a cylinder. Each morning on his way to the laboratory, von Kármán inquired of the student, "Herr Hiemenz, is the flow steady now?" Despairingly Hiemenz would reply, "It always oscillates."[2]

This condition stirred thoughts in von Kármán's perceptive mind. The workings of nature are not to be fought, changed, or overcome—they are to be understood and turned to men's advantage. Thus he took the student's problem and projected it into one of the major advancements in the science of aerodynamics, the Von Kármán Theory of Vortex Trails! The doctor gives a lay explanation of the intricate calculation in these words:

"It is very simple. If you observe a body in air or water—in any fluid —you get rotating motions behind the body. Now this motion that occurs is important, because it causes a drag—resistance. It was not always known that these asymmetric motions were useful. For example, behind a symmetric body—a circular cylinder—the eddies are alternating left, right, left, right.

"By mathematical calculation, I showed that this alternating is the means by which stabilization occurs. If they did not alternate, there would be unstability. My formula states the ratio of the distance between two consecutive eddies and the distance between the two rows. What I did is really not too much." His summation of the theory is evidence that greatness and humble simplicity appear as partners in his character.

The application of the Von Kármán Theory of Vortex Trails has come down out of the sky to aid the earth-bound endeavor of bridge building. The activity was occasioned by a letter von Kármán wrote in 1940 to the Governor of the State of Washington. It was a simple warning about Galloping Gertie. This suspension bridge across the Tacoma Narrows had just taken her last ride, propelled by a forty-two-mile-per-hour wind. She ended in a watery grave at the bottom of the Narrows; but no sooner had her wake ended than plans were announced to rebuild the bridge—a potential Galloping Gertie II—by the same plans. This brought forth the letter from von Kármán stating: "If you rebuild the bridge in the same way, it will fall in the same way."[3]

His advice was heeded. When a government committee was formed to look into the sad demise of Gertie, von Kármán was invited to participate. As he joined the others of the committee around the huge conference table, the introduction of each of the members brought forth an impressive list of affiliations—each man represented some highly specialized function of bridge building. The spirited aerodynamicist could not resist the disclaimer, "I represent only the vind!"[3] (Note: He may have conquered its behavior patterns, but no Hungarian will likely succeed in the pronouncing of the "w" in wind!)

Bridge-builders learned a vital lesson in this experience. Now they utilize such benefits as von Kármán suggested for the Tacoma span—that of using open grillwork on the deck and trusses instead of solid construction —and they also take the precaution of testing models of proposed structures in wind tunnels.

Though unlikely seeming to others, his venture into soil conservation was very logical to the learned doctor. "Soil erosion by wind is an inevitable thing. So I got a contract from the government to build a wind tunnel to determine how to bind soil. Dr. Frank J. Malina, my assistant, conducted the experiment with models of trees to see what position of planting best binds the sand and soil." Von Kármán followed this work with a nomadic trek into the desert, where he evolved a theory on the creation of sand dunes.

But the primary application of the Von Kármán Theory of Vortex Trails has always been in connection with aeronautics. He soon learned to confine his interest in airplanes to theoretical application when one of his first lessons in flying ended in a crash landing. Insult was added to injured pride when a German police officer accosted him and imposed a twenty mark fine with the admonition, "Don't you know that it is forbidden at this harvest time to walk through a potato field?" Von Kármán replied meekly, "Excuse me. I know this. But I was flying an airplane, and we had to make an emergency landing. We have to get out of the field somehow." Such an explanation failed to move the Teutonic heart. Von Kármán paid the fine—though the flying instructor was exempt because the policeman was impressed with the military uniform he wore.

Von Kármán continued to apply all his energies to his post as director of Germany's newly established Aeronautical Institute of the University of Aachen. But the skies he studied for their wind currents soon became blackened with war clouds and military orders determined his address for the next four years: the Austro-Hungarian Air Corps.

His early engineering background served him well in developing methods to protect fuel tanks and in adapting machine guns to the airplanes of the small forces. The most productive portion of this war period was the time that he spent developing a helicopter with two counter-rotating propellers. He is still convinced that this design will prove superior to the present helicopter configurations—but the years since his experiments have remained too crowded with other demands to permit his developing it farther. It remains as "unfinished business," like his sailboat-without-sails. Amazing? Not to the thinking of this creative mind. "It is done by means of boundary layer control. The sail is replaced with a porous cylinder. Inside is a small compressor to create suction—as a vacuum cleaner makes suction. By changing the distribution of the suction you can change the direction of the force in the case of the porous cylinder exactly like using a sail. I have made only model experiments so far. But, someday. . . ."

One hundred days of Bolshevism gripped Hungary to crown the tragedy of World War I. Philosophically, von Kármán—appointed a Group Leader in the Ministry of Education—saw benefit from it. "These one hundred days were useful for two reasons: First, I had direct information as to how the Communist system works; and, second, it saved me for all my life from having any belief in Communism—I saw it in operation and that was sufficient."

A return to the University of Aachen in 1919 started an era of bright achievement. Spurred by the war-time impetus, aviation was fast maturing. The Aeronautical Institute of Aachen, under von Kármán's direction, became a mecca for the air-minded. There were many demands on the services of this aerodynamicist, whose reputation was already established. In addition to extensive work with gliders and assistance to student-gliding clubs, von Kármán became consultant and patent expert to the Zeppelin and Junkers Companies.

The latter assignment had an amusing repercussion in 1931 when he was summoned to Henry Ford's office in Detroit. The famed automobile magnate sought von Kármán's opinion on a possible infringement of a Junkers' patent—he wished to make the wings on one of his first airplanes with an undulating steel sheet. With quiet dignity Mr. Ford inquired, "Do you really think we infringe on the patent?" Von Kármán replied in the affirmative. Forearmed for such a decision, Ford had a quick alternative suggestion. "All right, then, we will make the wing flat."

The aerodynamicist's failure to comment was more meaningful than a lecture. Mr. Ford grew uneasy. "Don't you think the airplane will fly? Reassuringly von Kármán replied, "Oh, yes, it will fly—but you will lose the wing." Mr. Ford decided to pay for the use of the Junkers' patent.

An international congress for physics was held in Europe in 1924. In attending, von Kármán founded a friendship that prompted his first trip to the United States. There he met the man whose work in the field of cosmic rays had won him the Nobel Prize the previous year, Dr. Robert A. Millikan. Immediate rapport was established between the two fine minds.

In 1925 Daniel Guggenheim established a School of Aeronautics at New York University with a gift of $500,000. Following that, he repeatedly asked his son, Harry F. Guggenheim, to find other universities where similar schools could be established. The son persuaded his father not to do this since, to his way of thinking, aeronautics could be better boosted in other ways.

Out of the father-son discussions which followed and a subsequent meeting late the same year with President Coolidge and Herbert Hoover, then Secretary of Commerce, came the Daniel Guggenheim Fund for the Promotion of Aeronautics, January 16, 1926. It was set up with a grant of $2,500,000.

Soon after its establishment, The Fund began to look for universities to which it might make grants for the promotion of aeronautics. Geographical distribution was a factor in this study, and for this and other reasons California Institute of Technology was one of the institutions considered.

At about this time Dr. Millikan heard of the project being contemplated by The Fund and came East to talk with Harry F. Guggenheim. In the discussions, Millikan pointed out, "You will make a great mistake if you do not give a considerable amount to Caltech, because California will become a center of the aviation industry. There are the vast acreages here which the industry demands, and the labor conditions are very favorable."

Millikan's wish was fulfilled by The Fund. In establishing the project the need for bringing a top scientist from Europe who could establish in the United States a position equal to that which Prandtl had established for Germany was stressed; though this country led in practical aeronautics in the Twenties it was Germany and England that set the pace for theoretical aeronautics and theoretical aerodynamics.

The outgrowth of the agreement between The Fund and Millikan prompted a cable to von Kármán—who was snatching a brief vacation at the seashore. The message was to the point "What is the first ship you can take to come to Caltech?"

The Hungarian had been discussing an assignment to build a research laboratory for the Kawanishi Aircraft Manufacturing Company in Kobe, Japan. Desiring to accept the invitation from Millikan instead, he then doubled the fee he asked from the Nipponese; to his surprise they met it unquestioningly. So both activities had to be scheduled into the agenda for the fall of 1926 and the spring of 1927. First came the visit to the United States, in company with his favorite companion, his sister Josephine, whom he fondly called Pipö.

Von Kármán and Josephine arrived in September, 1926, and Harry F. Guggenheim welcomed them to this country with an invitation to spend the weekend at his New York home. Constructed from the dismantled parts of an old French castle, it was a veritable museum. One of their delightful discoveries was to find a radio—at that time somewhat of a novelty in itself—hidden in a magnificent seventeenth century commode.

During that visit and in many conversations that followed, Guggenheim asked suggestions on how to best advance the standards of American aeronautical development. Von Kármán passed along several ideas, such as a series of handbooks revealing the present "state of the art" in the various areas; this idea led to the compiling of the respected William Frederick Durand's *Aerodynamic Theory, a General Review of Progress.* Secondly, the gregarious Hungarian pointed out that great benefits accrue from informal gatherings of scientists where there can be free exchange of ideas and news of current experiments; the European coffee houses provided an excellent opportunity for just such meetings. But Guggenheim declined the idea of going into the restaurant business—even for the purpose of furthering his favorite project!

Von Kármán consulted with Millikan regarding educational developments and the aerodynamical laboratory at Caltech which was to be constructed under The Fund's grant. Another feature of this important aeronautical training program was the lecture tour that the noted scientist made, visiting Stanford University, New York University, the University of Michigan, and the Massachusetts Institute of Technology.

He arrived at the latter bastion of scholastic endeavor on a Wednesday near the end of November. The following day there was to be a Thanksgiving dinner. Von Kármán was touched that his visit was to be marked with such an honor; he had not expected his fame in Europe to bring him such quick tribute in this strange land. But dutifully preparing for the occasion, he visited the near-by barber shop. There, to his chagrin, he learned that Americans have this day of thanksgiving every year, and that it had nothing to do with his visit.

A treasured experience was his meeting with Orville Wright in Akron, Ohio. The two men lunched and puffed cigars and spoke of a world removed from ordinary understanding—a world filled with such terms as airfoil, angle of attack, center of pressure, compressibility effects. Between these two men, dissimilarities of nature, habit, and background dissolved before the parallel devotion they shared to the skies above their heads. With deep pride the air-pioneering American showed his honored Hungarian visitor the wind tunnel in which he and his brother, Wilbur, had logged 200 hours of model tests prior to their momentous flight at Kitty Hawk.

Of von Kármán's other first impressions of America, he still recalls his wonder at beholding the Grand Canyon. As he and Pipö marveled at the red and gold spectacle of nature, he puzzled why it was that dimensions in American scenery are so big. The world's largest trees are within our boundaries. Even the biggest meteorite ever to fall from the skies landed on American soil. Propounding these facts, he tried to evaluate this influence on the character of its people. Had this played a part in inducing the expansive thinking that comes so naturally to Americans? Whatever the elements of this formula were they fused into a national personality very much to von Kármán's liking.

On his return to Germany, the sensitive scientist became increasingly aware of change. The mechanics of fluid flow he had mastered. Now his subconscious was monitoring the undercurrents of human emotionalism which were manifesting themselves in disturbing ways.

At the International Symposium planned to celebrate an extension of the Aeronautical Laboratory at the University of Aachen an unsavory episode developed. Students, steeped in nationalism, protested to the rector against a ceremony that was to bestow honorary degrees on four foreign scientists. Moreover, they felt deliberate insult because it was to be held on the Day of Mourning—the anniversary of the Treaty of Versailles. When the rector bowed to student demands, the usually genial von Kármán was livid. Compromise was finally reached. The honorary degrees were given, but in private ceremony.

The status of compromise was not allowable by the Hungarian's standards. His lifelong search was for truth in its many forms. He even beheld festering change within his own field—in aviation there was a secret rearming. His subsequent attempted warnings of Germany's clandestine air build-up found no receptive ears in United States governmental circles.

Von Kármán stood at a crossroad. His position as the world's leading authority on wind tunnels was indisputable—he had supervised construction on all the leading ones in Europe, Japan, and America. As early as 1906, he had set down concepts that aided materially in the structural design of aircraft. Now, when frictional design was preoccupying airplane designers, von Kármán had already turned his attention to problems others had not yet anticipated—the theory of turbulence. An honorary doctorate of engineering had been bestowed by the *Technische Hochschule* of Berlin. His ties were all with Europe. Yet how could he longer ignore these rumblings of the continent beneath him?

Pipö, with her sisterly devotion, her ready adaptability, and keen intuition, would support his plan for establishing a new life in America. As companion and assistant to her father, Professor de Kármán, hers, also, had been the world of intellect and achievement—one not bound by flags or customs barriers.

But what of Mrs. Helen de Kármán, aged seventy-six? With every root in the soil of Europe, how could she be urged to cut the lines of her full and active life? Furthermore, she was concerned at the position her brilliant son would occupy; she did not feel United States professors were given the same social respect as in Germany. Still, von Kármán knew what must be done. Urge he would, insist if he must that as lovers of truth and freedom they belonged in America. To the delight of Dr. Robert A. Millikan, von Kármán accepted the associate post offered at the Guggenheim Aeronautical Laboratory, California Institute of Technology, known as GALCIT.

After the bags and trunks were unpacked in Pasadena, California, and the new occupants had grown familiar with their rambling home, what then did his mother feel about this change? "She liked very much the country. She spoke good English—better than I do—but not American. She had trouble understanding the American dialects. My students liked her very much. She was to them quite an example of an old lady! I remember after she had been here a year, she said one day as I came home, 'This is a real funny country. Today I saw for the first time a horse, and the horse was riding in an automobile!' She had great wit, my mother."

The son rightly inherited this quality. The following year, after he had been appointed Director of GALCIT and the graduate school, he was host to a distinguished scientist who was visiting from Boston. As von Kármán showed him around and introduced him to his colleagues, some of whom came from such far-off places as China, India, and Hungary, the proper Bostonian inquired, "How does it happen you employ so many foreigners?" Von Kármán looked at him indignantly. "What should I do?" he demanded. "Hire a Navajo Indian?"[1]

It might be added that von Kármán became a citizen in 1934. And what was his most difficult problem in becoming an American? "Learning to speak English. But I vill yet improve, no?"

The greatest change for von Kármán in America was not in a way of life but in teaching. He has found the educational system vastly different. "The high school education in Europe is much more serious. They tell me the American approach is due to the philosopher, John Dewey, who propounded the idea that students learn only what they like. In Europe education is a 'must' and not just for the subjects the students are interested in.

"So far as the university education is concerned, the European system has one great advantage: The fundamentals are taught by first-line scientists. At Caltech a poor troubled student came to me once; I asked him who was his first mathematics teacher. He could not remember. My mathematics teacher was Hilbert, one of the greatest mathematicians of the world. I see him yet after fifty years. Here the student does not ever meet the really good scientists unless he works with them in the highest class in research.

"At Caltech they never let me teach the elementary classes; these, which are really the most difficult ones to teach, are usually given by teaching fellows. In Europe, I had classes of 150 students, but here we have only twenty-five or thirty to a class so that there are not enough great teachers to go around. Our system is based on control—that every student do every calculation. The European system is freer—good for those who are interested, bad for those who are not. So each system has advantages."

In retrospect von Kármán views education of the past years. "We engineers neglected physics and chemistry. And so very many discoveries which really were in the engineering field were made by non-engineers. For example, Heinrich Hertz first verified the existence of electromagnetic waves, and the whole wireless telegraphy was based on his discovery—he was a physicist. Why did this happen? Because we engineers learned only how to make big machines, not how to produce electromagnetic waves. During the war, physicists solved the problem of the production and direction of microwaves, making radar possible. This was really an engineering problem. Physicists made the fundamental discovery of atomic power and suggested applications; but the first utilization of atomic engineering was directed by military engineers.

"The solution is that engineers should get a very fundamental education in physics and chemistry, because engineering comes more and more in the scientific fundamentals. They should try to gain a deep understanding of the natural sciences. I think this is the most important. I do not believe in making scientists of every engineer, because the engineer has to design and create hardware. But today they need more fundamental science, or for those with an interest in management, more social science."

As von Kármán continued to intersperse his teaching with research, he started his "hot wire" experiments, which brought about a friendly rivalry between him and his former teacher, Prandtl. Each drew upon his finest skill and ingenuity to develop a theory for the laws of turbulence. The hot wire was an instrument to measure the velocity of the air—it was found best for following very fast changes in velocity, magnitude, and direction. In this experiment, the simple wire was heated, exposed to the wind, and the temperature changes were compared by measuring the variance in the electric resistance. These changes are very fast—perhaps 100th of 1000th of a second.

Tension grew in the scientific world as former student competed against master, each determined to present a solution before the Third Congress at Stockholm in 1930. Von Kármán was working on this gigantic problem in the Dutch town of Voals. One evening his assistant and former Caltech student, Frank Wattendorf, had been with him until a very late hour— the time most productive to the gifted Hungarian. The last streetcar left at midnight, and von Kármán escorted his collaborator to the car line, continuing the scientific discussion en route.

Just as the streetcar arrived, a new idea struck. Von Kármán fished a piece of chalk from his pocket and began using the side of the streetcar for a blackboard. The conductor waited respectfully; von Kármán continued in his frenzied writing of equations. As the writing and discussion continued, the conductor's patience was finally exhausted. Mathematical figures were scribbled until the car started to roll; Wattendorf jumped aboard and then was faced with a great perplexity—how was he to note the elaborate calculations which were too lengthy to remember?

The window proved to be in the wrong position as he tried to peer out at the valuable writing. The only alternative was to hop off at every stop, furiously copy down a portion, then scramble back on the clanging streetcar. This continued until Wattendorf's destination of Aachen. Luckily, it was a tied race. He just managed the final bit of the copying as the car rolled from the station and thus preserved some of the most vital computations in the "hot wire" experiment.

The nations of the world beckoned, storing their problems in aeronautics and aerodynamics until the schedule of von Kármán could accommodate the demand. To the Orient he journeyed to be consulted on how to build up China's air force. "How does a wind tunnel function?" Madame Chiang Kai-shek asked him. At the end of an hour, when he concluded his explanation, the lady responded, "I do not understand a word you said but, from the way you talked, it must be very important. China will have a wind tunnel."[4]

The Suicide Club was born in 1936. Its aims and objectives were not really what the name might imply. Its members were the most farsighted, intelligent, imaginative, and patriotic group which might assemble, and the name was their ironically humorous reminder that they were dealing in a dangerous endeavor—the development of rockets.

Von Kármán was advisor, cheer leader, and father confessor to the founding group of six: Frank J. Malina, John W. Parsons, Edward S. Forman, A. M. O. Smith, H. S. Tsien, and Weld Arnold. The latter enthusiast supplied the finances for this early research—a gift of 1000 dollars in cash which he presented in a newspaper-wrapped bundle.

It was even whispered by students that Millikan was so enraged by this activity of his prize Hungarian professor that he threatened to remove him from the staff. But, long before, von Kármán had dedicated himself to the skies; now he saw the possibility of going farther, faster, more furiously, with the ear-shattering blasts of rockets.

A sudden respectability and stature was given to the work of the rocketeers two years later when the remarkably progressive General H. H. Arnold determined that the Army Air Corps should have rockets to assist its heavy bombers in take-off. Both Caltech and MIT were allowed the opportunity to tackle this problem; Dr. Jerome Hunsaker of the eastern institution waved it away from his honored portals with the ready concession that von Kármán be the one to pursue the "Buck Rogers job with rockets."

The first Air Corps contract granted to von Kármán and his group for this research and development was for $1000—a suprisingly reasonable figure for those days. General Arnold's assistant was Major Benjamin Chidlaw (now a retired general), and as he discussed a second contract he dubiously inquired of von Kármán, "Do you really believe that the Air Corps will spend $10,000 for such things as rockets?"

Jauntily, the professor with the ready wit and superb skill approached the problem of shooting planes off the ground with rockets. There was nothing especially reassuring about the prospect, from the viewpoint of that day. There were premature explosions, misfires, greater thrust than anticipated—experience was small, and the danger was great. At a later date, Jack Parsons of the Suicide Club made a fateful experiment in his laboratory; but during the early development of JATO—jet-assist-take-off—the heavens showered a blessed immunity from accident on their awkward first attempts.

With von Kármán in the role of director, the great drama entitled "Jet-Assist-Take-Off" got underway. The rehearsal period was brief to transform theory into practicality. Equations and calculations were set forth. Clumsy first models were constructed, tested, and refined. Then came the all-important "dress rehearsal," when the final model was put on a test-stand and fired. All went well. But in the theater, a good dress rehearsal is an omen of a bad performance!

Time for the big "opening night" arrived! The leading man, Captain Homer A. Boushey, was cast in a potentially deadly role—that of performing in a flimsy Ercoupe airplane, propelled by the fury of burning explosives attached to its wing tips. His big scene was about to be played! Six deadly rockets were ignited, and the spotlight was focused upon his skill and daring. With perfect craftsmanship, he made history in the first JATO flight. The curtain fell on the thunderous applause of success. With courage and verve, Boushey repeated the performance sixteen times—indeed a record long-run for so hazardous an experiment!

Boushey is now one of the Pentagon's prized occupants, with the rank of Brigadier General, and continues to plan on the objectives of space as Air Force Director of Advanced Technology.

It is estimated by Andrew G. Haley, leading authority on space law, that by 1970, the astronautics industry will be many times its present size—in dollars and people—and many times the size of the automotive industry. Yet in 1940 not one American corporation could be persuaded to build rockets. Von Kármán, ever dauntless, was ready with an alternative. He and five friends—with $1500 each—would create a company to build the rockets. Aerojet was their brainchild.

Momentum developed in the rocket program under von Kármán's direction at Caltech. The war created demand for rocket boost in take-off. Yet this was viewed as an accessory—an adjunct to existing aircraft—not as an end in itself. The rocket was still floundering in its gangling childhood, insofar as military acceptance was concerned. Only the visionaries like von Kármán peered beyond the existing horizons and bounced a signal off projected plans that revealed a giant new phase of air and space in the offing.

In 1943, von Kármán, Malina, and Tsien (who later left for Red China) had urged the Army to institute a missile program. Now Allied Intelligence reports were bearing out the warning which was long before voiced by von Kármán—that Germany was developing a missile of great proportions. At last we got into the race, but even genius cannot stand such handicap; the lead horse was three quarters around the track before our favorite was allowed to leave the starting gate. When Germany's V-2 rockets showered down upon Britian and the Continent in catastrophic profusion, there was sorrow in the heart of a man sitting at his desk in Pasadena. In frustration, he remembered how desperately he had tried to sound the call.

The science-fiction writer, from the time of Jules Verne, had drawn the roadmaps into space. Von Kármán told an amusing story when he presided over the First Space Symposium in San Diego, sponsored jointly by the Air Force Office of Scientific Research and Convair. *Newsweek,* in the March 4, 1957, issue, reported it in these words:

"Research into the capabilities of animals to withstand the rigors of space began, Dr. von Kármán reminded the astronauts, with a balloon experiment above Paris in the eighteenth century. French scientists sent up a goat, a duck, and a hen to the 'incredible' altitude of 8000 feet. Upon landing, the goat and duck were healthy; the hen, tattered. The savants, von Kármán said, hastily drew the conclusion that space was fine for ducks, bad for hens. One persistent experimenter later looked in the goat's mouth. There was clear evidence of chicken feathers."

So it was that the smart man ridiculed the serious consideration of space travel. Only the brilliant man stopped to consider how to make it a reality. Von Kármán soon determined that the first step—the attaining of supersonic speeds—must be taken.

After three years of preparation he presented a paper to the Fifth Volta Congress in Italy in 1935 on the theory of supersonic flight. During World War II, fighter pilots bore out his theories on the problems of flying Mach one (Mach designates the speed of sound and was named to honor the Austrian physicist, Ernst Mach). Fliers related strange behavior of their aircraft in long dives. The details varied with the imagination of the individual, but all agreed that there was a powerful unseen force at work, buffeting and rending their airplane. "Man will never pierce the sonic barrier," some dourly predicted. "It's a brick wall in the sky," others added. "The limit of speed has been reached," many experts felt. Von Kármán disagreed.

Lockheed Aircraft Corporation called him in for consultation about strange flight characteristics that had developed on their P-38. "I am like a doctor," he commented. "I examine the patient. I consult my knowledge. Then I look out of the window and maybe the answer comes."[3] He diagnosed the trouble, but engineers were not capable of providing the "antibiotic" to effect a cure: thin wings and additional power.

There the case rested, until it was revived on the surface of a tablecloth, which, for mobility and ease of reference, certainly surpassed his earlier choice of the side of a streetcar! America was still in World War II when he was summoned to the Wright Air Development Center at Dayton, Ohio. He was rushed from the field to an urgent meeting with Brigadier General Franklin O. Carroll, who posed the question plaguing the finest engineering minds: Can an airplane ever fly faster than sound?

Von Kármán had been thinking seriously about this question since 1932; yet he asked for the reprieve of a few additional hours before rendering the final momentous verdict. The next morning he met the General for breakfast. It was a leisurely session on an overcast Sunday, but it decided the direction of long-range planning for the aircraft of the future. With his tablecloth equations, von Kármán showed the officer how supersonic flight could be attained. Four years later, the Bell X-1 proved him right. Colonel Charles "Chuck" Yeager piloted the rocket craft to a speed of 967 miles per hour, the first man to fly faster than sound!

"So far as my participation in the military is concerned," says von Kármán, "my conviction is that even though the research and development is made for the military, the experience is evidenced in civil aviation profits. So I believe that in helping the military in research, I am not only bettering our capacity to make war, but contributing very much toward the progress of technology in general. Now, if we truly go into space, it is no more necessary to make war, because it is most impossible to make war."

Von Kármán might well carve his initials on half the aircraft now flying in the sky. For in theoretical, advisory, or consultant capacity, his know-how was one of the major determinants that got them airborne.

Still, there were those who would challenge the merit of the "newfangled" theories and devices, as evidenced in this story which *Air Force* magazine related in the October, 1957, issue:

"Once at Wright Field, a group of scientists and pilots were discussing the consequences of automation. 'Automation can do many things, but you still need a human being in the cockpit,' insisted a veteran test pilot.

'For instance,' he added, 'where can you get a servomechanism that can react instantly, make decision based on judgment, yet weigh only 150 pounds?' Commented von Kármán, 'Yet you must remember that there is a lead-time of twenty years or so before the servomechanism of which you speak can become operational. However,' he added, suppressing a smile, 'there are things in its favor. It can be created with unskilled labor.' "

Strains and pressures took a toll on von Kármán's well-being. He required major surgery in 1944 and was tended by a doctor of finest repute. However, when he healed with a hernia, he angrily admonished the surgeon, "In an aircraft factory, if a mechanic makes as poor a welding as you did with my intestines, he would be fired!" The medical man was so startled at this complaint that he informed von Kármán's sister that the patient was having some mental disturbance. But it is safe to assume that Pipö knew well her brother's sense of humor and was not alarmed.

Von Kármán's recuperation at Lake George was interrupted by a telephone call from General Arnold. With apologies for intruding on his convalescence, the General asked if a meeting might be arranged at La Guardia Airport the following week regarding a vital matter.

As the Hungarian waited at the end of the airstrip in a limousine, the General's airplane touched down. What could be this urgently important, he wondered, as Arnold sent the chauffeur out of earshot. "World War III," Arnold astonished him by saying; then added, "I want to know what airpower can do to prevent it!"

The General told him that World War II was already won. Now, with utmost energy and determination, they must begin a new battle—a preventive one. Jet propulsion, rockets, missiles, radar, and all the new electronic development—what does it mean? What will be the shape of aerial warfare in ten to twenty years? What will 1965 bring?

This was the avalanche that fell upon von Kármán. It was a challenge unequalled in his vivid career. Like a strange charge that changed the polarization, the weakness of his body was transformed into vigor. The momentary occupation of his mind with his own physical condition was replaced with the mightier concern for the condition of the world. Now, as victory was in sight in the struggle against the ghastly disease of war that had been a scourge for the past four years, there was suddenly a vital plan to keep the world well. All the elements that could nourish its defenses must be employed. New "treatments" must evolve from brain and laboratory to insure that it would never again fall victim to the holocaust of war.

"What do you want me to do?" von Kármán asked the four-star General who commanded our Air Force. "Kármán, I want you to come to the Pentagon and form a group of scientists, one or two for every domain of the new technology. And with these scientists, you shall work out a blueprint for future research and development." The Hungarian agreed with one proviso, "I will do it, General, so long as no one gives orders to me, and I don't have to give orders to anyone."

Thirty-one giant brains, known as the Air Force Scientific Advisory Group, undertook this crusade, with standard-bearer von Kármán charting their course. They traveled extensively to laboratories and development centers of the United States and hopped oceans to probe the advancements of Japan, England, and Switzerland. The first product of this collective effort was succinct, a thin volume entitled *Where We Stand*. Then followed a gusher of information, interpretation, and prediction—twenty volumes with the hopeful name *Toward New Horizons*.

The advancements that you will read about in tomorrow morning's headline were anticipated in chapters of this series; many new projects that still remain as classified were planned and instigated by this monumental report.

Among the visionary projects detailed in this 1944 report were: an earth satellite, intercontinental rockets and missiles, antimissile defense, automatic celestial navigation, and supersonic bombers and interceptors. These are but a few of the vital contributions contained in the committee's lengthy work.

During the thousands of miles he covered for this committee, von Kármán once became annoyed at a five-hour take-off delay and filled out one of the "complaint forms," with the suggestion that passengers be given rebates in event of such inconvenience. In due time a reply was forthcoming, firmly rejecting the idea, with the name of the president of American Airlines signed to it; but it would appear a fourth assistant must have dictated the letter, for it stated, "Obviously, Mr. von Kármán, you do not understand the basics of aviation."[4]

As one block builds upon the next, von Kármán's traveling for the Scientific Advisory Group made him aware of a serious condition: the world direly needed scientific co-operation. War had left in its wake the devastation of many laboratories, and there was lacking the kind of interchange that could formulate progress. Scientific talent was floundering in the heavy seas of upheaval, and a lack of communication between groups and areas stymied the onrush of potential developments.

A plan formed in von Kármán's mind for the greatest scientific effort ever attempted—it would be international in nature, encompassing all the aeronautical sciences in its scope!

This was an audacious undertaking. Rivalries, language barriers, inborn suspicions, lethargy, ignorance—von Kármán would encounter these and a hundred more reactions instinctive to the human race when faced with a new idea. But his plan was solid—undeniably important—and his was the faith to carry it to fulfillment.

AGARD, the Advisory Group on Aeronautical Research Development, gave its first gurgle of life in the spring of 1952. Its parent was NATO, the North Atlantic Treaty Organization. The godfather was von Kármán's own Air Force Scientific Advisory Group. As for the inspired aerodynamicist who had been creator and catalyst for the effort, he was ready to bow out and allow it to mature under other tutorage.

But the post of Chairman of AGARD had to be filled. Where could they find an internationally recognized scientific figure of great stature who has the human understanding to blend the diverse temperaments and tangents of a multi-nation group? Where would there be a triple character: scientist, diplomat, raconteur? Wrote *Newsweek* magazine on March 4, 1957, "Von Kármán, with his many languages, eminence, and friendships with everyone in the field, is perhaps the only man alive who could make the thing work." All of these qualities were brought into play soon after von Kármán took over as Chairman of AGARD. The October 1957 issue of *Air Force* magazine related the incident in this manner:

"Probably the greatest victory for von Kármán diplomacy, however, occurred last fall during an international scientific conference at Brussels which was attended by scientists from both sides of the Iron Curtain. During the opening session, four of von Kármán's former Caltech students, who had returned to Communist China, invited their former teacher to dinner. Von Kármán accepted but asked them to come to his hotel room first for cocktails. Later in the day, five Chinese who were former Caltech students but were now teaching in the United States or in Formosa asked von Kármán to dinner. Without batting an eye, he accepted, and asked them, too, to his room for cocktails at the same hour he had invited the Communists. The Communists arrived first and were already having apéritifs when the other group arrived. All nine, together with von Kármán and a lady friend, went to dinner at a Chinese restaurant. The following day, the nine former students posed with von Kármán for a picture. One thing still perplexes von Kármán about the incident, however. 'I do not know who picked up the check,' he says."

To those who may mistakenly regard United States' participation in AGARD as a "one-way street," von Kármán observes that Europe has long been more advanced in some phases of aeronautical science than has America. For instance, in 1939, we were late in the introduction of jet propulsion; the Germans flew the turbojet Heinkel-178.

When we did introduce jet power, we copied a British engine designed by Sir Frank Whittle. In applying the design of the swept-back wing, we followed experiments of the Germans. So a program of international aeronautical research will bring benefits to our country, as well as to the other NATO nations.

From the broad and challenging expanse of the subject, five areas were selected for the initial effort: combustion, flight testing, wind tunnel design, aeromedicine, and documentation. The latter is a detailed program efficiently to catalog, abstract, and distribute important aeronautical papers and publications; the publishing of AGARDographs makes specialized material, not otherwise readily accessible, available to scientists.

Friends of von Kármán's saw in his great AGARD activity a two-way blessing. Just before the founding of this organization, he lost his beloved sister Pipö. She had been his perfect companion throughout life. Following World War I, she had been general manager and hostess at a meeting that may have inspired AGARD; at Innsbruck, von Kármán had brought together experts from many nations on aerodynamics and hydrodynamics.

Pipö could understand him intellectually (holding a doctorate of her own in the history of art) and intuitively arranged his home life to obviate disturbing influences; she wove into their family activity a certain emphasis on art and literature to balance the scientific activity.

Two of the loving tributes that now stand in memory of Pipö are the scholarship that von Kármán founded in her name for the education of Europeans in America, and the portrait of Pipö and her brother unveiled at the dedication of the Air Force Gas-Dynamics Facility in Tullahoma, Tennessee. At the ceremony, Dr. Hugh Dryden averred, "We join in a belated public recognition of her contribution to science and technology through a lifetime of assistance and inspiration, guidance, counsel, and companionship to an illustrious, creative scientist."

Under the classification of "Unfinished Business" in his scientific career, von Kármán files statistical theory of turbulence. "Fluid motion—air or water—in most cases is not smooth motion. (The smooth motion they call laminar.) If it is turbulent, that is when the particles go random. But every random phenomenon, we believe, must have fundamental statistical laws. These were first started by Sir Geoffery Taylor in England; I took them up and made them more mathematical and more general, working with an English student of mine, Leslie Howarth—now a professor in Manchester. Others of my excellent students contributed, like C. C. Lin, a professor at Massachusetts Institute of Technology. But I have not finished the building up of a whole system of the turbulent air."

Conveying the complexity of this problem, von Kármán relates, "The famous German physicist, Arnold Sommerfeld, once said to me, 'Before I die, there are two things I really would like to understand: the real sense of the quantum theory, and the real basis of turbulence.' However," says von Kármán, "if I have not understood them before I die, I shall call upon my Creator to explain only the quantum theory—the turbulence is so difficult that even the good Lord cannot explain it."

Though first and last a dedicated scientist, the Hungarian has always participated in an active social life; and it would appear from the following story that he tells that all his research has not been limited to the laboratory: At a meeting of the Royal Aeronautical Society, famed British aviatrix, Amy Johnson, asked von Kármán to explain the mechanics of a tailspin. He replied, "Young lady, a spin is like a love affair. You don't notice how you get into it, and it is very hard to get out of."[1]

To say that von Kármán has never married is only literally true. His has been an eternal union—one with knowledge, truth. From this perpetual enigma, he has wrested solutions to some of man's perplexities. He has fathered offspring endowed with immortality through their place within the sum total of existing knowledge. These theories that he has created answer to strange names—Aerothermochemistry, Aerothermodynamics, Vortex Trails—but they are obedient children, dedicated to the service of mankind.

What time he isn't shuttling to Rome, Paris, London, or Washington on a vital mission, von Kármán lives in his beloved old ranch-style home on a spacious plot of ground in Pasadena. Secretary Marguerite Williams and housekeeper Marie Roddenbery efficiently care for the details of his busy life, and even manage to provide him with occasional spare moments to indulge in such luxuries as playing with his black French poodle, Koko Mephistopheles. He deeply deplores one feature of his life which he will even term a weakness: "I cannot maintain a schedule. I am always late. When I promise an article, it is always in at the last moment, or after the last moment."

The fault here would not seem to be with his manner of maintaining a schedule but rather with the quantity of work he attempts to pack into each twenty-four-hour period. Until the elasticity of time can be realized, there appears no reconciling of the two.

To this man—who has received awards, medals, and citations from almost every leading nation of the world—these were the honors which touched him most deeply: the appointment by Pope Pius XII to the Pontifical Academy, and the presentation from the German Society for Aeronautical Research of the Prandtl Ring, an honor named for his first great teacher-hero. In June, 1960, he was awarded one of the highest honors of his profession, the Lamme Medal "for his outstanding, creative, and inspiring teaching; for his unique leadership in and creative influence on engineering education; and for his active leadership toward international cooperation in science and engineering."

Deep-thinking von Kármán gives his opinion on the ever intriguing question of whether there are living beings on other planets: "I do not think there are living intelligent beings on other planets of our solar system. But I believe there are beings in other solar systems. However, we will not be traveling to those solar systems in the foreseeable future. They are very far away." Then with a twinkle, he reminds us that space travel is really the cheapest type of travel. If you calculate the trip to Venus and back, then divide the cost—though it be tremendous—by the hundred million miles you would be traveling, you will find the cost per passenger mile less than any other mode of travel! But what does he regard as the greatest product of this Space Age so far as mankind is concerned? "Knowledge. I think it is more a question of intellectual curiosity than conquest."

Von Kármán has been actively guiding our own space effort from the earliest days; he was chief consultant on the development of the Atlas, our first operational intercontinental ballistic missile. Yet, at the International Astronautical Federation Congress in Barcelona, when discussing the orbiting satellites of each nation with the Russian scientists, Professor L. I. Sedov and Mrs. Alla Masevitch, von Kármán said, "It appears to me that the good Lord in putting the moon into its present orbit did a better job than our two countries either have done or probably will do."[5]

Such words are starkly revealing, for while much attention has been given to what von Kármán has been teaching, they illustrate that he has also been learning. He has mastered the lesson life teaches its great ones —humility.

REFERENCES

1. *Astronautics,* 3:42–43+, June, 1958.
2. Von Kármán, Theodore: *Aerodynamics—Selected Topics in Light of Their Historical Development,* Ithaca, N. Y., Cornell University Press, 1954.
3. *Saturday Evening Post,* 230:24, August 3, 1957.
4. *Air Force,* 40:41–48, October, 1957.
5. *Interavia,* 12:1227–1228, December, 1957.

*Mathematical giant who was
responsible for today's
high-speed electronic computers*

JOHN VON NEUMANN

The genius and the man seemed inexorably intertwined. John von Neumann had a mathematical brilliance that was legendary; he designed one of the most remarkably complex machines ever built—yet was intrigued with children's toys. He possessed the magnetism to mesmerize friends and associates—yet was shy when meeting strangers. From the depths of a fantastic memory, he could draw out facts, dates, and figures concerning any phase of history with an encyclopedic accuracy—yet he could not recall the names of guests in his home. His theories influenced the economic trends of the world—but he often went out without taxicab fare. He could tackle the incomprehensibly huge project of altering the earth's weather with calm—but he would grow agitated should a train not be on schedule.

Here, also, was a very warm and human man, given to certain frailties, but possessed of the strength to be himself. His contributions greatly hastened the ending of World War II, he persisted in crusading until he put into motion one of our mightiest capabilities for defense, and his theories have influenced many major decisions. Yet, in the same paradoxical fashion of his personality, his name is little known outside the scientific community.

History is crowded with the narratives of bright children who were ignored or punished by parents who were too ignorant to appreciate them. As these children grew to adulthood, though they might have deserved to rank among the world's mental giants, they were often faced with heartbreaking privation, struggle, and ridicule. Such has been the fate of many unusual ones because, in a sense, they were misfits, not conforming to the average, the norm.

But John von Neumann was so individual that his story doesn't even fit the pattern of a misfit. He came of wealthy parents, was appreciated, understood, and encouraged in his spectacular ability which evinced itself from childhood. *Wunderkind,* wonder-child, was what people termed the boy; and the Budapest banker, Max von Neumann, was more proud of this praise than he was of the decoration given him by Emperor Franz Joseph. John's mother, whom everyone fondly called Gita, added her own great strength of character, urging the boy to follow pursuits of the mind.

Ordinarily, the first son would be expected to carry on the family enterprise; but another career was indicated from the agility of John's young brain—at six he could divide two eight-digit numbers in his head; before he was ten he had mastered college calculus. Moreover, he possessed a phenomenal photographic mind, which enabled him to glance at the page of a telephone book, then repeat the names, addresses, and phone numbers of an entire column. He was a kind and thoughtful child, congenial with other youngsters, but usually preferring the companionship of a history book or studious conversation with adults—who did well to hold their own with him!

John was aware that he was unusual, but he was not made to think that he was strange. Deep pride in his capacities was instilled in him and a respect for the Creator who had endowed him. He must have been conscious from an early age that he was drawing on more than mortal reserve, for he commented often throughout his lifetime that mathematics was a subconscious process; the most difficult problems he would drop into his mind for solution during sleep.

A chain of circumstances seemed to formulate, providing opportunity for his development: The Lutheran High School in Budapest was one of the finest in the world. Its teachers, measuring up to rigorous scholastic standards, provided real stimulus to John. Many elements help to mold a young person; the Hungarian capital abounded in an atmosphere of culture, a respect for accomplishment, and the chance for the inspiring companionship of a distinguished group of mathematicians. While still in high school, he was guided by the distinguished mathematician Leopold Fejer of the University of Budapest. It was Fejer who entitled him "Our Country's Greatest Jancsi," (Jancsi being the nickname for John). The young man upheld the honor.

Practicality crept into Max von Neumann's thinking as his son approached university level. The positions open to a mathematician were almost exclusively in the realm of teaching—which, while respected, by the family's standards was low in remuneration. Could there not be another, a more materially promising path, that his son might follow? He sought council from Dr. Theodore von Kármán, the distinguished teacher and aerodynamicist, who had made important research contributions, even as early as that year of 1920.

Recalls von Kármán, "John was an outstanding seventeen-year-old boy when his father brought him to talk with me. It was a good visit, and both were satisfied with the compromise I suggested—that he study chemistry, a field which then appeared to hold more financial promise than mathematics." The years at the University of Berlin were followed by another two at one of the finest engineering schools in all of Europe, the *Technische Hochschule* in Zurich; there he became a student of Hermann Weyl. But though John von Neumann thus followed the letter of the "compromise," the spirit was not there. So after being awarded a degree in chemistry in 1925, he returned to his first dedication by winning a Ph.D. in mathematics from the University of Budapest the following year.

This was a place and an era of most remarkable scientists. From Hungary emerged four brilliant men, who have been dubbed "The Martians"; von Neumann, von Kármán, Dr. Edward Teller, and Dr. Eugene P. Wigner. Another scientist of this background was Dr. Leo Szilard. These five men have made scientific contributions to the United States that are beyond estimating.

Von Kármán relates the story of having worked with von Neumann during World War II at the Army Ordnance Laboratories at Aberdeen, Maryland. After the War, the commander, in an interview to the *Washington Post,* commended the help of both von Neumann and von Kármán and remarked on the coincidence that they both were from an obscure Hungarian village—the name of which he could not recall. Von Kármán pointed up the amusing slip by phoning the General and saying, "I want to call your attention to the fact that Buda, half of Budapest, was already a big city before Washington, D. C., was founded!"

But the "big city" of Budapest was not a happy city in 1926. Unrest and a succession of regimes had produced a stormy period after World War I. There followed 100 days of Communism, then the counterrevolutionary government finally gained control with Admiral Horthy as its regent. Under this force there were heavy reprisals against leaders of the workers and also against those of a minority faith. John von Neumann left his native city for Hamburg, the German center for mathematicians.

Later, at the famed University of Göttingen von Neumann spent two years as a Rockefeller Fellow and met another student who was to influence his life, H. P. Robertson. At the age of twenty-three he made his first major contribution to his chosen field—a treatise entitled *Mathematical Foundations of Quantum Mechanics*. In this he proved the mathematical equivalence of Erwin Schrödinger's wave mechanics and Werner Heisenberg's matrix mechanics. Thus he aided the firm foundation of modern physics, for all atomic and nuclear physics are based on the quantum theory—the theory that energy is not a smoothly flowing continuum but is the emission and absorption of energy in atoms.

It was to the young man's personal credit that his great ability was not accompanied by boastfulness. The dimensions of his grasp were becoming apparent at this early age; had he not been imbued with wisdom, as well as intelligence, the honor and acclaim might have altered his personality. There was quiet assurance in efforts, but a ready admission, "I can't solve it," should a problem stump him—though few did. This childlike candor remained a part of his reaction throughout his eventful life.

During the same year that he wrote his famed treatise, von Neumann was invited to become a Privatdocent at the University of Berlin. As assistant professor, he lectured to students scarcely two or three years his junior. Teaching provided the stimulation that von Neumann needed. He began a most remarkable habit of lecturing without notes, selecting a problem which he had not yet solved and tackling the solution of it as he lectured!

Three hundred years ago, the Bernoulli family was the first to figure odds of probability for the gamblers of France. Von Neumann was fascinated—not by the card games, but by a parallel which he drew between parlor games and some important phases of living. In games of strategy, such as poker, there is a human factor in making choices, and the pay-off of the game can depend on making guesses about what cards the other fellow holds while concealing one's own cards; there are the elements of deception and of counterplay. How this rivaled situations in life von Neumann realized! But it was a tremendous challenge to determine the best choices in games of strategy—far more involved than figuring odds on pure games of chance, such as dice games. Yet from his ponderings and deductions came a theory of games clearly defining (1) pure strategy, a plan formulated in advance by a player for playing the game from beginning to end, and (2) mixed strategy, a method of choosing a pure strategy by having chance select the strategy for a player.

Zermelo and Borel had previously projected similar thinking, but von Neumann's *Minimax Theorem* firmly established the theory: Minimax is the crucial point at which the greatest gain that Player #1 can be sure of making and is equal to the amount to which Player #2 can definitely limit Player #1. Importantly, a similar concept, that of imputation, could be applied to games in which more than two players are involved, thereby opening the way to groups, or alliances.

Throughout this study, which lasted for decades, it is interesting that von Neumann always played an average poker game—perhaps consistent with the theory he had set forth. That was of little consequence, for the game was but a tool for study; mathematicians generally work with models instead of the real problems they are attacking. In this instance, von Neumann had used a game to represent a contest of any sort between human opponents, taking into account the opportunities that might be present and the decisions that would have to be rendered. This theory of games applied helpfully to such diverse areas as the buying-and-selling habits of people in the world of economics and to specific military problems. Its scope was consistent with the always diverse interests of the young mathematician. Though von Neumann was but twenty-five when he first published his paper on this notable theory in 1928, there have been no revisions in the over-all concept.

Opportunity soon provided the answer to desire when Princeton University extended an invitation to him to occupy a chair of mathematical physics. This was arranged through his friend of Göttingen days, Dr. H. P. Robertson. The political festering of the Right he had sought to escape by leaving Hungary had spread to Germany, and he envisioned that it would in time assume the epidemic proportions of war. Also, his keen understanding of history gave him a thorough appreciation of America's magnificent experiment, and he was eager to explore firsthand the workings of this unique democracy.

That the outstretched hand of freedom which we extend also returns to us benefits manyfold was emphasized by Senator Henry M. Jackson of the State of Washington on April 29, 1957. When pleading the case for a continuation of the Hungarian refugee program, he cited Dr. John von Neumann, "the world's greatest mathematician," as a refugee whose "contributions to the security of our country are so numerous that it would require a long time to enumerate them."[1]

It may seem surprising that von Neumann could not be rated as an exceptional teacher, but this is readily understandable when it is qualified "not exceptional for the ordinary student." The mathematician's lightning-fast mind sent him speeding ahead of the usual grasp—not only of students, but of his colleagues as well. As he plowed through problems, he would soon fill a blackboard with formulas, then erase and continue, which brought forth the wry comment from one befuddled mathematician, "I see. Proof by erasure."[2]

While this facileness was discouraging to most, the student capable of following von Neumann's lectures was greatly stimulated. And the teacher's schedule was never so heavy that he could not find time to assist a promising student or a worth-while project. When he had this individual contact, or was lecturing to a lay group and was conscious of keeping his level of discussion consistent with their capability to absorb, he could score by conveying the most complex problems in lucid terms, pausing and smiling to verify that they were "with him" as he progressed.

An interesting characteristic was von Neumann's response to challenge —he worked well and speedily under pressure. This trait, when extended to other areas, was not without its complications. When faced with the complexity of a traffic jam, he would rise to the demand with increased pressure on the throttle, terrifying any passengers. But when there was open road ahead of him, he relaxed into a disinterested slow gait. His accidents from this method of handling a car soon mounted, and he had the dubious honor of having the intersection of his most frequent mishaps dubbed "Von Neumann Corners." His touching explanation of one of his encounters with the law of impact went as follows: "I was proceeding down the road. The trees on the right were passing me in orderly fashion at sixty miles per hour. Suddenly one of them stepped out in my path. Boom!"[2]

But his driving was not the only point for discussion among his associates at Princeton. They responded to his great warmth and talent for entertaining. Gatherings and parties at the von Neumann home were high points of any season, for there was an air of complete enjoyment, combined with the keen stimulation of his discussions.

Von Neumann could make contact with the understanding level of a child or with the comprehension of a scholar. Subject matter was no barrier. His expert knowledge covered mathematics, physics, and economics; added to that was a "hobby" of history which was of such proportions that it shamed most who had made this their specialty. One time a world expert on Byzantine history attended one of his parties; he and von Neumann got into a discussion concerning a minor historical point. They did not agree on a date; verification proved von Neumann right. When next asked to the von Neumann house, the expert agreed, on a half-serious condition: "I'll come if Johnny promises not to discuss Byzantine history. Everybody thinks I am the world's greatest expert in it, and I want them to keep on thinking that."[2]

So it was with this amazing Hungarian, that in utterly unrelated fields —whether it be trains, typhoons, or typography—he was alert and interested in everything except trivia. Since he possessed such profound powers of logic, he could adapt his thought pattern, quickly superimposing it over a strange area to give him a clairvoyant-seeming insight into it.

"Jancsi" or "Johnny," as friends called him, was a great wit. He had a repertoire of jokes and a flair for limericks; Dr. Edward Teller commented that he was the only friend with whom he could pun in three languages —adding that to pun in only one language was like painting a picture in black and white. Von Neumann also delighted in creating spontaneous poetry with his friend Dr. H. P. Robertson; they would concoct alternate lines of verse, each trying to outdo the other in wit and diversity.

One type of conversation was never heard from the mathematician—that was the derogatory form referred to as gossip. He had a faculty for perceiving what was worth-while in a person; and though with his astute mind he certainly saw the other qualities he discarded them in his consideration. This might well explain his difficulty in recalling names—he seemed to care not who a person was but merely what he was.

Von Neumann responded to good company and good food. In the midst of the music and confusion of a night club, he frequently snatched up paper and pencil and jotted down equations. Once when a secluded room was provided for his work, his unexpected response was one of hurt because he felt he was being kept from the center of activity.

A five-million-dollar donation from Mr. Louis Bamberger and his sister, Mrs. Felix Fuld, founded the Institute for Advanced Study at Princeton which opened in 1933. Abraham Flexner set about to gather a faculty. Appointed to a full professorship at this imposing venture into higher learning was Albert Einstein; another of the first invitations was issued to John von Neumann, who was not quite thirty years old. Although there are some activities which they share the Institute and the University are organizationally and administratively distinct. The Institute does not conduct classes in the usual sense; individual research projects are followed in fields ranging from mathematics to archaeology. This research center for eminent scholars awards no degrees. Requirements state that members must already have the highest degrees in their respective fields. It has been a lofty and most productive experiment into learning, offering a unique opportunity.

In a most advanced state the Institute bore similarities to the free and exploratory type of educational environment which helped to shape the mind of von Neumann in his youth; it has been speculated that the routine of our American undergraduate schools might well have hampered his progress, the thinking being that our great emphasis on conformity is apt to crush the spark of individualism in the unusual student.

Dr. Edward Teller says of von Neumann, "I still wonder how much of his great abilities were due to what a person would call a gift and how much of it was training; but I suspect that it was due to an early discovery of the joy of thinking and an almost perpetual exercise of this activity."[3]

The John von Neumanns are few—distressingly few, within the long annals of time. Yet, if one even approaching his capability is limited or thwarted the loss to the world is inestimable. There are greater crimes than "not belonging to the crowd"; not reaching the stature for which one is created numbers as a truly serious sin of omission.

The decade of the Thirties was eventful in von Neumann's personal life: He became an American in fact as well as in spirit. His circle of friendships continued to increase throughout the world's scientific community.

A daughter, Marina, was born; she early displayed a rightfully inherited superior intellect. He became a member of the distinguished National Academy of Sciences. His book, *Mathematische Grundlagen der Quantenmechanik* was published in German (later reprinted in English). His marriage to Mariette Kovesi was dissolved. He was awarded the American Mathematical Society's Bocher Prize. (He was a Gibbs Lecturer and a Colloquium Lecturer for that Society.) Scientific papers continued to flow from his pen.

Pressures for ever increasing productivity were felt through the steadily mounting numbers of United States military experts who sought counsel at the Institute. Technical ramifications continually arose to block defense preparations, and it was evident that the gravest need was yet to come. Von Neumann had sensed Germany's falling barometer in 1928 before he left for America; the war clouds had gathered relentlessly. The storm was clearly imminent when he briefly returned to Hungary in 1938.

While in his native country, he married a friend of many years, Klara Dan. Pointing up their diverse backgrounds, she relates, "I lived for fun—in England and on the Riviera. I had a marvelous time, but I actually did not know the meaning of the word 'science.' Then, in 1938, I married Johnny and was plunged into scientific groups. I listened to them and could understanding nothing."[4]

His was a world unto itself, with its own specialized forms of high excitement—peaked by such rewards as finding prime numbers! Klara recalls an evening spent in a hotel room in Washington, D. C., during which her husband and a mathematician friend spent hours searching their wallets and their memories for choice specimens of prime numbers—a prime number is one which can be divided only by one and by itself. They were thrilled by such big primes as 65537! Von Neumann was always searching for prime numbers on the license of every car that passed him.

The Institute for Advanced Study was an exceptional cloister for von Neumann's creativeness. Whereas his early interests had been centered about the theoretical, pure mathematics—quantum theory, mathematical logic, ergodic theory, continuous geometry, problems of rings of operators —the years at the Institute brought about a marked transition in his efforts. The practical application of his work assumed greater importance; and most of his colleagues concur that his best work resulted from this impetus.

Additional thought was given to his theory of games, first stated in the treatise published in 1928. If, for the word "games," the word "conflict" were substituted, and if consideration were given to man's consistent areas of conflict, none appeared greater than that of business, finance, economics. It was von Neumann's evaluation that the understanding of economics was at a stage of development similar to that of physics prior to Newton's contributions.

Professor of Economics at Princeton, Dr. Oskar Morgenstern, was von Neumann's close friend. Together they played an intellectual form of tennis, batting back and forth ideas that were returned when well placed or left when they went too wild. From such interchange sprouted the collaboration on the book, *Theory of Games and Economic Behavior,* published in 1944. This study broadened the viewpoint, loosened prior restrictions, and appraised the prospect of growth with a definitive formula: A uniformly expanding economic system can exist providing the rate of expansion is equalled by the rate of interest. So widespread was the influence of this new approach that the minds of other economists were stirred, resulting in a flood of comment in the form of articles and books. A not unusual estimation of this work ranks it as one of the major contributions since the turn of the century. And this was but one of the monumental donations from von Neumann's talents.

Once the science of mathematics contained only finite systems in which every question had a "black or white," right or wrong answer. Then came infinite systems, the "grey" areas where there are no definite answers. To those who think of mathematics as being as absolute as "two and two always equalling four," this may be difficult to understand. A simple illustration of the infinite systems might be this: The ratio of the circumference of a circle to its diameter is pi, approximately 3.1416. But if one wants a more exact figure for pi, how is it written? 3.14159265+? How many numbers beyond that + should be added? Is there ever a final number among the digits? Though this is a foolish-sounding question, it provocatively illustrates that in infinite systems there are certain mathematical questions that have no definite answers, for pi is an infinite number with no repeated sequence of numbers. This was one of von Neumann's favorite fields, one that he had explored since his teens.

Every profession has its own special brand of stories. Among mathematicians stories often veer from the joke category into tests of mental agility posed in humorous terms. When Viscount Cherwell, the late scientific advisor to Churchill, heard one such story, he eagerly awaited his next visit with von Neumann, which took place at Oppenheimer's home in Los Alamos. There he posed this puzzle: One morning bicyclist A and bicyclist B started riding toward one another from points twenty miles distant. They were each pedaling at ten miles per hour. As they started a precocious fly decided to enliven their journey by flying from the nose of A to the nose of B and back again to A and so on, flying twice as fast as the men were cycling and making as many trips as possible. The problem was to determine the total distance the fly traveled before A and B met and squashed the fly between their noses as they collided.

Von Neumann's alert mind had started clicking with the figures of diminishing distances and, by the end of the story, readily produced the correct answer. Someone asked him how he determined the answer so quickly, and he answered "by geometric series." An outstanding scientist who was present pointed up the true humor of the incident by remarking that the story was a trick and anyone could have come up with the answer, but that von Neumann had the ability to compute it in this most elaborate mathematical manner and come up with an answer as quickly as anyone else could have by seeing through the trick.

A vitally important event gripped the United States. We became involved in World War II.

Von Neumann was called on frequent trips to England in connection with a United States Navy assignment. His periods of absence afforded Klara von Neumann an opportunity she had long sought—to begin a study of his field. She was not content to continue sharing only a portion of his life, for the exposure to scientific activity proved too great a lure.

She accepted a post with a population-research organization; primarily it utilized her linguistic abilities, but it also afforded her the chance to become familiar with statistical processes. Delighted with her interest, her husband snatched moments between trips to tutor her and thereby test a belief he'd long held—that the learning of mathematics can be effectively accomplished, and be infinitely more fascinating, by plunging into advanced phases. As elementary theory was needed, she went back and picked it up. Klara's remarkable progress was proof of the plan. She achieved the capability of programming computers—which she terms a sort of "mathematical clerical work."

The work involved translating problems from terms that a mathematician would use into terms that the machine would understand. A very tedious and vexatious problem it becomes too, for the machine has very limited understanding compared with men; its vocabulary is generally limited to such language as "add, subtract, divide, take the number stored in this place and transfer it to here." Klara was pleased, and Johnny was proud. She could do it.

The most frequent comment from people who first come to the United States concerns the country's "wide open spaces." The vastness of our land, the great expanses that meet the eye on every side, impress visitors and may well be reflected in a certain quality of the American spirit—we are generally candid, open, frank about our thoughts, our shortcomings, and our plans. So it was almost miraculous that we kept so well guarded a secret of such importance and magnitude as the Manhattan Project. As whispers of it traveled through a few tight circles, as they were bound to do, the members of the press had closed ears. With a reporter few things can come before "getting that story." The survival of his country is one of the few. The news never leaked.

Lieutenant General Leslie R. Groves assumed the tremendous responsibility of directing this effort, and he quickly gathered the finest brains in the country. Von Neumann was among them. Guarded military transport planes made regular runs from Los Angeles, Washington, and other major cities, flying to a destination known only to passengers and crew—and even the crew knew nothing of what the project entailed.

Los Alamos. The name was never spoken out loud. The quiet New Mexico town played host to some of the most prominent scientists of the free world, but she could only greet them with a silent nod. They gathered. They went about their important business. Gates were guarded. Passes were checked with scrupulous care. Townspeople never asked questions. The announcement would come in time. It was to be the most thunderous roar ever heard by the ears of man.

Calculations indicating that 100 pounds of pure U-235 would give a colossal, explosive force, equalling 20,000 tons of T.N.T., had been made as early as 1942! The possibility was overwhelming in its significance. It became imperative that the United States, gripped with a losing war at that period, rush this project into action. But the aim was for 100 pounds of a material which, in 1942, did not exist—not even one millionth of a pound of it.

As three different methods were set up for the separation of the precious U-235 from its natural companion, U-238, one laboratory operated at Berkeley, California, another at Columbia University, and a third at Knoxville, Tennessee. Meanwhile, the fourth geographic location assumed top importance—Los Alamos. On a lonely mesa, thirty-four miles from Santa Fe, Dr. J. Robert Oppenheimer took over direction of the weapon development work.

Any weapon is the product of aim and result—of the objective and the attainable. How were the products of the production plants to be reduced to pure metal? By what method could it be fabricated to the required shapes? What was the size to be? What of the weight, which must be governed by the maximum load capability of the B-29 that would drop it. Would the intended explosive force endanger the airplane? How was it to be fused to detonate at the proper instant in the air above its intended target? The problems were multitudinous and formidable. The one of detonation was among the gravest. This giant that was being constructed on paper—which could never be fully tested—had to be meticulously triggered to unleash its unholy blast. But how?

Von Neumann considered this a proper problem, so he set about at once to solve it.

At this point in his scientific career, his colleagues had ceased to be amazed at the productivity of his mind, which roamed and scurried in a dozen different places at once, like a gently poised but always darting hummingbird. It was somewhat surprising that he was able successfully to avoid arousing the human reactions of jealousy and envy from others—often the harvest reaped by accomplishment. This fact was due in part to his utter lack of pomposity, a good measure was due to his ever willing attitude of helpfulness to everyone—but most of all it must be credited to the simple fact that he knew.

There were no doubts, no quibbling. If "Johnny" said this was the way, this was it. One of the top men in government voiced what all felt: If Johnny investigated a problem, it was not necessary to hold any further conferences or discussions. He would tell them what should be done. It was that simple.

Despite this vote of utter confidence from his peers, it still might have come as a shock if the great assemblage of brain power involved in the Manhattan Project were suddenly informed "Von Neumann will cut a year off your time!" The schedule was already pressed to the absolute maximum in speed and had the highest priority of the nation. Still von Neumann did it with his answer to the detonation problem: the implosion method. This means of detonation by an inward burst is the discovery that is credited with slashing one full year from the development period of the atom bomb!

The path marked "If" is crammed with turnings that prevent our looking through to any destination. Only one thing is dramatically evident: had the delivery of the atom bomb been delayed by one year, there would be more empty chairs in America today—chairs made empty by the additional invasion force that would most surely have had to be called upon to end World War II.

Throughout the years of the War, there was a consuming earnestness to von Neumann's efforts and a driving urgency to do what could be done in the fastest possible way. But there was never any but the most optimistic attitude reflected, for at the outbreak of war he had run involved computations at the Institute in Princeton as to the probable resolution of the conflict. The figures confirmed his belief: Even though we suffered a slow start, he knew that the Allies would be victorious because of our great industrial strength. His complete faith in the outcome, at moments when tremendous setbacks might have influenced top-level thinking, acted as an exceptional boost to morale—morale, that quality often associated with a GI but equally important to a general behind a desk.

Johnny von Neumann valued the power of laughter. He often recounted, with appropriate gestures, his introduction to Los Alamos: His orders had been given in strictest secrecy. The assignment was one vital to the nation.

He had proceeded to this isolated region of New Mexico with expectant awe and a good share of anticipation for the job ahead. He was met at the station by a government car and a close-mouthed driver who whisked him to a heavily guarded building where a top secret session was underway. He was cleared to enter, and arrived just as Oppenheimer was finishing his report regarding the meeting with the British in Toronto. There were the names of world leaders, such as Churchill, used appropriately in the report. It was revealed that an important British delegation would be visiting Los Alamos in a short time. Oppenheimer paused, scrutinized the assembled group of scientists and high-level military men, wondering if he had left any vital detail out of his important report. "Are there any questions?" he asked. From a far corner of the conference room, a voice boomed out, "Yes . . . when are we going to get a shoe repair shop up here on the hill?"

There were but few moments of release from pressure for the men guiding the production of the world's first atom bomb. Moreover, tension did not always end when the lights were put out. It invaded the privacy of dreams, assuming proportions more terrible than those of daylight, building into a nightmare that would awaken a man in a cold and clammy state.

Seemingly, it is nature's ever present balance wheel to instill conscience in partnership with capability. In most instances, both are to be found. The mind that can create a force will project itself into grave concern over its application.

It was von Neumann's conviction that "the terrible possibilities of mass destruction should not be viewed as typical of what the nuclear revolution stands for."[5] In reminding the world, and himself, that science and technology are neutral, awaiting man's application to give them meaning for good or destructive purposes, he assumed another responsibility: He felt it was his duty, and the duty of every person importantly involved in the development of a force such as the atom bomb, to aid in the administering of what they have created.

A religious scholar to whom von Neumann opened the innermost recesses of his thoughts recalls long conversations with him: "He was deeply conscious of the moral aspects of this wholesale destruction which the atomic bomb could achieve. He saw that as a moral problem; he felt that very, very keenly and was overwhelmed by the consideration. He said, 'We are now in a position to render the entire world first of all uninhabited (it is just a matter of putting up the various stations) and secondly, absolutely uninhabitable.' "[5]

During World War I it was commented upon that the admiral commanding the fleet could lose the British Empire "in an afternoon." Things have undergone great change. Now the prize is not one empire but the whole world, and the time has been shortened considerably—it would take but one fraction of an afternoon.

In the full awareness of this von Neumann said, "It must go on." More fully his reasoning was this: "It is not a particular perverse destructiveness of one particular invention that creates danger. Technological power, technological efficiency as such, is an ambivalent achievement. Its danger is intrinsic." But is there no possible separation? He continues, "Useful and harmful techniques lie everywhere so close together that it is never possible to separate the lions from the lambs." Perhaps all advances should be halted then. But to this he commented, "Prohibition of technology (invention and development, which are hardly separable from underlying scientific inquiry) is contrary to the whole ethos of the industrial age. It is irreconcilable with a major mode of intellectuality as our age understands it." Von Neumann sums it up by saying, "For progress there is no cure. . . . The only safety possible is relative, and it lies in an intelligent exercise of day-to-day judgment."[5]

His brilliance was occupied day to day and hour to hour. The Manhattan Project was but one phase of his myriad activities during wartime. He roamed between submarine warfare projects, ordnance problems, and economic intelligence projects. The pattern established by his prior consultant functions repeated itself here—each group would pigeonhole its "sticklers." These problems which no one else had been able to solve were then tossed on the conference table during von Neumann's next visit, and Johnny would read them; he'd look away in that blank manner which was indicative of a veritable cosmic bombardment of activity within his brain, then he'd scribble a formula, with a smile that seemed to say, "Here you are. This is the obvious answer." Obvious, but only to von Neumann.

The world's return to peace allowed him to make some choice of his range of activities. He promptly plunged into an idea that had been shelved for those several years—a concept for a giant, high speed computer!

Man had freed his back from the lifting of stones; he had freed his arms from the rowing in slave galleys; he had given wheels and wings to his movements; but still his brain remained in bondage. Complication in all fields promised a life sentence at mathematical hard labor unless a parole could be won through the mercy of a computer. Since ancient time when the primitive yet practical abacus had first helped man in his figuring, he had sought assistance. But problems had now so outdistanced progress in mechanical mathematical aids that the quicksand of complexity threatened his very future.

Von Neumann's imagination had been well stirred in his encounter with the ENIAC in Philadelphia before the war; he had utilized this computer to perform some of the tremendous volume of calculation required in the study of a hydrodynamic problem, the interaction of shock waves.

His approach was not commonplace. It couldn't be. This could be the greatest challenge science could ever undertake, for he saw as the ultimate in perfection a computer that could duplicate the processes of the human brain! With furious diligence he pursued studies of neurology, psychiatry; with doctors he discussed in infinite detail the workings and mysteries of this enigmatic nerve substance. The area of the brain's memory was especially fascinating to him. In the hours of dawn, when inspiration would shatter the protective fibers of sleep, von Neumann would hurry to his desk. A few more symbols and formulas were added to his resources.

The Von Neumann Computer emerged! Now he had evolved a prototype, an instrument containing all the basic principles for endless elaboration. It would be used not only in such fields as mathematics and physics, but also in industry and economics. All new tools must have their instruction sheets; this computer and the others that would evolve from it had a series of papers written for those who sought to utilize its benefits. The theory of the functioning and the organization of the computer was stated, also the theory of programming and coding the computer—for these machines must be fed proper information before they will regurgitate the answers.

A name applied to the Los Alamos member of this high-speed computer family was MANIAC, mathematical analyzer, numerical integrator, and computer. Von Neumann's next achievement was the NORC, delivered to the Navy, for the purpose of making a full day's weather prediction in a matter of minutes. The Rand Corporation version was named JOHNNIAC, in honor of its creator. His principles were put to use in the building of the ORDVAC and the UNIVAC, which became a television star in its own right in giving the 1952 presidential election returns.

The government, industry, and the military were quick to seize the advantages of high-speed computers, for as von Neumann stated in an article appearing in *The New York Herald Tribune,* June 11, 1952, "Problems which seem interesting to scientists, but which formerly were impossible for practical reasons, can now be undertaken with this new tool, thus widening the range of scientific investigation."

Von Neumann wore his honors well, perhaps through long practice. He became the world's foremost authority on the "electronic brain."

But his appetite for its eventual state of development was insatiable. His goal was clear: "In principle, he reasoned, there was no reason why some day a machine might not be built which not only could perform most of the functions of the human brain, but could actually reproduce itself, i.e., create more super machines like it."[2] A friend felt it was almost as if von Neumann wanted to design something that could function without human emotions, yet have other human attributes. This he would begin to evolve. But the present state of his theory would produce equipment capable of handling a formidable task he saw upon the horizon—the calculations necessary to produce the H-bomb. Time performs the inevitable disservice of rendering man's products obsolete. The atomic bomb was quickly becoming old-fashioned.

But a dangerous split in scientific ranks occurred! There was diversity of agreement about whether or not to begin the planning of the hydrogen bomb. This occasioned an action from von Neumann which was not consistent with his usual nature—he started a crusade. Always before, his favorite expression had been, "I like to get things done with kinetics, not dynamics." He had not "gone to bat" for any ideas or desires. For the most part, he had not needed to, for the logic and right of his thinking was so clear that it was not necessary to change any minds in his favor.

Now it was imperative that action be taken, and he waged an all-out battle to begin not next week, not tomorrow, but today; and, if someone suggested it be started at nine o'clock this morning, he would counter with eight o'clock. When a temporary impasse was reached, he was so faithful to his goal that he went of his own accord to Los Alamos and began the most elaborate planning of how to program the gigantic numbers of calculations that would be involved in the H-bomb. He was in close contact with his friend, Dr. Edward Teller, who is known as the "father of the H-bomb." The work of programming Teller's theories was undertaken with zeal. Again his efforts "collapsed time." Through his diligence, through his persistence until the H-bomb deadlock was broken and the decision to proceed was reached, and through his great high-speed computers that could ride roughshod over the mountain of calculations to be done, von Neumann hastened this vital project by many months.

For his efforts von Neumann was rewarded on February 15, 1956, with the Medal of Freedom. President Eisenhower commended him for "exceptional meritorious service in promoting the scientific progress of this country's armament program." In April of the same year, the Enrico Fermi Award was bestowed upon him, which carried with it the tax-free gift of $50,000. The citation stated in part that von Neumann anticipated more than anyone else the importance of the high-speed computer in the nuclear energy program and in the general advancement of science. He also was presented with the Air Force Association's Science Trophy for 1955.

It was a source of considerable amusement to the friends of Johnny von Neumann that his agile mind was so smoothly geared to "big things," yet could be thrown into a state of agitation when faced with the "little problems" that most people take in stride. His long-time friend, Dr. Nicholas C. Metropolis, now with the Institute for Computer Research at the University of Chicago, recalls one small but amusing incident involving Johnny von Neumann:

"He and Dr. Ulam and I were once going to Los Angeles from Los Alamos to attend a meeting and were planning to go by train. Von Neumann was especially meticulous about all his travel arrangements, always arriving at the station or airport well in advance of schedule. The slightest impedimenta to the smooth function of his travel schedule always loomed much larger than the fact. So on the morning of the day that we were to leave Los Alamos to be driven to the station at Lamy, New Mexico, we were advised that the Super Chief would not stop that day at Lamy and were advised to take the small airplane from Los Alamos to Albuquerque and board the train there.

"That the train would not be making its regularly scheduled stop seemed so irregular and illogical to Johnny that it caused him a certain amount of excitement. I tried to put him at ease by suggesting that one of the bridges had probably been washed out and that the eastbound Super Chief would probably go as far as Albuquerque and turn around and head back to Los Angeles, whereas the westbound train would go to the nearest point on the other side of the bridge and also turn around with the passengers being exchanged in between. He admitted this as a possibility since we had had some recent thunderstorms.

"We arrived in Albuquerque around 2:10 P.M. with a scheduled departure at two-thirty. There was only one ticket agent on duty, and there was a line of about five people ahead of us. Eyeing the clock and noting the amount of time it took for each customer, Johnny rapidly concluded that our chances of getting our tickets in time to board the train were less than 1%. But shortly thereafter another agent opened his window, and von Neumann quickly dashed over. Just as he was beginning to relax, I heard him excitedly say, 'I knew they would make that mistake!' He had planned to arrive in Los Angeles the next morning, give his talk, and return that same afternoon on the eastbound Super Chief. Someone along the line must have forgotten, so made his return reservation a day later. After a few desperate moments suffered by the agent, he was able to confirm the return accommodations.

"At 2:30 P.M. an announcement was made that a bus was leaving for Belen to board the Super Chief there—there *had* been a washout and the train had been rerouted south. We boarded the bus, and things seemed to be going well until von Neumann looked up and saw a 'Detour' ahead. This again put him into a state of consternation. He asked us whether we thought this detour had been taken into account in the schedule and whether there was now some doubt as to whether we would catch the train.

"I amused him, I believe, by telling him that when we got to Belen the train would not be there. Instead we would go by mule pack to Flagstaff and presumably would hitchhike the rest of the way. The incredible part of the story, but indeed factual, is that when we were disembarking from the bus, the loud, clear braying of a donkey broke the stillness! Von Neumann jumped, turned around and said, 'Great Scott! I think you are right!' "

The steppingstones into space were not necessarily recognized as such at the time each was laid. But without the broad base of these developments and discoveries there would never have been the prospect of man's exploring the universe. And, it is a cold fact of history that military support has furthered the rate of progress of many fields—aviation and the specialized science of radar are but two striking examples.

The real story of space does not begin, therefore, with the launching of the first courageous astronaut—100,000 men "flew the mission" before him from their desks, conference tables, and laboratories. This advance guard constituted the forty-niners of the era, trekking along uncharted trails, facing obstacles never before experienced, pitting determination against disappointment to clearly mark the way.

The advances of science occur in seemingly unrelated fields, but often one builds upon the other as a pyramid is fashioned. The foundation of the space monument has a few unexpected stones in it. Von Neumann laid some of the most important.

The intercontinental ballistic missile (ICBM) became a possibility only after the occurrence of what is termed the "thermonuclear breakthrough," the H-bomb. The weight of an atomic bomb was too great to constitute a practical war head for a rocket; but the hydrogen bomb, with its greatly increased explosive force and reduced weight, would serve. Therefore, one of von Neumann's most vital contributions to the space story is the relentless campaign he waged for the development of the H-bomb.

When a farsighted Air Force officer, Colonel (now Lieutenant General) Bernard A. Schriever was first urging the investigation of the possibility of a long-range missile, it was von Neumann he contacted for a study and projection regarding the yields and weights of nuclear war heads. (Von Neumann was then the chairman of the Nuclear Weapons Panel of the Air Force Scientific Advisory Board. He had been a member of the General Advisory Committee of the Atomic Energy Commission since 1952.) The study prepared at Schriever's request did much to "push the button" on further ICBM activity.

The forceful and persuasive Trevor Gardner, who was then Air Force Special Assistant for Research and Development, set into motion his dramatic battle for an ICBM program by enlisting the aid of von Neumann in October, 1953; under his chairmanship, a group was organized which became known by the code name, the Teapot Committee (official name, Strategic Missiles Evaluation Committee).

Why would a Princeton mathematician be called upon to function in this position—a position so vital that his recommendations would influence the direction of one of the nation's major defense weapons? Because labels are deceptive. He was not just a mathematician, nor just the leading expert on computers; there was a breadth to von Neumann's interests and capabilities that uniquely qualified him for the spot. It is exemplified in this comment by an officer who was present at one of the first meetings of the committee: "None of the specialists nor experts ever discussed any phase of the technicalities of their individual fields but that von Neumann seemed to know all about them. And more than knowing these separate scientific disciplines, he could integrate the pieces into a whole and complete concept. There was such interplay between the separate elements which the committee had to evaluate that no rigid mind could have properly analyzed the overall."

An added factor which figured into this chapter of the early struggles toward space is the personal prestige of the man von Neumann. The report which the committee would formulate on the possibilities of the success of an ICBM program had to carry with it such weight that it could revamp the prevailing atmosphere. Not many sober statesmen were considering the future of space weapons at this period, and the scientists who talked out loud about space were most likely to be smiled at. The nation's capital was not only skeptical about this stranger who was trying to move into their society; they were downright unfriendly in their reception. Furthermore this would be a most expensive addition to the family, and government was in a strong budget-cutting mood.

But von Neumann's name on a favorable ICBM study would immediately render it a "hot document"—too hot to be ignored or pigeonholed. This Trevor Gardner knew when he enlisted the scientist's support.

Aside from this technical aspect, there was a personal consideration. It is an irrefutable, though often overlooked, fact that everyone is first a "person"—whether he be President, chief of staff, or congressman. His position does not render him immune from human reactions, preferences, influences. Aside from the occupation of lighthouse keeper and certain religious orders, those in almost all other endeavors rely in varying degrees on the matter of this personal relationship. Here, as in so many other ways, von Neumann was superior.

Recalling the first meeting of the Teapot Committee which he attended, Colonel Beryl Boatman speaks descriptively of von Neumann, "At first glance, he appeared just an average height, rather plump man; I received no strong impression. But then the meeting started. He became dynamic and vibrant, with a personality that no one could resist. The very air around him seemed to become supercharged with a kind of magnetic force. He would allow nothing to stand between him and what he believed to be the basic truth and fact; he would sift these things out of all hours of discussion to come up with what I call 'pearls of truth.' He would isolate those focal points which everyone could crystallize on and select a unified course of action. In a few seconds, he could thus summarize a discussion which had taken thirty or forty minutes. Then he would follow through with an almost mathematical approach to the problem—'if this is what you are saying, doesn't it follow that this is your most probable course of action?' In almost every instance everyone agreed. The two principal things he expected in others were objectivity and an open mind. Because of the person he was, people were ready to extend these."

Von Neumann was always ready to listen to others, and for long periods of the meetings he would sit quietly, staring off into space. As he responded to ideas, he would jot down a figure on the pad before him, then carefully tear the paper into tiny bits; ash trays were filled with "von Neumann confetti" by the time a meeting was adjourned. During one of the most pressing periods, he hurriedly asked Schriever for his home telephone number; when Schriever started to write it down, von Neumann merely closed his eyes, repeated the number, and smiled brightly saying, *"Ad infinitum."* No doubt the number did remain with him from then on.

"The Three Musketeers of the ICBM" might be an appropriate designation for von Neumann, Gardner, and Schriever. After von Neumann and the others of his Teapot Committee determined that such a missile as the H-bomb was theoretically possible, Gardner set the governmental and political wheels in motion, urging them to faster turning through his own urgent conviction. Then it became Schriever's responsibility to set up the Western Development Division (later renamed the Ballistic Missile Division, BMD) and transform plans into hardware; with unrelenting devotion he managed the production of the Atlas, Thor, and Titan in less than 50 per cent of the usual development cycle.

Colonel Otto Glasser, project officer for the Atlas, recalls, "One of the unusual aspects of the BMD arrangement, as I see it, was the leadership of the von Neumann committee. From the outset and following on through as the program progressed they periodically sat down in review with those of us on the project—what had we been doing, what problems were we facing, what successes were we achieving, what were new routes that should be explored, where were backups needed, where were they no longer effective or economical, things of this sort. They gave a tremendous amount of guidance to the entire program, for some of the most brilliant minds in the country comprised this Teapot Committee."

On one of von Neumann's trips west he was summoned for an important conference at the Santa Monica, California, offices of the Rand Corporation. This government-sponsored research organization was made up of some of the leading figures of science, but their combined mental reservoir could not produce a trickle of an answer to a problem with which they were faced. So they were seeking advice on the construction of a giant super-computer with which to handle this enormously complex matter.

Von Neumann could not detail the specifications of such a computer without knowing the problem; so the intricacies of it were related. In turns the scientists spoke, producing formulas, diagrams, and tables to convey fully its ramifications. After two hours they had finished. They waited for von Neumann to begin describing the type of computer that might solve their dilemma. But instead he said, "Gentlemen, you won't need a computer." He paused for a moment, staring blankly into space, then scribbled a few figures. "Here is your answer." The conference room was thunderstruck. At last one man spoke up, "We'll still need the computer, because we won't have a von Neumann around."

In light of later occurrences, the remark became sadly prophetic.

Fellow scientists have speculated that perhaps one of von Neumann's greatest efforts, the high-speed computer, was prompted by his innate desire to help others. This was a strong characteristic throughout all his life—helping anyone with a problem. Many of the most esteemed scientists have said that they learned more from him than from any other source, for his approach not only handled individual problems, it was so well-founded that it often influenced wide areas of thinking.

In all fields of endeavor, in art forms for example, the attainment level of the leading figures does not necessarily influence the level of the lesser lights nor contribute to their uplifting. But in science, the output of the guiding few determines to a tremendous degree the value of all lesser levels of ability. Each time science is advanced, the entire community tends to rise a step on the climb toward truth. It is in this frame of reference that the actual scope of one magnificent mind must be measured.

When the pressures of his wartime duties subsided, von Neumann was able to return to the Institute at Princeton and devote himself in greater measure to exploring some avenues of automata utilizing his cherished computers. Nuclear physics, aerodynamics, shock waves, the statistical distribution of stars—all of these areas received his attention. In particular, his work in meteorology was significant, for his calculations gave a fresh approach to the science.

As his work progressed, it expanded into this interesting channel: "the control of weather or, to use a more ambitious but justified term, climate. . . . All major weather phenomena, as well as climate as such, are ultimately controlled by the solar energy that falls on the earth. To modify the amount of solar energy is, of course, beyond human power. But what really matters is not the amount that hits the earth, but the fraction retained by the earth, since that reflected back into space is no more useful than if it had never arrived. . . . Microscopic layers of colored matter spread on an icy surface, or in the atmosphere above one, could inhibit the reflection-radiation process, melt the ice, and change the local climate. . . . The most constructive schemes for climate control would have to be based on insights and techniques that would also lend themselves to forms of climatic warfare as yet unimagined."[5]

How vividly von Neumann could focus our thoughts on the future through his eyes. He thought, understood, planned on a scale almost incomprehensible. His great contention was that the world had run out of room. With each development in our technological process, we had absorbed more and more geographic area. Suddenly there is no room for expansion, for each successive step brought about larger scale operations, and we lack the "safety valve" of former times, when there was room to expand and release built-up pressures or tensions. He lays this growing stress to three factors: more and cheaper energy, more control over the actions and reactions of people, and greatly accelerated communications.

For all of his sober realization of the stupendous problems facing the world, his conclusion reflects the faith that always kept a smile on his face: "The one solid fact is that the difficulties are due to an evolution that, while useful and constructive, is also dangerous. Can we produce the required adjustments with the necessary speed? The most hopeful answer is that the human species has been subjected to similar tests before and seems to have a congenital ability to come through, after varying amounts of trouble. To ask in advance for a complete recipe would be unreasonable. We can specify only the human qualities required: patience, flexibility, intelligence."[5]

Von Neumann's extensive experience and knowledge was well utilized when on October 23, 1954, he was named to the important five-man Atomic Energy Commission. Close upon this came another honor most pleasing to him—an invitation to deliver the Silliman Lectures at Yale University in the spring of 1956. Though his AEC duties were very absorbing, he planned to steal time from his evenings to prepare this lecture series, which was so highly regarded among scholars. His topic: The Computer and the Brain.

But no sooner had he transferred his residence from Princeton to the Georgetown area of Washington, D. C., and adjusted himself to the routine of his daily AEC activities, than a grave illness overtook him. Surgery revealed a secondary cancer in the shoulder region. When able, he returned to his desk, cramming in appointments at a furious pace. Time, that element he had never computed into his life's plan, was suddenly running out.

He continued to attend important conferences, even after he was confined to a wheel chair. When he was moved into Walter Reed Hospital, the Secretary of Defense and other top officials came to his room, seeking his advice on key government decisions. But soon the decisions were more difficult to render. Utter, absolute frustration tormented this scientist, for he had never before encountered a situation in which he was helpless.

When the solace of his mother's regular visits stopped, he suspected the truth—members of the family had insisted that she herself go into the hospital for a checkup, and she was gone within two weeks, the victim of cancer. With valiance and incredible fortitude, she had kept the secret, hoping to outlast her son.

Summoning his secretary to his bedside, he made pathetic efforts to complete the Silliman Lectures—for Yale had agreed that someone else might read them if he could conclude the paper. The attempt was futile. But his great amount of thinking on the matter of the computer and the brain did serve one complete purpose—it closed the circle of his faith. He said to the clergyman who brought him comfort and scholarly companionship in his last days, "I've given much thought and study in my life to the human nervous system. I know what extraordinarily complicated machinery the human intelligence can devise. I also know something of the complication of the human nervous system. There is no comparison between the human nervous system and the most complicated machine that human intelligence has ever devised, or can devise. No man can tell me that behind the complications of the human nervous system there is no such thing as a greater intelligence. For me, that other intelligence is God."

On February 8, 1957, John von Neumann closed his eyes, never to open them again. Then it became clear that the genius and the man were not inexorably intertwined, for it was only the man who was taken. The genius that he created will always remain.

REFERENCES

1. *Congressional Record—Senate,* vol. 103, pt. 5, 85th—1st session, pp. 6116.
2. *Life,* 42:89–90, February 25, 1957.
3. *Bulletin of Atomic Scientists,* 13:150, April, 1957.
4. *Good Housekeeping,* 143:3:80–81+, September, 1956.
5. *Fortune,* 51:106–8, June, 1955.

Colonel, United States Air Force.
Heroic and skillful experimental
test pilot who first pierced the
sonic barrier in the X-1

CHARLES E. YEAGER

This was the boy's first trip to Washington, D. C., and he entered the National Air Museum of the Smithsonian Institution with a breathless kind of eagerness. His eyes darted about, not tarrying to drink in the treasures before him but merely taking quick sips from each. Then his gaze came upon the X-1. There it remained, fixed in fascination, on the needle-nosed rocket ship.

"That's really something to admire, isn't it, boy?" The stranger was staring transfixed too. As the boy nodded solemnly, the old man shook his head a little, as if still disbelieving, and continued: "Can you imagine—that little airplane crashed through a brick wall in the sky? And I knew the pilot who was at her controls, Chuck Yeager. When I first got to know him in Hamlin, he was about your age, young fellow. He was just an ordinary American boy, but he grew up to do very extraordinary things!"

Straddling the Mason-Dixon line, Hamlin, West Virginia, abounded in the qualities that were ideal for a growing boy. The townspeople numbered no more than 1000, so they looked after one another, and shared both joys and setbacks. Picnics and church suppers were among the favorite activities

—with most of the folks that is. But not with young Chuck Yeager. Even from boyhood days he found greatest pleasure in his trips into the woods, hiking beside the streams so filled with fish and hunting with Dad or brother Roy.

Then there was another kind of excitement that flowed through him when he devoured—chapter by chapter—the adventures of Tom Swift. It stirred a response in him that he never wanted to talk about; he was not at an age for talking. The right thing was to help Mom with the chores around the farm, study enough to get by with school (except for arithmetic, which was fun), play football and basketball with all his might, and save the remaining dreams locked safely away. They were nothing but dreams, for how could exciting things ever happen to anyone in Hamlin? At that time it had never really occurred to him that he'd ever leave West Virginia.

It wasn't the fact that World War II had started in Europe; it wasn't just the influence of an Army recruiter visiting Hamlin; it wasn't even the scarcity of jobs in the town that influenced Chuck Yeager. It was simply that since high-school graduation, he had been ready for something that he couldn't define; now he had blocked off more thinking and was just following instinct. With the cautious approval of Mom and the solid advice of Dad, he left in September of 1941 to start the training of an Army pilot.

To apply for cadet training required two years of college and a minimum age of twenty-one. Chuck could fulfil neither qualification. But, as he relates, there was another category into which he could fit: "There was a program for enlisted pilot training, which required just a high-school education. Following this plan, you went through flight training as an enlisted man and then graduated as a staff sergeant pilot. Back in those days, Congress put a limit on the number of commissioned officers that the Army could have in the Air Corps. So, in order to have a larger pilot force, this class, known as enlisted pilots, was set up—very much as the Navy or the Royal Air Force had done."

Two circumstances could have proved disastrous to his budding career: Yeager was so cocky, now that he had set out on the trail of his yearning, that he wore his hat at too rakish an angle; this, plus the attitude that it reflected, nearly got him washed out of training. The second great factor was that he grew deathly airsick for the first few times he was taken up. But he straightened both his hat and his attitude, and nature took care of the second complaint as soon as he was given some function in a plane that served to occupy his mind.

Having first been schooled as a mechanic at Victorville Army Air Base (he now commands the 306th Tactical Fighter Squadron at George Air Force Base, Victorville, California), there was both skill and respect in his approach to an airplane. Yeager says today in appraisal, "You don't find people who can fly an airplane through talent or instinct the way some people can sit down and play any musical instrument. An airplane is a complex mechanism built by man and has certain limitations; so you can't inject a man to make it perform like a musical instrument. There's no natural born pilot—you have to learn the job. Co-ordination and operational routine— you cannot fly unless you learn these things."

Yet the term most often applied to Yeager by the press reporting his accomplishments, by his fellow test pilots, and by his commanding officers, is "natural born pilot." When pressed about these comments, Yeager will modestly say, "It's all a matter of being in the right plane at the right time." Then he adds a comment so significant that it proves the key to the entire matter, "Certain people have a feeling for machinery. If you have this, you don't abuse your machine; it will last longer and work better. A lot of pilots have been killed because they abused their aircraft. It's this same way in research. When you're flying an experimental or research airplane, the engine and all the systems are new and they are stressed to get the most performance. If you abuse the plane, it will blow up. If you respect it, it will deliver for you!"

This basic belief was evident from the time Chuck Yeager first soloed in a little Ryan plane at Ryan Field, Hemet, California. He had thought through every second of it the night before as he lay in his bunk, just the way he used to plan each step of a deer-hunting trip. With eyes closed, he could see the instrument panel with such clarity that it seemed tatooed on his eyelids. His hands would clutch the air and move about, giving him complete command of the imaginary stick. The actual solo flight was just another repetition of the routine; he had been through it so many times before in his mind.

Yeager was given his wings in March of 1943, but still more training followed to equip him for the rendezvous he would have with Messerschmitts and Heinkels over the skies of Germany and France. There were grueling hours to learn formation flying, night flying, acrobatics, dog fighting, and gunnery. A bright spot in the period proved an assignment to Wright Field to do accelerated service testing on the P-39. While there, Yeager also flew the P-47 Thunderbolt, the A-36 inverted gull-wing dive bomber, and the twin-boom P-38. The pilot was served a sampling of his future calling, and he responded with the enthusiasm of a child reveling in a storehouse of new toys.

But these were not toys; they were powerful and intricate instruments to defy the law of gravity. Now, not satisfied with this feat, scientists were beginning to wonder if another of nature's seeming barriers might be smashed. While Yeager tested existing aircraft at Wright Field, a highly secret conversation was underway in another section of the Field on the matter of supersonic flight. The eminent aerodynamicist, Dr. Theodore von Kármán, had been summoned to give an opinion on the matter; his answer threw the switch—he said it was possible.

John Stack, a brilliant research scientist who worked for the National Advisory Committee for Aeronautics, had also probed the question and was formulating proposals for the aircraft that might achieve the victory.

There was yet another thread being spun that would weave into Yeager's future. This one was in a small village in France, where oppression had descended upon freedom-loving people. How could the independent spirit of proud French farmers endure servitude under a Nazi boot? Could the patriotism of a people be stilled simply because they could not fight an open battle? There was yet a way, and French men, women—even youngsters— learned it. The Maquis! The people in the village of Angoulême were already about the grim, dangerous business of the underground.

Yeager, unaware of these overtones that would soon turn his life into a crashing cacophony, was impatient. Now that he had savored the skies, eagerness was straining like a wild beast within him. Fighter pilots were trained to fight. He had done with mock battles. He wanted live ammo and free reign. In just such spirit was he transferred once more—not overseas but to Oroville, California.

It wasn't that Chuck Yeager felt strange around girls—after all, hadn't he grown up with his sister Pansy Lee—even though they'd never been as close as he and Roy? Then, in Hamlin, there were always plenty of girl-type social activities around the school. But things were different now he told his buddies. They were ready for combat, steeped in banks and turns, stalls and rectangular patterns. Why divert such concentration? But he was badly outnumbered. All his buddies went to the USO, and he was delegated to see about a dance for the group.

Glennis Dickhouse felt sorry for the men. She knew how little activity there was in Oroville, especially for those who had come from some bustling area like Chicago or St. Louis. At least the USO gave them a place to congregate. So she put in every moment she could spare from her secretarial jobs—two of them—in pouring coffee, serving doughnuts, and talking with an endless procession of smiling fellows. But this one wasn't smiling. In fact, he seemed pretty grim about asking her if she could arrange a party with the money from his outfit's Snafu Fund. She did, at the Elk's Club.

Before that evening was over, Chuck was amazed at how many things they shared—a love of hiking, swimming, horses, and the comforting feeling of their similar small-town, farm-family backgrounds. She worked for a dairy, and he'd milked cows back home in Hamlin. They had so much to talk about; but, all too soon, he was transferred again.

"Glennis!" As he rallied from unconsciousness, the face before him sharpened into focus. Something was wrong. It was not a small face framed in black hair.

"Lie very still. You'll be all right, Flight Officer Yeager." The authoritative voice verified that he was in the Base Hospital. "Your friend, Glennis, left a message that she was returning to Oroville."

Chuck felt sick. While he had been sent on an unexpected flying assignment from the base at Casper, Wyoming, Glennis had been waiting for their long-planned meeting in Reno, Nevada. Slowly, the events of the day dropped into sequence in his mind. Explosion in his P-39. Fire! The horrible clawing and struggle to get out of his ship. The falling, falling while he grappled for the rip cord. Then the violent jerk as the opening of his chute flipped him over. There his memory ended. The hospital report finished the story. A cracked vertebra.

"Glennis." He murmured it again before his mind blurred, for there had been something very important he'd wanted to discuss with her at that Reno meeting. Now she was gone—back to Oroville.

January of 1944 was a cold gray month in England. It was a cold, sodden anticlimax to every expectation. Somehow Yeager had felt that war was activity, duties, excitement; he had pictured himself taking off at dawn, engaging enemy planes in hairy dogfights, picking up a little flack, then limping back to his base. Now, he decided he had read too many novels about how a war is fought. It wasn't any of those things—at least not for the first month he was overseas.

Monotony dragged the hours by in heavy procession. At a muddy, cold base north of Ipswich, Yeager and his buddies waited, so eager for combat they even welcomed the routine of school once more to teach them the facts about the P-51. When the airplanes arrived, they were briefed and ready. Idleness evaporated. Action materialized.

One mission. Another. Another. Now it was all making sense to Yeager. The planning, the tactics, the briefings—everything was called into play when there were ME-109s in the air around him. March 4th was a day to be marked, for he'd been flying fighter escort on this first big daylight bombing raid on Berlin, and he had shot down his first and second aircraft.

Though the light was bad in his Nissen hut, he'd balanced a writing tablet on his knee to describe the incident in a lengthy letter to Oroville. "Glamorous Glennis came through!" he wrote to the girl whose name adorned the nose of his Mustang. This was the last letter Yeager was to write for a long, long while.

The news spread through Hamlin, West Virginia, like a dark and dreadful cloud. "The Yeager boy has been lost! Reported missing in action over France! Flying a combat mission!" Neighbors came calling. Forced encouragement was offered to the disturbed parents. The usual things were said. Everyone waited—and prayed.

In Angoulême less talking was done, but no less praying. There had been anxious witnesses to the aerial onslaught that shattered Glamorous Glennis and set her afire. The same witnesses saw a body hurtling through the air; finally a parachute blossomed. Courageously they rushed into the woods, hoping to be the first to find the downed flier. The sight they finally beheld was heartbreaking. Blood streamed from the gash on his head. His feet were filled with flack. His slight body was lost in the bulk of the flying suit. "Just a boy," the French mother repeated again and again. But Chuck Yeager was not a boy playing at war. He was in it, enmeshed in the horrible web of it, in German-occupied French territory. The two who had come after him rushed him to the temporary safety of their barn. Soon German bayonets jabbed into the hay; but as if it were the clever manipulations of a magician sticking swords through the box containing his assistant the steel miraculously missed piercing Yeager's body. Helpless, hurting, hardly breathing, he lay in the loft for an interminable time.

Another misery had been added to his torment, for now he knew other lives would be taken if he were found. He made a game of trying to remember the unreal-seeming events since he had struggled from his burning airplane. There was an older man with a big, black mustache—Bertrand. A woman, too—there was a woman. She looked tired from war and worry he recalled from the one glimpse, but she was not old—a daughter perhaps.

Fearful of unconsciousness, he had cautiously slipped a Benzedrine from his pack. If it cleared his mind, it was only to heighten the concern. Who were these people? Why had they taken the terrible risk of coming after him, hiding him? What was he to do now? Where could he go surrounded by German patrols?

Like the white ball on a roulette wheel, the dogged questions spun and spun in his brain. The pain was great—he must continue to think of something, so he turned to other questions, equally unsolvable. Why do men fight wars? Why was I shooting at the FW-190s and the ME-109s? Why did they blast Glamorous Glennis? The struggle for answers ceased. He would just concentrate on the memory of a smiling, pert face. Huddled in the suffocating, dusty haystack, he waited—and waited. At last he was moved into the house.

What had this farmhouse been like before it was permeated with the terrible effects of war Yeager wondered? As an invalid mother supervised, the old man and the daughter bathed his feet and cleaned his head; he could almost see his Mom's kitchen and smell one of her wonderful pies. He was awfully hungry. They gave him soup, some heavy bread, and sour wine.

Then it happened. He beheld the most disturbing sight of all.

A small, frightened child appeared in the doorway. Her huge eyes stirred his soul, and again the harassment began within him: "Now there is also a child to worry about. If you are found here, the Germans will kill her too."

The approach of marching feet stiffened the room. As the sound grew to its peak then gradually decreased, another breath could be taken. Pain and exhaustion were finally the victors. Chuck Yeager closed his eyes in sleep.

The agony of concern was repeated as he rode—for two days and two nights without stopping—with another mysterious stranger who took him the next step on the road to escape. As Yeager pressed the bicycle pedals with his wounded feet, his thought still dwelled on these quiet, unassuming people who were such a mighty force. They formed a dangerous daisy chain, smuggling out the hapless Allied fliers who had been shot down from the skies above.

Another farmer, his wife, his son—the stay here was a blur of days of jumpy unrest and nights of horrible dreaming. Then a move to the town of Nérac, where his "host" was Gabriel; there, also, was Dr. Henri. At last a medical man could tend his poorly healed wounds, but the stay was not for long. The final lap of the journey was to make previous dangers fade by comparison.

For four days and four nights the ghastly footrace persisted without letup. French guides, three other pilots, and Yeager drew deeply from that well of human endurance that seems bottomless when dire peril is imminent.

When the self-imposed torture subsided, it proved but a false reprieve. The guides pointed to the snow-covered mountain that towered above them and whispered, "Spain." With a gesture of good luck, Godspeed, the guides slid into the blackness of the night, and four pilots stood less than two miles from freedom.

There was a guarded road to cross they had been warned. The first man dared it and won. Luck held with the second. The third man lunged, then was hurled back as a rifle bullet found its mark. Yeager bent over the man as blood oozed from his knee. What had he said his name was? In a ridiculous moment of release from the taut strain of days into weeks, he remembered—the tentmaker! Omar . . . Omar Patterson. The man was half cursing him, "Go on . . . leave me. Go on!"

At last Yeager felt no constraint! No other lives were hanging in the balance, none but his and Patterson's. No one would be tortured if things misfired. He could act!

Tugging, he got Patterson up to the road again, and bullets peppered the dirt as they scrambled across and started the conquest of the mountain before them.

Scientists can chart the human body and diagram its muscles and nerves. But no formula nor mathematical equation could ever prove that there was enough strength left in Yeager to get the injured man to the top of the mountain.

As he scrambled and clambered, clawed and clutched, his headway was measured in inches. Numb and bleeding, he paused only long enough to pour sulfa into Patterson's wound, then blindly fought on—never daring to look up at how far away the peak yet hovered.

The Spanish jailer pointed to his head in a gesture clearly indicating insanity. Here were two ragged, battered men in his cell, and all they did was laugh in an exhausted, hysterical manner. What was he to think of this pair who were brought in by his border guards? Were the Allied forces waging a war with lunatics? What were they laughing about? This was clearly too much for him to fathom. He had best be rid of such prisoners. But first let them rest a bit and enjoy plates full of *paella,* for indeed there was not much flesh on their bones.

At SHAEF headquarters Yeager was questioned endlessly about every phase of his bail-out and escape. Then he was officially informed that he could not fly any further missions, for now he was an "evadee"—one who has evaded capture, but knows too much about the workings of the French underground to risk being captured by the enemy.

Yeager protested, loudly. His appeal was even carried to the Supreme Commander, General Dwight D. Eisenhower, who listened with understanding when Yeager insisted that he did not want to be sent back to the States. General Eisenhower explained that it was one of the regulations, but he would contact Washington to see if a change could be made so that evadees could be returned to combat.

Frustrated in the hopes he had of rejoining his buddies in their missions, Yeager then had an additional wait at headquarters until someone could come to identify him.

"This man claims to be Yeager?" Tiedy—who had been a part of Chuck's group since he first arrived in England—sat solemnly before him, no glimmer of recognition lighting his devilish face. Yeager was stunned at first; then he began to see the possibilities of the situation, so he played along with it, pretending to get a bit ruffled. The farce kept up long enough for the headquarters' officers to suspect excitedly they had an enemy agent in their clutches!

When it was revealed as a joke, discipline was threatened; but anger finally softened into a kind of pity. "Guess the chaps have to be a little balmy to fly," the officers muttered and bundled the two pranksters back to their squadron before any more trouble could develop.

Seeds implanted in earth in a dozen different locations will send forth sprouts at about the same time. Similarly, progress is seldom the handiwork of any single man. The present facts, coupled with the prospective manner of improvement, usually lead many brains along a similar path in approximately the same evolvement period.

Several brilliant scientific minds had been puzzling the matter of "top" speed limits for the aircraft of the 1940's; they had listened to the alarming tales of buffeting and incontrollability that pilots experienced when they approached the mysterious sonic barrier; and they reached about the same conclusion: Wind tunnels were inadequate to define and solve the problem. A "flying laboratory" must be designed to crash through and gather the necessary data.

So in December of 1943 when the National Advisory Committee for Aeronautics discussed high-speed flight with representatives of each branch of the military and of industry, the time was ripe for a move. Representatives of the Bell Aircraft Corporation were very much interested and submitted a suggested design for an aircraft.

Similar thinking had been underway at Wright Field, where the gifted teacher and engineer, Ezra Kotcher, had started a project for the design of a rocket ship. But Wright Field had no production facilities, so he wrote every major aircraft company, soliciting their interest in such an undertaking. Since it was still wartime, he was doubtful that he would receive any favorable response. Then, to his delight, he learned of the Bell Aircraft Corporation's activity; Bell was equally pleased to be offered an Air Corps contract.

Lawrence D. Bell, the president, relished the challenge of promising to deliver a research aircraft that would fly at the fantastic speed of 1700 miles per hour and climb to altitudes of 80,000 feet. X-1 was the designation given this proposed craft.

Another force was in motion also—training, sharpening, molding the abilities of the man who was to fly it. Chuck Yeager had returned to his squadron; it was about two weeks after D-Day, and the regulation prohibiting evadees from combat flying was lifted.

The critical days were at hand. The skies were black with enemy aircraft. The tide had turned, but the battle was yet a stiff one. Days rolled into nights and into days again. Yeager performed automatically, almost flawlessly. He listened to briefings, studied maps, planned missions, and there was never a tiny fray indicating that he'd had more than his share. He piled up fifty-five additional combat missions, bringing his total to sixty-four; this represented 270 combat hours—hours of wily keeping Messerschmitts off his tail, of dodging flack, and downing enemies (eleven of them, to be exact, and a twelfth shared with a buddy). Finally, it was over.

The next mission took him to Oroville.

He picked up the girl who had waited, who had written faithfully, and had banked the savings that he had sent. They went to his parents' home in Hamlin for the wedding on February 26, 1945, then lazed in the Santa Monica, California, sun for a month at the Re-Distribution Center.

Successive instructor assignments at Perrin Field and Lubbock Air Base suddenly became rough duty for a hot-shot pilot. But the gray dawn changed to rosy pink when the Air Force came forth with a policy allowing former prisoners of war—escapees or evadees—to choose their base! Yeager was among the first in line.

"I selected Wright Field because it was the nearest base to West Virginia where my Mom and Dad live. The fact that this was the center for flight testing didn't occur to me. When I reported and they saw from my records that I had about 1100 hours of flying time, had a maintenance background, and had been a GI and crew chief, they decided to put me in the Flight Test Division as an assistant maintenance officer." But you can't keep a good pilot on the ground! "One thing led to another. When the crew had finished working on an aircraft, I used to fly it and check it out. When the Lockheed P-80 was ready for accelerated service testing, we went to Muroc Army Air Field (later renamed Edwards Air Force Base). I did quite a bit of the testing, and Colonel Boyd liked the way I flew."

Albert Boyd, now a retired Major General, had a strong and favorable impression of Yeager. He invited the flier to attend test pilots' school, then sent him all over the country putting on air shows. Boyd recalls, "When the X-1 program was assigned to my division, we had at that time 125 pilots doing flight testing. I'd had an opportunity, of course, to become fairly well acquainted with the majority of them and had observed their performance as test pilots as well as their behavior as men.

"In making a choice for the important testing of the X-1 my deputy, Colonel Fred J. Ascani, and I, narrowed the field down to Bob Hoover and Chuck Yeager. I had hoped to find a man who wasn't married for this very difficult task. At that time, in early 1946, we didn't know if we could succeed in flying the X-1 at a speed in excess of Mach 1 [Mach equals the speed of sound].

"However, we always came back to Yeager in our selection; and the reason was his demonstrated capability as a test pilot, his performance in the many air shows that we were having during that period, and his obvious stability. I think anyone who knows Chuck will recognize a man who is capable, extremely stable, reliable, and determined. These were the qualities, with his demonstrated outstanding ability as a pilot, that won him the opportunity of making the first supersonic flight in history," Boyd summarized.

Reliable? Stable? These adjectives might describe a banker or a judge. Aren't test pilots wild and reckless, devil-may-care in their whole approach to their work? Explains Boyd, "I had a few daredevils, and they didn't last very long. It's a very tedious job in which we must fly with great precision. Test pilots must have an analytical, scientific approach toward the work. This is one place where you don't dive and zoom!"

When Yeager was summoned to Boyd's office and the hazardous proposition of testing the X-1 was laid before him, he faced one of the most difficult decisions of his life. He had never shirked responsibility and he thrived on difficult assignments. But now there was Glennis, Donald, a year and a half old, and baby Michael. It was the same feeling, almost, that he'd experienced toward the brave French people who had hidden him—the fate of others hinged on his actions.

The big issues of life are usually complex, with no straight yes-or-no possible. There are considerations, obligations. What is a man's first duty? To his wife? To his country? To his children? To himself? Must they conflict? Can't each stay neatly in its own box and not overlap the other?

Yeager's inclination was an eager, unqualified "yes," but he deliberately thought through every aspect. The words from Boyd were echoing through his mind when suddenly the answer became clear—it was his commanding officer's opinion that he could test the X-1 better than anyone else! That was it. If the help, guidance, experience of his lifetime enabled him to do this job better than the other men, this was his first obligation.

It was not simply an assignment that Colonel Boyd was suggesting Yeager perceived—it was a chance to be a part of history. How often on hikes had he wished that he might walk where no one else had ever walked or look at a tree no other eyes had seen. Now it seemed within his grasp to accomplish what no one else had ever done—indeed, what most people thought might never be done. This could be one of the first breakthroughs in man's lunge into space—for without supersonic speeds there could never be penetration of space.

Boyd was speaking again, about the honor and tradition of the Air Force, about the importance—the absolute necessity—that the project succeed. "Do you think you could do it, Yeager?" At last a simple answer could be made: "Yes, sir. I believe I could do it, with the right co-operation and teamwork." Boyd felt obligated to warn Yeager of the enormous danger others saw in the program—others, not he. There would be no extra pay, no fat bonus such as a civilian test pilot had demanded for the attempt. There would be no privacy afterward, for the world would claim a part of the life of any man who performed such a feat. Yeager's eyes said, "I will do it, sir," but his words were more properly phrased, "I would like to try, sir."

Crimes and accomplishments share one element—motive! Why had this project been started? Why was the X-1 designed? Why must a human life be risked—Yeager's life—to see if it were possible to smash through that unpredictable sonic barrier? There was, of course, sound motive.

As Boyd expressed it, "We were an experimental flight test organization and were, of course, interested in the unknown, as all engineers and scientists are. It is this that man always seeks—it's a natural human attitude, to want to fly faster and higher, go farther and explore the unknown. Also, there was a definite military need for supersonic flight, because the faster the machine the sooner you can get to the target and, therefore, the safer the pilot and the machine surely would be."

The tiny X-1 was built to furnish answers to two questions: Was it possible for a straight-wing airplane to fly faster than the speed of sound? Could a pilot ever control the battering and buffeting of an airplane traveling at such speeds? The wind tunnel tests were negative. Data collected by the X-1 on early flights at slower speeds cast gravest doubts on the possibility. Grim jokes were being passed wherever pilots gathered. The consensus was that whoever tried for Mach 1—the speed of sound—would get himself "clobbered." But the opinion was not unanimous. The prime dissenters were those who made up the X-1 team.

Each man knew his job, and respect was high between them. Said project engineer, Richard H. Frost, "Charlie Yeager is completely nerveless. . . . He's the coolest guy I've ever seen, and it's been my business to see a lot of pilots preparing for flights of doubtful outcome. He is a perfectly natural airman, if there is such a thing. He flies a plane as if it were a part of him. In his test work he does exactly what the aeronautical engineers request, and he brings back the answers."[1]

Frost schooled Yeager in the inner workings, past history and future expectations of the rocket ship. It was a load to drop on a man, but luckily Yeager had help in the person of Captain (later Colonel) Jackie Ridley, the man whom Boyd had assigned as engineering officer on the X-1. Ridley was a pilot, and had earned his Master's Degree in aeronautical engineering from the California Institute of Technology. He was straightforward, proud of his Oklahoma heritage, loved to hunt and fish—and was the perfect complement to Yeager.

They established an immediate and close rapport. Just as every teacher learns, it helped Ridley to do his job more thoroughly to have to explain and discuss the highly technical aspects with Yeager. The pilot credits Ridley with being "the brains behind the X-1." Ridley in turn rates Yeager the finest of fliers and also declares, "He never studied engineering, but he blots up the stuff as fast as it's poured."[2]

Penicillin is a deadly mold, and yet it helps to make men well. Few elements are absolute in themselves—the essence of good or bad. The arid expanse of Mojave desert was sinister and threatening to the wagon teams that trekked across it before the turn of the century. Yet that same desert, with its gigantic dry lake of hardened clay, in recent times has saved the lives of countless pilots in trouble and served as an outstanding research center.

The farsighted General H. H. "Hap" Arnold first discovered "nature's gift" to the Air Force in the early Thirties while he was stationed in California as commander of March Field. The air of mystery that surrounded the testing of secret aircraft in the area did not introduce a particularly new note to the old-timers—they recalled the day when there was just as much secrecy occasioned by bootleggers whose stills were hidden along the edge of the lake.

The census taker could convey the real change in the area. New people—40,000 of them—claimed residence in the desert section during the war years. But by July of 1947 the tents and temporary barracks had given way to neat rows of houses and substantial-looking quarters. It is evident that the Air Force had found, in Edwards Air Force Base and Rogers Dry Lake, the ideal terrain for experimental test flying.

It was a fat-bellied B-29 that carried the valuable X-1 across the country from the Bell plant in Buffalo to Edwards AFB, much as a mother kangaroo conveys her young. The bomber sacrificed her bomb-bay doors so that a proper nest might be provided for the tiny experimental craft.

For all its sleeping innocence as it was ferried beneath the bomber, this was a dangerous "baby." Her 6000 pounds of thrust was created from rockets that had acquired the aggravating habit of exploding. None of the pilots who had previously tested her—Jack Woolams, Alvin M. (Tex) Johnson, Chalmers H. (Slick) Goodlin—had ventured into the supersonic speed range; the buffeting they experienced as the speed mounted cooled their faith in the craft. But now the bronco might as well stop bucking, for there was a rider named Yeager about to climb on her back, and he intended to ride her out.

Later, when he was solicitously asked about the phase of the X-1 flights that he most disliked, Yeager gave an unexpected reply: "The ride in the B-29." The X-1 could not expend her brief spurt of life on take-offs; if all four chambers of the rocket engine were fired simultaneously, she had two and a half minutes of power, or ten minutes if they were fired in sequence. So she was borne aloft by the mother ship and dropped at an altitude of 30,000 feet.

As the bomber reached 5000 feet, Yeager started the difficult routine of getting down into the X-1. He could not ride in the craft from the time of take-off for this reason: the B-29 had a climbing speed of 180–190 miles per hour. The stall speed of the X-1 was 240 miles per hour. Should any emergency have arisen whereby the X-1 had to be dropped before the B-29 reached a speed of 240 miles per hour, the rocket ship would have been in dire trouble.

Yeager's transfer from the B-29 into the X-1 was not exactly a maneuver designed to reassure his insurance company. First, the dexterity of a tight-rope walker was required to tread the catwalk back to the ladder—there was no protective mesh of a safety net spread below him in event of a misstep. Next came a function borrowed from the fire escapes on buildings—a ladder that slid down under his weight, putting him in reach of the X-1 door. The sure-footedness of early-day wing-walkers was required for the transfer from ladder to X-1 cockpit, for the wind was in a tug-of-war with Yeager's firm grip.

The seal of the cockpit was accomplished when Ridley lowered the door to the X-1, then heaved and pounded it into place. The routine continued. Yeager hooked up his oxygen supply—badly needed after that amount of exertion at 10,000 feet. Next he plugged in his communications system, so that the X-1 would not be isolated from either the crew of the B-29 or from the tower below.

The first drop Yeager made in the X-1 was a glide drop, without power; Captain Bob Hoover, chosen by Boyd as backup pilot on the project, was flying "chase." It was a firm rule of Boyd's to have a chase plane escorting every test flight, for he'd learned that by thus watching an experimental aircraft in flight indications of trouble can sometimes be detected before they grow too serious. The great difficulty in flying chase on the X-1 was that it outdistanced any other craft in the sky when its rocket engine was fired.

Even on this simple first glide flight, Yeager's enthusiasm reached a new peak. The fledgling X-1 had been pushed from the nest, only to fly like a veteran! He exclaimed it was the "best darned airplane" he had ever flown. Now the problem was one of holding back throttle on himself, for it was his inclination to try to crash that sonic barrier on the next flight!

Now there was a new Glamorous Glennis, and Yeager was frank to admit she supplanted all the previous ones in his career. But his pride in her performance didn't alter the carefully laid plan of progress. Boyd had stipulated that this be accomplished in "easy nibbles"—a nonchalant description at best, since nothing about the project was easy, and the nibbles were bites into the unknown.

Yeager paused in the test schedule long enough to bring Glennis and the boys from his parents' home in Hamlin to Muroc. On their first evening out, by way of familiarizing his wife with one of the chief gathering spots near Edwards AFB, Chuck took her to Pancho's Fly Inn. Pancho was a most unusual lady, whose never-used name was Florence Lowe Barnes. Tales were always related to newcomers to Edwards about her background—how her grandfather used balloons in the Mexican and Civil Wars and how there was a flying field as well as a mountain in California named after him. But Pancho did not have to rely on family prestige, for she'd built up a store on her own. She was a favorite entrant in the Bendix and Tom Thumb Races of a few years back, speaking the fliers' lingo because she was one of them. Her dude ranch was a favorite with some of the Air Force's most distinguished generals, and many a mission was reflown at her tables.

But moments of relaxation at Pancho's were most rare, for Yeager's schedule of work was demanding. Data from each flight of the X-1 was being reduced and analyzed by the National Advisory Committee for Aeronautics representatives, Walt Williams and De E. Beeler. Since this was a joint effort between the government agency, Bell Aircraft Corporation, and the Air Force, reports were then wired to Boyd, who commanded the operation from Wright Field, Ohio.

Exact aims of each mission were spelled out at preflight meetings; the function of the specialized craft was scrutinized at postflight sessions. These involved Ridley, Frost, Williams, Beeler, and Gerald Truszynski, the "brain" who knew the function of every black box in the system.

After three X-1 glide flights, power was supplied. Recalls Yeager of this first taste of the ship's real performance, "I fired one of the four chambers —the rocket motor consisted of four chambers, each having roughly 1500 pounds of thrust. As soon as I turned the switch on, I could feel a tremendous boost. I turned on a second cylinder and turned off the first, so that I never had more than one running, and flew around for three or four minutes just checking out the various systems on the aircraft. I turned them off, glided down and buzzed the field, then lit all four and shot up to about 45,000 feet and reached Mach .87—that is, eighty-seven per cent of the speed of sound." The X-1 had been flown in twenty powered flights before Yeager was assigned, yet none of them had reached this speed!

Nibbling, did Boyd say?

On this particular flight, Yeager was supposed to have stayed below Mach .8. "What is your explanation for this?" Boyd had demanded. Yeager's reply to his commanding officer was semiapologetic and pseudotechnical, but his simple explanation to himself was, "I had all the confidence in the world in the X-1. I *knew* that airplane wouldn't start flying apart or start swapping ends without giving me some sort of warning." At some point the science of flying must allow for this kind of human intuition!

"Tomorrow?" The mechanics were standing in a patch of shade near maintenance. There was a nod between them—tomorrow. These questions and answers had been traveling around the base for weeks. No project was ever named in the conversation. Everyone knew what was meant. The questions were simple, direct. "Any trouble today? Do you think he'll make it? What happens if there's fire?" They were overly casual, wrapped in the camouflage modern man adopts to hide emotions he's not supposed to have. The word continued to spread throughout the buildings. Tomorrow. A crewman from another project volunteered, "I'd sure hate to be doing it." The X-1 group neither heard nor saw him; this was no matter for an outsider to be discussing, and particularly not in that manner.

As Yeager sped along the highway, making the forty miles from home to the base on the old English Triumph motorcycle Pancho had loaned him, he saw the first red streaks of sunrise in the cloud-strewn sky. Suddenly they looked like tongues of flame to Yeager. His usually well disciplined imagination was momentarily wallowing in the area of his greatest fear, fire! Ruling out emotion, he logically thought it through. If the red light on his instrument panel should suddenly flash its dreaded warning, he would have to appraise the situation quickly and make a decision about jettisoning fuel—for if, when he touched the release to rid his craft of 13,000 pounds of volatile fuel, the fire had burned through a jettison line the procedure would drench the tail of the craft.

With detachment, Yeager acknowledged that there were no alternatives open to the pilot in case of serious trouble. Escape? How? The parachute he wore was comforting, but there was little chance of crawling out the small opening, especially if the craft were out of control. That could be ruled out. "Yeager," he lectured himself sternly as he turned in the gate at Edwards, "you just stay out of trouble and ride her up to Mach 1. This is the flight you hack it!"

With the gentleness that a lumbering dog might evidence toward a baby, the yellow bulldozer towed the X-1 from the protection of the hangar and backed the craft down into a pit. There she was winched up into the B-29's gaping bomb bay, and together they traveled to the second pit for fueling.

Yeager donned his pressure suit and insulated boots. He carried his electrically heated gloves, helmet, and parachute aboard the B-29; after they were airborne this gear would be adjusted by the flight surgeon who was along on this special flight, Dr. John Paul Stapp (then at Edwards with his own rocket-sled testing program).

As Boyd had said, experimental test flying consisted of a methodical series of small advances. There was, perhaps, a higher degree of tension among the X-1 crew on this particular mission, but it was still routine. At 7000 feet altitude, Major Robert L. Cardenas, pilot of the B-29, gave Yeager the signal to make his risky transfer into the little sycophant that hung below.

Then for forty-five minutes Yeager waited. His electrically heated pressure suit provided inadequate protection for his back, which rested against the liquid oxygen tank with its temperature of 290° below zero Fahrenheit.

At fifty minutes after ten on the morning of October 14, 1947, the radio crackled, and Cardenas asked, "Are you ready?" Yeager had trained, studied, and practiced for this moment; he'd had daydreams and nightmares about it. He was ready. The countdown barely crawled from second to second it seemed so slow. "Drop!" The word was the knife that cut the X-1 free from her shackles.

Yeager dropped, lifting from his seat with the giddy sensation a teen-ager experiences when he rides over the top in a roller coaster. From the comparative darkness of the cockpit when the airplane was sheltered, Yeager suddenly faced the blinding brightness of a clear desert sky. His fingers were well schooled, however, and automatically sought out the switch to turn on the rocket motor. With three of its chambers ignited, it zoomed to a fantastic 35,000 feet in less than a minute!

Leveling off, Yeager fired the fourth chamber. "This is it," he shouted into the microphone attached to his helmet. The crew of the B-29, Hoover and Ridley in chase planes, the ground team clustered in the tower, were all living the seconds with Yeager. They well knew the buffeting to which he was being subjected in the transsonic speed—the dangerous transition zone when the air rushing past the craft was partly at subsonic speed and partly at supersonic speed.

Shattering blows tore at the X-1, but she was stressed to take eighteen g's—eighteen times the pull of gravity. Like a wiry fighter she took this buffeting from Mach .88 to Mach .96 and even stayed upright when Yeager lost stability at Mach .94. For thirty tortuous seconds the beating continued, then Yeager climbed in speed to reach Mach 1!

The buffeting subsided, though strain still caused the X-1 to shudder and only his expertly delicate touch on the controls kept the craft from turning over. Security regulations prevented him from shouting this triumph into the microphone. What words could ever have conveyed this moment had he been allowed to speak?

Man was free—in a new dimension in space. His knowledge and design technique had gained him passage through the barrier that mighty air currents had erected. Once he only dared to fly as the birds. Now he knew he could fly faster than their song traveled. Superstitions crumbled. Plans soared. The beginning period of aviation ended, and the aerospace era started at that instant when Charles E. Yeager first flew at supersonic speed!

Though orders from Washington, D. C., clamped a "secret" classification on the event, word of it spread like seeping water around the base. In the midst of congratulations, his friends never suspected that Yeager was quaking over his next assignment—he had to make a presentation to the "brass" about the flight. Boyd sent through word that most of the Air Force's key generals would gather at Wright Field to hear Captain Yeager brief them. It was enough to scare a fellow!

This was but the first of many, many speeches, the first of endless appearances and press conferences scheduled for the flier. Boyd had warned him at the beginning that such activities would become a part of his life. Yeager fulfilled the new obligation as thoroughly as he had other phases of the assignment. No personal feeling crept into his talks except when he conveyed that he was proud to have been in an Air Force uniform when he accomplished supersonic flight.

In June of 1948 the Air Force Chief of Staff, General Hoyt S. Vandenberg awarded Yeager the Mackay Trophy for the outstanding military aviation performance of the year; in December another honor was added when President Harry S. Truman made the presentation of the Collier Trophy to Yeager and two other recipients, Lawrence D. Bell and John Stack. The committee which made the selection deemed this achievement "the greatest since the first successful flight of the original Wright Brothers' airplane."[1]

Another honor was added—an Oak Leaf Cluster to Yeager's wartime Distinguished Flying Cross. For his World War II participation he also had been awarded the Silver Star with an Oak Leaf Cluster, Bronze Star Medal, Air Medal with six Oak Leaf Clusters, and the Purple Heart.

Competition, in its varying forms, has been a key factor in the history of expansion and growth of America. It has prompted states into friendly rivalry and spurred individuals on to greater effort.

When Yeager heard that the Navy D-558 Skyrocket—a jet-powered craft with a rocket engine in its tail—was making supersonic runs from ground take-offs and that there were those men in blue who said the X-1 could never duplicate this record, the Air Force flier yearned to prove his craft. He discussed it with Bell, who urged him to present the idea to General Vandenberg and Stuart Symington, who was then Secretary of the Air Force.

Authorization for an attempted ground take-off of the X-1 was granted. Loaded with only 60 per cent of maximum fuel, with Yeager urging her on, the rocket ship proved that she not only could negotiate a ground take-off, but could attain supersonic speeds in a vertical climb! This, Yeager said, is the only time an American aircraft has ever taken off on rocket power alone.

Yeager continued at Edwards by testing every new, experimental aircraft that came along. Each, with its different procedures and systems, had to be carefully mastered; and he was often flying two, three, or four different aircraft in a single day. Among them was the XF-92A, "the first delta wing ever flown in the world," Yeager recalls.

He wanted Glennis to see this airplane that was then drastically different from the conventional design, so phoned her when he was ready for the first take-off. The end of the runway passed near their home; she went outside to watch—and beheld the horrifying sight of the craft's getting fifty feet off the ground and then crash-landing! Instead of running, scrambling, climbing fences to try to get to him, Glennis went back into the house and telephoned the tower to see if he were all right!

Such an action is evidence that the wife of a test pilot must also be a special breed. When asked to describe her husband, she smilingly said, "He's definitely lazy. This is not an unkind remark—he has to be. He doesn't become wound up over things the way most people do, and this contributes to his being the kind of test pilot he is. I don't think others would have come out of that X-1A test flight alive."

The X-1A, a modified version of the X-1, had the same wing and tail plane, but the fuselage was seven feet longer for extra fuel. It also had better visibility from the cockpit, which Yeager noted as a questionable improvement—especially for his peace of mind, "because I saw a lot of things I'd rather not have seen. When I looked back, I could see the wings buffeting and the shock waves on them."[3]

Bell Aircraft Corporation had called upon Yeager to test the X-1A; their test pilot, Skip Zeigler, had been killed in an accident with the X-2. An aim and a timetable for the X-1A were spelled out: to achieve a speed of Mach 2 before the fiftieth anniversary of powered flight on December 17, 1953. The old team gathered—Frost, Ridley, and Yeager.

The fourth flight of the X-1A nearly proved to be the last flight Yeager ever made. "That was probably the most trouble I've ever been in," he vividly recalls. Launched, as usual, from the B-29 at 30,000 feet altitude, Yeager fired three chambers and climbed to 45,000 feet; with the fourth chamber he then took the X-1A to 72,000 feet and pushed it over the top in a parabolic curve—the profile that is flown to simulate zero gravity, or weightlessness. In a fantastic burst of speed, 1650 miles per hour was reached—not the Mach 2 that had been aimed for, but Mach 2.5, two and a half times the speed of sound!

Then, as the fuel was exhausted, the sudden deceleration caused a complete loss of stability. It was like a car skidding wildly on ice. For one ghastly, frantic minute, Yeager lost all control of the X-1A. It started "swapping ends," spinning earthward with a horrific force. Yeager was being thrown and battered about, almost to unconsciousness, as his helmet smashed the inner liner of the canopy. The momentum of the spin increased until it was making two complete rolls per second, giving him blurred glimpses of sky, desert, and mountains; he was pulling ten positive and four negative g's (being alternately thrown upward with four times the pull of gravity, then forced downward with ten times the pull of gravity), plus a violent side load, like going around steep curves.

Two oxygen bottles were flying about in the cockpit and jagged pieces of the broken plexiglass inner canopy added to the debris. Down, down, and down it spun. In trying to recover, trying to do something to make the airplane respond, he got his head down on the stick, the crash helmet caught on the trim button on the stick that moved the whole horizontal stabilizer down, the forces increased to over eleven g's, and Yeager blacked out. His pressure suit—which probably could have prevented the blackout—had not automatically inflated, though the cockpit pressure had reached about 44,-000 feet.

He relates, "The airplane's gyrations changed to an inverted spin at about 34,000 feet. I remember recovering enough to correlate the controls with the spin direction. (We spin airplanes a lot, so that recovering becomes second nature to us.) The X-1A recovered from the inverted spin and flipped into a normal spin; at about 25,000 feet I was able to recover from that. I was hurting pretty badly by the time I got the airplane on its back." He had spun down an incredible 51,000 feet in fifty-one seconds!

The anxious crew realized the significance of the minute of silence from Yeager. With studied calm they repeated the call, "This is Ridley, Chuck. Where are you? Do you read me?" Barely coherent, gasping for breath, he mumbled, "I'm at 25,000 feet over Tehachapi. I don't know whether or not I can make it back to base."

"Are you sure you're at 25, Chuck?" Ridley was prompting him to double-check his reading.

Yeager wasn't too sure of anything at that instant. "I don't know if I've torn anything up . . . something isn't right." Captain (later Major) Arthur "Kit" Murray was flying chase on the mission. He cut in, "Tell us where you are, if you can, Chuck." He was scanning the sky, trying to get within sight of the X-1A and help survey the damage.

With supreme effort Yeager shook some of the fuzziness from his mind. "I think I can get back OK now, Jack. Boy, I'm not going to do *that* anymore!" Even in their wildest imaginings, the listening crew could not have guessed the real extent of "that." Then, with the quiet humor that he could still summon at such a time, Yeager quipped, "The engineers won't have to run a structural demonstration on this airplane!" The strains and stresses which the X-1A had withstood were gigantic.

The Bell crew on the ground cut in, "Jettison the tanks, Chuck." Training had guided Yeager's actions. Though he had no memory of it, he had jettisoned the liquid oxygen and fuel but had left the hydrogen peroxide tank alone, fearing the jettison line on that might be damaged and cause dreaded fire. He continued accurate landing reports. From having been so high in the cold temperatures, the inside of the windshield was now becoming fogged with the warmer moist air. The chase plane finally caught up with the X-1A on its landing approach. Murray augmented Yeager's hazy visibility by counting off the altitude, "50, 30, 20, down, 5, 2 . . . you have it made, Chuck."

As speeding trucks and an ambulance reached the craft, Yeager climbed out unaided. In the same tone that he might have commented that it was a nice day, he mentioned, "I got in a little trouble up there." A member of the Bell crew summed it up: "Wow!"

The day had started with a duck hunt at three that morning—before the flight—and it ended by Yeager's driving to Los Angeles to make a speech to the Army-Navy Club. He told the assembled group about "the routine day in the life of an experimental test pilot," and, of course, did not mention the event that had made the day far from routine.

This event won Yeager the Harmon Air Trophy Award, the Distinguished Service Medal, the Air Force Association Flight Trophy, and the General William Mitchell Memorial Trophy (shared with General Curtis E. Le-May).

General Nathan F. Twining, who had taken over the position as Chief of Staff of the Air Force, contacted Yeager with some alternative proposals: He could stay at Edwards, but not do any more test flying; he had been at it for nine years and had strained his luck to the breaking point. Or, he could go to Germany and take command of a fighter squadron.

Yeager reluctantly made plans to leave Edwards. One of the arrangements he had to make was for the sale of "the car." A legend had grown up around this battered old Model A Ford, its brush-marked paint a terrible shade of blue which had oxidized. It had first been the property of Major Joe Wolf, who bought two Fords for twenty-five dollars each, brought them from Los Angeles to Edwards, and tore one down to put the other in good shape, with Yeager's help. When Wolf was killed, his widow sold it to Major Neal Lathrop. A B-51 accident claimed Lathrop, and it was sold to Yeager. The tradition was established. The Ford had to be sold for $100 and only to another test pilot. Yeager sold it to Colonel Frank K. "Pete" Everest. (Subsequently, Everest left and sold it to the late Major Iven Kincheloe; his widow sold it to Captain Bob White.)

The entire town of Nérac turned out in a gala, daylong celebration when Yeager revisited the French village where he had hidden and saw his wartime helpers, Gabriel and Dr. Henri. So many faces were familiar to Yeager, except that they had since changed to happy faces. The Mayor proclaimed a holiday, and at a festive banquet endless toasts were proposed to the "brave M. Yeagaire" and the "charmant Mme. Yeagaire!"

Before he ended his duty in Germany, the squadron Yeager commanded had taken top honors in air-to-ground competition in the world-wide gunnery meet of 1956. Yeager traveled widely for the Air Force, tested the MIG-15 that a north Korean pilot had flown to Okinawa, and got better performance out of it than had ever before been recorded. The pattern held —whatever Yeager did, he did better than anyone else.

Personally, Yeager is happiest working as he is now, commanding a fighter squadron at George Air Force Base, having the feeling of companionship and teamwork that goes with such activity. As he says, "Flight testing is very hard work. You can't enjoy the flying because of the work." But it was work well done, for it opened the skies to speeds that men had feared would never be reached, and once Yeager had shattered that imaginary sonic barrier the whole infinity of the universe was suddenly within reach of man!

Since being displayed in the Smithsonian Institution, the rocket ship X-1 has reminded countless visitors of the momentous event. The young boy visiting the National Air Museum there was still held captive, his eyes fixed on its sleek configuration. As the old man finished telling him the story of test pilot Yeager, the boy was silent for a moment. Then he wondered out loud, "Are there any barriers left for me to break?"

REFERENCES

1. *Collier's,* 122:30–31, December 25, 1948.
2. *Saturday Evening Post,* 223:26–27, July 1, 1950.
3. *Aviation Week,* 59:15–16, December 28, 1953.

Index